MATHEMATICS FOR A LIBERAL EDUCATION

MERLIN M. OHMER
College of Sciences, Nicholls State University

ADDISON-WESLEY PUBLISHING COMPANY
Reading, Massachusetts
Menlo Park, California · London · Don Mills, Ontario

This book is in the
ADDISON-WESLEY SERIES IN INTRODUCTORY MATHEMATICS

Consulting Editors:
GAIL S. YOUNG
RICHARD S. PIETERS

Preface

Many students in college today require only a two-semester terminal course in mathematics to continue their programs. It has been traditional to prescribe the standard college algebra and trigonometry sequence to those terminal students. However, in view of the revolution in school mathematics, it seems somewhat anticlimactic and inconsistent to force such students into the algebra-trigonometry sequence. *Mathematics for a Liberal Education* is written to fill the needs of the terminal student in mathematics who needs a clearer idea of mathematics as a logical discipline rather than mathematics as a mechanical system. Since it does not depend on any particular high school mathematics sequence, the major prerequisites are maturity, curiosity, and open-mindedness. The emphasis is on logical development motivated and tempered by intuition rather than on manipulation of symbols. The definitions and theorems are concise, precise, well motivated, and illustrated by examples. If the proof of a theorem is simple and straightforward, it is included. If the proof is long, tedious, difficult, or too advanced for the student, it is omitted. The instructor may wish to omit some of the proofs which are included in the text or to supply some of the proofs which are omitted. The end of each proof is indicated by the symbol "QED," for "*quod erat demonstrandum.*" The exercise sets illustrate the theory, and some exercises in the sets extend the theory for enrichment purposes. Some exercises are fairly simple and straightforward, and others are somewhat more involved and require clear thinking. The answers to selected exercises are included so that the student can check his progress periodically.

At Nicholls State University we have taught the text in manuscript form according to the following two-semester schedule. The instructor may wish to modify the schedule to fit the needs of his particular students. For example, in a class of above-average students, a one-semester course may consist of Chapters 1, 2, 5, 7, and 8.

I am indebted to many persons, especially to the many students who have studied *Mathematics for a Liberal Education* in manuscript form. In particular, I would like to express my gratitude to Dr. Gail S. Young of Tulane University and the University of Rochester for his detailed suggestions, comments, and criticisms of the manuscript; to President Vernon F. Galliano and the members of the Mathematics Department of Nicholls State University; to Dr. C. V. Aucoin of Clemson University, my coauthor in other projects, for his advice and encouragement; to the staff of Addison-Wesley Publishing Company for their valuable assistance and advice; to Mr. Jimmy Broussard and Mr. Dale R. Hester for their painstaking job of reading, correcting, teaching, and improving the manuscript and for writing the *Instructor's Guide* to accompany the text; to Mrs. Pearl Ameen for class testing and commenting on the manuscript; and to Miss Stephanie Caballero, Mrs. Paula Goff Stentz, and Miss Marcella Bourgeois for typing the manuscript.

Finally, I am grateful to my wife and children for their patience, understanding, and encouragement during the preparation of the manuscript and production of the book.

Thibodaux, Louisiana   M. M. O.
August 1970

Contents

*Dedicated to my wife Beverly,
and my children Carol, Merlin, and Susan*

George Boole was born in Lincoln, England, on November 2, 1815. His father was a poor shopkeeper. Education was nearly inaccessible to anyone born in Boole's class, but Boole managed to educate himself with little formal schooling and very little help from his parents. By the age of 14, Boole had mastered Latin and Greek and had acquired a very limited knowledge of mathematics.

At the age of 16, Boole accepted the first steady job available—that of an "usher" (assistant teacher), and contributed to his parents' support until their deaths. His job as an usher enabled him to continue his studies, and at the age of 20 he opened a school of his own. Boole found it necessary to study mathematics so that he could better prepare his students. In his studies he developed contempt for the mediocre and poor textbooks available. With very little help he studied the works of the masters, and before he was 21 years old he mastered Laplace's *Mécanique céleste*, one of the most difficult masterpieces ever written.

Boole's first contribution to mathematics (a paper on the calculus of variations) resulted from his study of Laplace's masterpiece. Continuing his elementary teaching and his private and lonely studies, he developed the theory of invariants, which was later to lay the foundation necessary for the development of the theory of relativity by Albert Einstein.

The works of Boole impressed prominent mathematicians, many of whom became his close friends. In 1849, through the influence of his friends, Boole was appointed Professor of Mathematics at Queen's College in Cork, Ireland. That same year Boole published *The Mathematical Analysis of Logic*, a booklet which was only a promise of greater things to come. In 1854 Boole published his masterpiece, *An Investigation of the Laws of Thought, on which are founded the Mathematical Theories of Logic and Probability*. In his revolutionary work Boole reduced logic to an extremely easy and simple type of algebra and thus logic itself was incorporated as a discipline of mathematics. Today symbolic (or mathematical) logic is indispensable in any serious attempt to understand the nature of mathematics and the state of its foundations. Unfortunately, not all mathematicians recognized the significance of Boole's work, and as late as 1910 some eminent mathematicians considered it a philosophical curiosity.

Boole's continual yearning for social respectability probably had some influence on the choice of his wife, Mary Everest, the niece of a professor of Greek at Queen's College. On December 8, 1864, Boole died of pneumonia, which he had contracted after delivering an important lecture. At his death his fame was growing rapidly throughout the world. Boole's dream had come true—he had been honored during his lifetime.

The Bettmann Archive

BOOLE
(1815–1864)

Chapter 1

Introduction to Logic

1.1 SENTENCES—STATEMENTS AND OPEN SENTENCES

The purpose of this chapter is to present a brief introduction to the elementary principles of logic, an understanding of which is extremely valuable in the study of mathematics. We do not attempt to build a complete logical system, but only to include the fundamental concepts and principles of logic.

For the sake of understanding, consistency, simplicity, and nonambiguity, we should define each technical word precisely in accordance with certain established rules, or we should leave it undefined. The reason we leave certain mathematical words undefined is that any attempt to define *all* mathematical words leads to circular definitions, a simple fact which some of the greatest mathematicians and philosophers of the past centuries did not realize.

If we seek the definition of an unfamiliar word in a typical dictionary, we discover that the definition of the unfamiliar word is phrased in terms of other words. If we seek the definitions of the other words, we discover that they too are defined in terms of other words. Eventually, one of the new words turns out to be the original word whose definition we are seeking. For example, in an attempt to determine the meaning of the word *collection*, we might find the following in a dictionary:

collection—group

group—assemblage

assemblage—collection.

Once we have selected the relatively small number of words which we leave undefined in the mathematical system, we define the other words of the system in such a manner that the definitions obey certain laws. In general, every *definition* should be:

1. expressed in terms of the undefined words and/or the previously defined words and the common, nontechnical English words;

3

2. consistent with itself and other definitions;
3. meaningful and relevant;
4. expressed in such a manner that it includes all desired cases and excludes all undesired cases.

Just as we begin with certain undefined words, we also begin with certain statements (declarative sentences) which we assume to be true. The assumed statements are called *postulates, axioms,* or *assumptions.* Although Euclid distinguished between *postulate* and *axiom,* we do not make such a distinction. Briefly, a *postulate* (or *axiom*) is a statement which is assumed to be true. Among other things, the postulates prescribe the relationships among the undefined concepts. For example, in many developments of modern Euclidean geometry the words *point, line,* and *plane* are left undefined, but the relationships of points to lines and planes are prescribed in the postulates.

Accepting the axioms and the laws of logic (rules of inference), we prove new statements (called *theorems*) from the axioms, definitions, and previously proved theorems.

The reader is familiar with the word *sentence,* which includes exclamatory, imperative, and interrogative sentences as well as declarative sentences. We now define the word *statement.*

Definition 1. *A* **statement** *is any declarative sentence which is either true or false, but not both true and false.*

From Definition 1 we see that *a statement must be meaningful and unambiguous.* The following examples are statements.

Example 1. My father has brown hair.

Example 2. All cats are quadrupeds.

Example 3. Some mice are quadrupeds.

Example 4. No cats are quadrupeds.

Example 5. George Washington wore a wig.

Example 6. $7 + 8 = 15$.

Example 7. $7 + 5 \neq 5 + 7$.

Example 8. 4 is equal to 15.

Example 9. All college freshmen study mathematics, and some college freshmen study German.

Example 10. If Robert comes home, then his wife will go out.

Although we could deny that Examples 1, 5, and 10 are statements because one cannot determine, for example, whether Example 10 is true until he knows who *Robert* is, we agree that any name appearing in a statement specifies a particular person, object, number, etc. In everyday conversation, when an acquaintance tells us that Dan Roy is ill, we know that he is referring to a particular Dan Roy, in spite of the fact that there may be numerous persons named *Dan Roy*. Actually, Example 6 is similar to Examples 1, 5, and 10. We would ordinarily say that Example 6 is true. However, we could argue, as we did in Example 10, that we really cannot determine whether it is true until we know what numbers the symbols "7," "8," and "15" represent. When we write "$7 + 8 = 15$," we mean "seven plus eight is equal to fifteen." The symbols "7," "8," and "15" are similar to the names *Robert, George, Dan*, etc. They symbolize or represent the numbers just as the names *Robert, George*, and *Dan* symbolize or represent the persons. In Chapter 3 we will learn that the symbol "15" may represent some number other than *fifteen*. However, when we write "$7 + 8 = 15$," we know that we are referring to particular numbers. To avoid ambiguity, we agree to regard each *statement* as uttered by a specific person at a specific time and place.* Although the sentence "$14 + 2 = 16$" is a statement, the similar sentence "$x + 2 = 16$" is *not* a statement because "x" does not specify a particular number. Until we know that the symbol "x" specifies a particular number, we cannot determine whether "$x + 2 = 16$" is true or not. For example, if $x = 14$, we can say that "$x + 2 = 16$" is true; whereas, if $x = 25$, we can say that "$x + 2 = 16$" is false. A symbol such as a letter, triangle, etc., which represents a number or person or object is called a *variable*. For example, the letter "x" in the sentence "$x + 2 = 16$" is a variable. Since replacement of the variable "x" by a specific number converts the sentence "$x + 2 = 16$" into a statement, we say that the sentence "$x + 2 = 16$" is an *open sentence*. In a similar manner the *open sentence* "B drinks tea" can be converted to a *statement* by the replacement of the variable "B" by the name of a specific person.

Definition 2. *A sentence which contains a variable and which is not a statement but which is converted to a statement by replacement of the variable by the name of a specific number, person, or object is called an* **open sentence**.

The reader should observe that an open sentence may contain more than one variable. The following examples are open sentences.

Example 11. $x + 2 = 5 \times 7$.

Example 12. $x + 9 = 9 + 3x$.

Example 13. $5x = 4 + x$.

Example 14. $x^2 + 5x + 6 = 0$.

Example 15. $b + 4 \neq 2y$.

Example 16. $6 + 3x = c + ay$.

---

*   The reader is cautioned that removing a statement from its context may render it ambiguous, may change its truth value, or may even give it the appearance of an open sentence.

Example 17. $ax^2 + bx + c = 0$ and $a \neq 0$.

The following examples are neither statements nor open sentences.

Example 18. Karl, shut the door.

Example 19. Is $2 + 2$ equal to 4?

Example 20. $4 + 6$.

Henceforth, in this text, the word *sentence* will refer to either an open sentence or a statement, but will not include exclamatory, imperative, or interrogative sentences. According to this convention, the English sentences in Examples 18 and 19 are not considered to be sentences in the mathematical sense. Since Example 20 is not an English sentence, it is neither a statement nor an open sentence.

EXERCISE SET 1.1

Classify the following as *statement, open sentence,* or *neither*.

1. Peggy went swimming.
2. All of the students in the class did the assignment.
3. $3 + 5 = 6 - 2$.
4. No man lives forever.
5. $2x + y = 5$.
6. All men are mortal.
7. Vance plays football.
8. Is Guy attending school?
9. If x is less than 6.
10. There is some number t greater than 11 and less than 21.
11. If the sum of two numbers is zero, then both of the numbers are zero or neither is zero.
12. $100 - 4 + 69$.
13. $x + 2$ is greater than 6.
14. $6 + 7 = 4$ and $5 + 3 = 8$.
15. Is 5 less than 8?
16. 11 is less than x.
17. $2y - 3 = 6 + 8$.
18. Is $2x - 1$ equal to 5?
19. $x/5 = 10$.
20. Yvonne, study your mathematics.
21. $x/4 + 4/5$.
22. $a + 0 = a$.
23. Run home.

1.2 QUANTIFIERS

An open sentence is not really a statement. However, an open sentence can be converted to a statement by the replacement of the variable with the name of a specific number, person, or object. For example, the open sentence

$$x + 2 = 7$$

is converted to the *true* statement

$$5 + 2 = 7$$

by replacement of the variable "x" by the numeral "5." Replacement of the variable "x" by the numeral "3" converts the open sentence

$$x + 2 = 7$$

to the *false* statement

$$3 + 2 = 7.$$

The replacement method is not the only method of converting an open sentence to a statement. For example, we could assert that there is a number x such that $x + 2 = 7$. The assertion

There is a number x such that x + 2 = 7

is a statement; in fact, it is a *true* statement. Similarly, the assertion

For all numbers x, x + 2 = 7

is a statement; but it is a *false* statement. The open sentence

$$x + 3 = 3 + x$$

becomes a statement if we prefix the phrase "for all x." Thus

For all numbers x, x + 3 = 3 + x

is a statement; in fact, it is a true statement. The reader should observe that the sentence

There is a number x such that x + 3 = 3 + x

is also a *true* statement. Although the sentence

$$x + 3 \neq x$$

is not a statement, the sentence

For all numbers x, x + 3 ≠ x

is a *true* statement. The reader should notice that the latter statement has the same meaning as the statement

There is no number x such that x + 3 = x.

Observe that we have converted an open sentence by prefixing the phrase

for all numbers x

or the clause

there exists a number x such that.

Since both convey the idea of quantity, the words *all* and *there exists* [or *some*] are called *quantifiers*. The statements

All dogs are quadrupeds

and

Some dogs are quadrupeds

illustrate the use of the quantifiers *all* and *some* [or *there exists*]. The reader may wonder whether there is a third quantifier. Since the word *no* [or *none*] also conveys the idea of quantity, it is also called a *quantifier*. The statement

No dogs are quadrupeds

illustrates the use of the quantifier *no* [or *none*].

Throughout this chapter, unless specified otherwise, the word *number* will mean *counting number*; i.e., every number we consider is one of the numbers $0, 1, 2, 3, 4, 5, \ldots$.* We will consider negative numbers, fractions, and irrational numbers subsequently in the text. Thus the sentence

For some number x, x + 3 = 1

is *false*. If we included the negative numbers, the sentence

For some number x, x + 3 = 1

would be *true*. Thus we realize that *a quantifier* refers to a *specific collection of numbers, persons, or objects*. The statement

The base angles of an isosceles triangle are congruent

means

For all isosceles triangles t, the base angles of t are congruent.

Hence the quantifier here is *all* and refers to the collection of isosceles triangles.

Whenever the writer [or speaker] of a sentence omits the quantifier which converts that sentence to a *true* statement, and the reader [or listener] supplies that quantifier, we say that the quantifier is *implied* rather than *expressed*. For example, in the sentence

$x + 3 = 3 + x$

the quantifier *all* is implied. That is, the open sentence

$x + 3 = 3 + x$

---

*   The three dots are approximately equivalent to the word *etc.* That is, the three dots indicate that the pattern established is to be continued. In $0, 1, 2, \ldots, 10$, the three dots represent $3, 4, 5, 6, 7, 8, 9$. However, in $0, 1, 2, \ldots$, the three dots represent all of the counting numbers beginning with 3.

is used, whereas the statement

For all x, $x + 3 = 3 + x$

is understood. In informal mathematics, we usually use such open sentences as if they were statements and frequently refer to them as *statements*. However, even if it is used as a statement, the reader should realize that

$x + 3 = 3 + x$

is an open sentence and *is not a statement*. Similarly, in the sentence

$x + 2 = 5$

the quantifier *some* is implied.

The quantifier *all* is called the *universal quantifier*, and the quantifier *some* [*there exists*] is called the *existential quantifier*. Since the quantifier *no* [*none*] may be expressed in terms of the universal or existential quantifier, it is not given a special name. For example, the statement

No odd number is divisible by two

may be expressed as either

There does not exist an odd number which is divisible by two

or

For all x, if x is an odd number, then x is not divisible by two.

The symbol for the universal quantifier *all* [or *every* or *each* or *any*] is "$\forall$," and the symbol for the existential quantifier *some* [or *there exists*] is "$\exists$." Thus the statement

For all x, $x + 3 = 3 + x$

may be expressed

$\forall x$, $x + 3 = 3 + x$,

and the statement

There exists x such that $x + 3 = 3$

may be expressed

$\exists x$, $x + 3 = 3$.

In summary, we list the methods of converting an open sentence to a statement:

1. *Replace the variable by the name of a specific number, person, or object.*
2. *Quantify the variable.**

---

*   When a quantifier is *implied*, it is understood to be the quantifier which converts the sentence to a *true statement*. If both the existential quantifier and the universal quantifier convert the sentence to *true statements*, then the *universal quantifier* is understood to be the implied quantifier.

EXERCISE SET 1.2

I. In each of the following statements identify the quantifier or quantifiers as *all*, *some* [*there exists*], or *no* [*none*].

1. All birds fly.
2. Some birds fly.
3. Some students will become teachers.
4. No reptiles can fly.
5. Some numbers are odd.
6. There is a smallest number.
7. For every number, there is a larger one.
8. There is no largest number.
9. $\forall x,\ x + 6 = 9$.
10. $\exists y,\ y + 5 = 2$.
11. Some birds fly and no dogs fly.
12. $\forall x$, if x is positive, then $x + 6$ is positive.
13. For each number x, either x is even or x is odd.
14. Any even number is divisible by two.
15. $\exists x$ such that x is a man and x has blue eyes.

II. State whether each of the following sentences has an *expressed quantifier*, an *implied quantifier*, or *no quantifier*.

1. $2 + 7 = 15$.
2. For all x, $x + 2 = 2 + x$.
3. Men are mortal.
4. There is no y such that $y = y + 2$.
5. $6 + 2 = 2 + 6$.
6. A hexagon has six sides.
7. Galileo is mortal.
8. An orchid is a flower.
9. 0 is a counting number.
10. An equilateral triangle has congruent angles.

III. Identify the quantifier in each of the following sentences.

1. $y + y = 2y$.
2. $x + 3x = 4x$.
3. $xy = yx$.
4. $x + y = y + x$.
5. Roses are red.
6. Violets are blue.
7. $\forall x,\ x \cdot 0 = 0$.
8. $\forall y,\ y + 0 = y$.
9. A counting number is never negative.
10. An even counting number is not odd.
11. $\exists x,\ x$ is divisible by both 2 and 3.

12. $\exists y$, y is divisible by both 4 and 3.

13. $x = x$.

14. $x + 1 = x$.

15. $\forall x$, $x + 2 = 5$.

IV. Quantify each of the following open sentences by use of each of the three quantifiers [*all, some, none*]. Determine whether each of the resulting statements is *true* or *false*.

1. $x + x = 2x$.   2. $x + 5 = 11$.

3. $5 + t = 5$.   4. $y + 4 = 4$.

5. $7 + x = x$.   6. $n + 5 = n$.

7. $t + 6 = 6$.   8. $2t + t = 7t$.

9. $b + 6 = 5$.   10. $5 + a = 3$.

1.3 CONNECTIVES, COMPOUND SENTENCES, AND SIMPLE SENTENCES

In mathematics, as in English grammar, we study simple sentences and compound sentences. However, the definitions in mathematics differ slightly from those in grammar. In order to define *simple sentence* and *compound sentence*, we first name the undefined words *not, or, and, if ... then ...*, and *if and only if*.

Definition 3. *The words **not, or, and, if...then...**, and **if and only if** are called **connectives**.*

Definition 4. *A sentence which does not contain a connective is called a **simple sentence**.*

Definition 5. *A sentence which contains a connective is called a **compound sentence**.**

The reader should observe that Definitions 4 and 5 include both statements and open sentences.

Since any sentence either does or does not contain a connective, we see that every statement or open sentence can be classified as either compound or simple. However, the reader should be aware that the connective may not appear explicitly; i.e., a substitute may appear in its place or the connective may be implied. For example, the sentence

Joan is enrolled in mathematics, but Joan is not enrolled in Russian

is a compound sentence. Although the connective *and* does not appear explicitly in that sentence, the English substitute *but* does appear.

Moreover, in the sentence

Joan is enrolled in mathematics; Joan is not enrolled in Russian

the connective *and* is implied.

---

*   The reader is cautioned that the word *and* in the simple sentence "The flag is red, white, and blue" is not a connective, and the word *or* in the simple sentence "The money will be paid to John or Mary" is not a connective. We agree that a connective is a *sentential connective* rather than a word connective.

The dots in the notation

if ... then ...

signify that some words have been omitted. For example, in the sentence

If it rains today, then the golf match will be postponed

the connective consists of only the two words *if* and *then* and is usually written *if ... then.** The omitted words are

it rains today

and

the golf match will be postponed.

The following are examples of simple sentences.

Example 1. Kathleen was late for her mathematics class yesterday.

Example 2. $7 + 5 = 5 + 7$.

Example 3. $4 + 3 = 16$.

Example 4. This bird can fly.

Example 5. x is larger than 8.

The following are examples of compound sentences.

Example 6. Some birds can fly, but no monkeys can fly.

Example 7. $4 + 5 \neq 12 + x$.

Example 8. If it rains today, then I will take a nap.

Example 9. Phil will score twenty points in the basketball game if and only if he plays 30 minutes.

Example 10. It did not snow Saturday.

Example 11. Jeff will attend Tulane or Tom will attend Yale.

Connective	Symbol
not	$\sim$
or	$\vee$
and	$\wedge$
if ... then	$\rightarrow$
if and only if	$\leftrightarrows$

Fig. 1.1

We symbolize the connectives as shown in Fig. 1.1.

---

*   Although the complete connective is *if ..., then ...*, we usually write *if ... then* and say *if-then*.

We represent sentences by the lower-case letters

p, q, r, etc.,

and in particular we represent open sentences by

p_x, q_x, r_x, etc.

The following examples illustrate the use of the connectives in the symbolization of compound statements.

Example 12. Let p, q, and r be the following sentences.

  p: *Carol went home.*

  q: *Susan studied violin.*

  r: *Beverly prepared dinner.*

Then $\sim q$ [read "*not-q*"] represents the sentence

  Susan did not study music;

$p \vee r$ represents the sentence

  Carol went home or Beverly prepared dinner;

$p \wedge q$ represents the sentence

  Carol went home and Susan studied violin;

$p \rightarrow q$ represents the sentence

  If Carol went home, then Susan studied violin;

$q \leftrightarrows r$ represents the sentence

  Susan studied violin if and only if Beverly prepared dinner.

Since the connective $\sim$ does not connect *two* sentences, but is used with a *single* sentence, no ambiguity results when it is used with another connective. Hence no punctuation is necessary. For example, we agree that

$p \vee \sim q$	means	$p \vee (\sim q),$
$p \wedge \sim q$	means	$p \wedge (\sim q),$
$\sim p \vee q$	means	$(\sim p) \vee q,$
$p \rightarrow \sim q$	means	$p \rightarrow (\sim q),$
$p \leftrightarrows \sim q$	means	$p \leftrightarrows (\sim q),$

and

  $\sim p \rightarrow q$ means $(\sim p) \rightarrow q.$

Moreover, we agree that

  $\sim \sim p$ means $\sim (\sim p).$

This agreement eliminates the excessive use of parentheses.

Example 13. Symbolize the sentence "Paul will attend Tulane but not Yale."

Let *p* represent "Paul will attend Tulane" and *q* represent "Paul will attend Yale." Then $\tilde{\ }q$ represents "Paul will not attend Yale." By recalling that *but* is an English substitute for *and*, we see that $p \wedge \tilde{\ }q$ represents "Paul will attend Tulane but not Yale."

Example 14. Symbolize the sentence "Stephanie will go to a movie; Susan will not."

Let *p* represent "Stephanie will go to a movie" and *q* represent "Susan will go to a movie." Then $\tilde{\ }q$ will represent "Susan will not go to a movie." Hence we may write $p \wedge \tilde{\ }q$. The reader should observe that the semicolon used in this manner is merely a substitute for the connective *and*.

Example 15. Symbolize the sentence "If Tommy does not make a passing mark in this course, then Tommy will not receive a scholarship."

Let *p* represent "Tommy does make a passing mark in this course" and *q* represent "Tommy will receive a scholarship." Then $\tilde{\ }p$ represents "Tommy does not make a passing mark" and $\tilde{\ }q$ represents "Tommy will not receive a scholarship." Thus we write

$$\tilde{\ }p \to \tilde{\ }q.$$

The following definition *names* the five basic forms of compound sentences.

Definition 6

  a) *The sentence $\tilde{\ }p$ [read "not-p"] is called the* **negation of p.**

  b) *The sentence $p \vee q$ [read "p or q"] is called the* **disjunction of p and q.**

  c) *The sentence $p \wedge q$ [read "p and q"] is called the* **conjunction of p and q.**

  d) *The sentence $p \to q$ [read "if p, then q"; or "p only if q"; or "q if p"] is called a* **conditional sentence.**

  e) *The sentence $p \leftrightarrows q$ [read "p if and only if q"] is called a* **biconditional sentence.**

Written Statement	Spoken Statement	Type of Statement
$\tilde{\ }p$	not-*p*	negation
$p \vee q$	*p* or *q*	disjunction
$p \wedge q$	*p* and *q*	conjunction
$p \to q$	1) if *p*, then *q* 2) *p* only if *q* 3) *q* if *p*	conditional
$p \leftrightarrows q$	*p* if and only if *q*	biconditional

Fig. 1.2

In Fig. 1.2 we summarize the use of the connectives in the formation of compound sentences.

EXERCISE SET 1.3

I. Classify each of the following sentences as *simple* or *compound*. Name the connective(s) of each compound sentence.

1. $4 + 7 = 7 + 4$.
2. $4 + 2 \neq 2 + 4$.
3. 7 is not equal to $2 + 5$.
4. $(4 + 3 = 7)$ or $(5 \neq 3 + 2)$.
5. $(5 + 0 = 5)$ and $(4 + 3 = 7)$.
6. $(6 \times 0 = 0)$ or $(4 + 2 = 21)$.
7. $(4 + 8 = 12)$ or $(6 + 1 = 7)$.
8. If $1 = 3 - 2$, then $4 = 7 - 2$.
9. If $3 + 3 = 7$, then $3 \times 3 = 9$.
10. If all birds fly, then some fish swim.
11. All dogs bark if and only if some birds talk.
12. If there exists a number x such that $x + 2 = 5$, then there exists a number y such that $2 = 4 + 3y$.
13. If $2 + 3 \neq 5$, then $\exists x$ such that $2 + x = 4$.
14. There is no number y such that if $y + 2 = 2$, then y is not zero.
15. For no number x, $x + 2 \neq x$.
16. $\forall x, x + 2 = 2$.
17. If $6 = 7$ and $4 \neq 3$, then $1 = 17$.
18. If there is no number x such that $3 + x = x$, then there is no number y such that $4 + y = y$.
19. If $4 \neq 6$ and $7 \neq 4$, then $2 = 5$ and $7 = 6$.
20. $\forall x, x$ is greater than zero if and only if x is positive.
21. $\exists x, 2x + 4 = 56$ only if $x = 1$.
22. Today is Saturday if and only if tomorrow is Sunday.

II. Classify each of the following sentences as *simple* or *compound*. Let p, q, and r represent simple sentences, and represent each sentence in terms of p, q, r, and the connectives.

1. If Gary is in college, then he is not living with his family.
2. $42 - 12 = 22 + 1$ and $5 = 4 + 1$.
3. x is greater than 0.
4. x is not negative.
5. If $\frac{1}{2} + \frac{1}{3} = \frac{1}{6}$, then $\frac{1}{3} + \frac{1}{4} = \frac{1}{12}$.
6. 8 is less than 4 or 4 is less than 10.
7. $\sim(3 + 4 \neq 7)$.
8. $6 + 7 \neq 6 + 5$.

9. Either mathematics is a science or mathematics is not a science.

10. Either mathematics is a science or mathematics is an art.

11. $4 + 6 = 5$ and $3 + 6 \neq 9$.

12. If x is positive or if x is negative, then x^2 is positive.

13. $4 + 7 = 8$ only if $2 + 3 = 1$.

14. If x is greater than y and if y is greater than z, then x is greater than z.

15. $a + 0 = a \times 0$.

1.4 NEGATION

In the previous section we studied the five connectives and the five basic compound sentences. In this section we investigate the conditions under which the negation of a given sentence is true. The *truth value* of any true sentence is *true*, and the *truth value* of any false sentence is *false*. For example, the truth value of the sentence "$4 + 5 = 5 + 4$" is true, whereas the truth value of the sentence "$3 + 7 = 7 + 2$" is false.

The following definition states the conditions under which the negation is true.

Definition 7. The negation of p [*denoted by* "$\sim p$"] **is a true sentence** *if and only if p is a false sentence.*

The words *if and only if* in a definition indicate that two statements are made. For example, Definition 7 is really a statement of the following:

1. If p is a false sentence, then $\sim p$ is a true sentence;

2. If $\sim p$ is a true sentence, then p is a false sentence.

The following examples illustrate Definition 7.

Example 1. Let p be the sentence "$5 = 7$." Then $\sim p$ is the sentence "$\sim(5 = 7)$." Then $\sim p$ is *true* because p is *false*.

Example 2. Let q be the sentence "$4 + 3 = 3 + 4$." Then $\sim q$ is the sentence "$4 + 3 \neq 3 + 4$." Then $\sim q$ is *false* because q is *true*.

Example 3. Let r be the sentence "All birds fly." Then $\sim r$ is the sentence "Not all birds fly." Then $\sim r$ is *true* because r is *false*.

Example 4. Let p_x be the open sentence "$x + 2 = 5$." Then $\sim p_x$ is the open sentence "$x + 2 \neq 5$." Then "$\sim(\forall x, p_x)$" is *true* because "$\forall x, p_x$" is *false*.

Although we may express the negation of "$5 = 7$" as either "$\sim(5 = 7)$" or "$5 \neq 7$," the latter is preferable. Similarly, we may negate "all birds fly" as "not all birds fly" or "some birds do not fly," but we prefer the latter form. The negation of "some triangles are squares" is "no triangles are squares," and the negation of "no birds fly" is "some birds fly."

The preceding examples illustrate three general rules:

1. The negation of

$\forall x, p_x$

is

$\exists x, \sim p_x.$

2. The negation of

$\exists y, p_y$

is

$\forall y, \sim p_y.$

3. An equivalent form of

$\forall y, \sim p_y$

is

for no y, p_y.

The truth value of $\sim p$ is true if the truth value of p is false, and the truth value of $\sim p$ is false if the truth value of p is true. If we use the capital letters "T" [for *true*] and "F" [for *false*], we may tabulate the truth values of the negation of p by a device known as a *truth table*. To compute the truth table for $\sim p$, we observe first that p has two possible truth values, T and F. For each of these we wish to know whether $\sim p$ is true or false. From Definition 7, we know that $\sim p$ is false if p is true and that $\sim p$ is true if p is false. The truth table for $\sim p$ is shown in Fig. 1.3.

p	$\sim p$
T	F
F	T

Fig. 1.3

The truth table exhibits all the information contained in Definition 7 and no extraneous information. Thus the truth table can be used as an alternative definition of the *negation*.

EXERCISE SET 1.4

I. Negate each of the following as in Examples 2, 3, and 4.

1. The moon is a planet.
2. Pluto is a star.
3. $3 + 4 = 7$.
4. $4 + 3 \neq 3 + 4$.

5. Every number is positive.   6. $0 + 0 = 2$.

7. $2 + 4 = 6$.   8. Some numbers are odd.

9. No number is even.   10. All numbers are not odd.

11. Some numbers are not even.   12. $\forall x$, x is prime.

13. $\exists x$, x is less than 5.   14. There is no smallest number.

15. Some numbers are greater than 25.

16. $\exists x$, $x + 2 = 7$.

17. $\forall x$, $x + 1$ is greater than x.

18. Some equilateral triangles are isosceles triangles.

19. $\forall y$, y^2 is not negative.   20. $\exists y$, $yx \cdot 3 = y$.

II. Determine the *truth value* of each sentence in Exercise I and then use Fig. 1.3 to determine the *truth value* of the *negation* of each sentence.

1.5 DISJUNCTION AND CONJUNCTION

In this section we study the truth values of the *disjunction $p \vee q$* and the *conjunction $p \wedge q$*. The mathematical usage of the conjunction is identical with the English usage. However, the mathematical usage of the disjunction differs from the English usage. The following definition, which states the condition under which the disjunction is *false*, highlights the difference.

Definition 8. *The **disjunction of p and q** [denoted by "$p \vee q$"] is a false sentence if and only if p is a false sentence and q is a false sentence.*

The reader should recall the meaning of *if and only if*. That is, Definition 8 is really a statement of the following:

1. If p is a false sentence and q is a false sentence, then $p \vee q$ is a false sentence.

2. If $p \vee q$ is a false sentence, then p is a false sentence and q is a false sentence.

We conclude the following:

1. If p is true and q is true, then $p \vee q$ is true.

2. If p is true and q is false, then $p \vee q$ is true.

3. If p is false and q is true, then $p \vee q$ is true.

4. If p is false and q is false, then $p \vee q$ is false.

The following examples illustrate Definition 8.

Example 1. $(4 + 2 = 8) \vee (5 + 3 = 7)$ is *false* because

$$4 + 2 = 8$$

is false and

$$5 + 3 = 7$$

is false.

Example 2. $(3 + 4 = 7) \lor (5 + 6 = 10)$ is *true* because

$$3 + 4 = 7$$

is true.

Example 3. $(2 + 7 = 16) \lor (6 + 8 = 14)$ is *true* because

$$6 + 8 = 14$$

is true.

Example 4. $(5 + 7 = 12) \lor (2 + 4 = 6)$ is *true* because

$$5 + 7 = 12$$

is true (or because

$$2 + 4 = 6$$

is true).

Definition 8 states that $p \lor q$ is false whenever p is false and q is false and that $p \lor q$ is true otherwise. Thus $p \lor q$ is true whenever *both* p and q are true sentences. This is the important difference between the mathematical usage and the English usage of the connective *or.* For example, the sentence

Next summer Bob will fly to New York or Bob will drive to New York

is usually considered to mean that Bob will fly to New York or drive to New York but not both. Likewise, the sentence

Paul will have tea or milk with his meal

is usually considered to mean that Paul will take tea or milk with his meal *but not both.* However, the sentence

Beverly will buy a dress or [*Beverly will buy*] *a coat*

is usually considered true even if she buys both a dress and a coat. The disjunction $p \lor q$ in the English language has a double meaning; usually it means

p or q but not both p and q

but sometimes it means

p or q or both p and q.

In the latter sense, it has the meaning of *and/or* in legal documents. In mathematics we avoid the ambiguity by adopting Definition 8. That is, in mathematics,

$$p \lor q$$

means

> *either p or q* [*or both*].

Thus the mathematical meaning of $p \lor q$ is the legal meaning of p *and/or q.**

To compute the truth table for $p \lor q$ we note that p has two possible truth values, T and F. For each of these, q has *independently* two possible truth values, T and F. Thus there are four possible combinations of truth values. For each of these combinations we wish to know the truth value of the disjunction $p \lor q$. From Definition 8 we know that $p \lor q$ is false whenever p is false and q is false and that $p \lor q$ is true in the other three cases. The truth table for $p \lor q$ is shown in Fig. 1.4.

p	q	$p \lor q$
T	T	T
T	F	T
F	T	T
F	F	F

Fig. 1.4

The truth table exhibits all the information we need to know about $p \lor q$; i.e., according to the truth table $p \lor q$ is true whenever p is true or q is true (or both p and q are true) and $p \lor q$ is false whenever p is false and q is false. Thus it exhibits all the information contained in Definition 8 and no extraneous information. Hence the truth table for $p \lor q$ can be used as an alternative definition of $p \lor q$.

The mathematical usage of the conjunction is identical with the English usage, as the following definition states.

Definition 9. *The **conjunction of p and q** [denoted by "p $\land$ q"] is a true sentence if and only if p is a true sentence and q is a true sentence.*

The following examples illustrate Definition 9.

Example 5. $(4 + 3 = 7) \land (5 + 8 = 13)$ is *true* because $4 + 3 = 7$ is true and $5 + 8 = 13$ is true.

Example 6. $(4 + 7 = 11) \land (5 + 2 = 6)$ is *false* because $5 + 2 = 6$ is false.

Example 7. $(2 + 3 = 6) \land (4 + 4 = 8)$ is *false* because $2 + 3 = 6$ is false.

Example 8. $(2 + 0 = 3) \land (4 + 4 = 4)$ is *false* because $2 + 0 = 3$ is false (or $4 + 4 = 4$ is false).

---

*   The symbol "$\underline{\lor}$" is sometimes used for the exclusive *or.* That is, "$p \underline{\lor} q$" means "p or q but not both p and q."

Definition 9 states that the conjunction $p \wedge q$ is true whenever both p and q are true sentences, and the conjunction $p \wedge q$ is false in the three remaining cases. The truth table for $p \wedge q$ is shown in Fig. 1.5.

p	q	$p \wedge q$
T	T	T
T	F	F
F	T	F
F	F	F

Fig. 1.5

The truth table exhibits all the information we need to know about $p \wedge q$; i.e., according to the truth table, $p \wedge q$ is a true sentence whenever both p and q are true sentences, and $p \wedge q$ is a false sentence in the remaining cases. Thus it exhibits all the information contained in Definition 9 and no extraneous information. Hence the truth table for $p \wedge q$ can be used as an alternative definition of $p \wedge q$.

EXERCISE SET 1.5

Compute the truth value of each of the following sentences.

1. $3 + 5 = 8$.
2. $5 + 2 = 2 + 5$.
3. $(5 + 6 = 11) \wedge (2 + 3 = 4)$.
4. $(2 + 1 = 7) \vee (5 + 6 = 11)$.
5. $(2 + 3 = 5) \wedge (6 + 1 = 7)$.
6. $(4 + 7 = 2) \vee (5 + 1 = 7)$.
7. $5 + 7 \neq 12$.
8. $(6 + 0 = 0) \wedge (4 + 2 = 7)$.
9. $(4 + 6 = 5) \vee (2 + 0 = 2)$.
10. $(4 + 3 \neq 6) \wedge (5 + 1 \neq 8)$.
11. Some numbers are even or some numbers are odd.
12. Some numbers are not even and no numbers are odd.
13. There is no largest counting number and there is no smallest counting number.
14. Some numbers are divisible by 3 or all numbers are divisible by 4.
15. $\forall x$, $[(x \text{ is even}) \vee (x \text{ is odd})]$.
16. $\exists x$, $[(x \text{ is even}) \wedge (x \text{ is odd})]$.
17. $\forall x$, $[(x \text{ is odd}) \vee (x \text{ is zero})]$.
18. $\exists x$, $[(x \neq 0) \wedge (2x = 0)]$.
19. $\forall x$, if $5x = 0$, then $x = 0$.
20. $\forall t$, $6t \neq 0$ if and only if $t \neq 0$.

1.6 CONDITIONAL AND BICONDITIONAL

Since many theorems in mathematics are of the form

$$p \rightarrow q,$$

it is important to study the conditional sentence. The following definition states the conditions under which the conditional sentence $p \rightarrow q$ is false.

Definition 10. *The* **conditional sentence p → q is a false sentence** *if and only if p is a true sentence and q is a false sentence.*

The following examples illustrate Definition 10.

Example 1. $(4 + 8 = 12) \rightarrow (3 + 0 = 3)$ is *true* because $4 + 8 = 12$ is true and $3 + 0 = 3$ is true.

Example 2. $(4 + 6 = 10) \rightarrow (1 + 1 = 7)$ is *false* because $4 + 6 = 10$ is true and $1 + 1 = 7$ is false.

Example 3. $(4 + 1 = 12) \rightarrow (2 + 4 = 6)$ is *true* because $4 + 1 = 12$ is false and $2 + 4 = 6$ is true.

Example 4. $(2 + 3 = 3) \rightarrow (5 + 6 = 1)$ is *true* because $2 + 3 = 3$ is false and $5 + 6 = 1$ is false.

There should be no difficulty with Examples 1 and 2 because their truth values follow directly from Definition 10. However, questions may arise about the truth values of Examples 3 and 4. It may seem strange to say that $p \rightarrow q$ is true when p is false. The only reason this seems strange to us is that we are accustomed to assuming that p is true in any sentence of the form $p \rightarrow q$. This natural assumption is usually made in any mathematical theorem of the form $p \rightarrow q$. Thus when stating a theorem

> *If p, then q*

we usually *prove* the theorem by *assuming* that p is true and then *proving* that q is true. If p is false, we do not bother to determine the truth value of q. Remember that Definition 10 states that $p \rightarrow q$ *is false if and only if p is true and q is false*; i.e., the only case in which $p \rightarrow q$ is false is the case in which p is true and q is false. In the three other cases, $p \rightarrow q$ is true.

The following example illustrates why we chose to define $p \rightarrow q$ to be true except when p is true and q is false.

Example 5. The weatherman makes the statement "If it rains all night tonight, then New Orleans will be flooded."

The weatherman's statement is the conditional statement $p \rightarrow q$, in which p is the statement

> *it rains all night tonight*

and q is the statement

> *New Orleans will be flooded.*

We wish to compute the truth value of his statement in each case. The following are the only cases that can occur.

1. p: it rains all night, q: New Orleans will be flooded;
2. p: it rains all night, $\sim q$: New Orleans will not be flooded;

3. $\sim p$: it does not rain all night, q: New Orleans will be flooded;

4. $\sim p$: it does not rain all night, $\sim q$: New Orleans will not be flooded.

In Case 1, we would certainly say that the weatherman told the truth, and hence $p \rightarrow q$ is true. In Case 2, we would have to admit that the weatherman did not tell the truth, and hence $p \rightarrow q$ is false. In Case 3, we would certainly give the weatherman the benefit of the doubt and say that he told the truth, and hence that $p \rightarrow q$ is true. He did not say what would happen if it did not rain. After all, New Orleans can flood from causes other than rain; for example, the levee containing the Mississippi River can break. In Case 4, we would again have to give the weatherman the benefit of the doubt and say that he told the truth, and hence that $p \rightarrow q$ is true.

Definition 10 states that $p \rightarrow q$ is false whenever p is true and q is false and that $p \rightarrow q$ is true in the remaining three cases. The truth table for $p \rightarrow q$ is shown in Fig. 1.6.

p	q	$p \rightarrow q$
T	T	T
T	F	F
F	T	T
F	F	T

Fig. 1.6

The truth table for $p \rightarrow q$ contains all the information in Definition 10, and contains no extraneous information. Hence the truth table can be used as an alternative definition of $p \rightarrow q$.

In the conditional sentence $p \rightarrow q$, the sentence p is called the *hypothesis* [or *antecedent*] and the sentence q is called the *conclusion* [or *consequent*]. In mathematical theorems of the form $p \rightarrow q$, the hypothesis p and the conclusion q are so related that $p \rightarrow q$ cannot be false; i.e., if the hypothesis is true, then the conclusion cannot be false.

Since many theorems in mathematics are of the form $p \leftrightarrows q$, a study of the biconditional sentence is important.

Definition 11. *The biconditional sentence* $p \leftrightarrows q$ *is a true sentence if and only if both p and q are true sentences or both p and q are false sentences.*

Definition 11 is illustrated in the following examples.

Example 6. $(2 + 1 = 3) \leftrightarrows (1 + 4 = 5)$ is true.

Example 7. $(2 + 4 = 6) \leftrightarrows (6 + 0 = 0)$ is false.

Example 8. $(4 + 5 = 7) \leftrightarrows (2 + 1 = 6)$ is true.

Example 9. $(1 + 1 = 7) \leftrightarrows (2 + 5 = 7)$ is false.

Definition 11 states that $p \leftrightarrows q$ is true whenever both p and q have the same truth value and that $p \leftrightarrows q$ is false whenever p and q have different truth values. The basic truth table for $p \leftrightarrows q$ is shown in Fig. 1.7.

p	q	$p \rightleftarrows q$
T	T	T
T	F	F
F	T	F
F	F	T

Fig. 1.7

The basic truth table for $p \leftrightarrows q$ contains all the information contained in Definition 11 and no extraneous information. Hence the truth table can be used as an alternative definition of $p \leftrightarrows q$. In the following section we will *derive* another truth table for the biconditional.

EXERCISE SET 1.6

Compute the *truth value* of each of the following sentences.

1. $\sim(2 + 3 \neq 5)$.
2. $(4 + 3 = 7) \wedge (7 + 2 = 6)$.
3. $(4 + 3 = 7) \vee (7 + 2 = 6)$.
4. $(2 + 3 = 4 + 1) \rightarrow (3 + 0 = 3)$.
5. $(2 + 3 = 4 + 1) \leftrightarrows (3 + 0 = 3)$.
6. $(4 + 1 = 2) \leftrightarrows (2 + 1 = 3)$.
7. $(4 + 1 = 2) \rightarrow (2 + 1 = 3)$.
8. $(4 \neq 3)$ only if $\sim(3 = 4)$.
9. $(4 + 1 = 5) \rightarrow (2 + 3 = 2)$.
10. $(6 + 0 = 0) \rightarrow \sim(2 + 1 \neq 3)$.
11. $(4 + 2 \neq 2 + 4) \leftrightarrows (6 + 1 \neq 7)$.
12. $\forall x,\ [(x + 2 = 7) \leftrightarrows (x = 5)]$.
13. $\forall a$, if $a \cdot 0 = a$, then $a = 0$.
14. $(2 + 5 = 6) \leftrightarrows (1 + 1 = 2)$.
15. $(4 + 3 \neq 7) \leftrightarrows (2 + 4 = 6)$.
16. If $4 + 2 = 6$, then $5 + 1 = 6$.
17. $7 + 4 = 8$ if and only if $2 + 1 = 5$.
18. $6 + 1 = 5$ only if $2 + 1 = 3$.
19. $7 + 1 = 2$ if $1 + 2 = 3$.
20. $1 + 3 = 4$ only if $2 + 3 = 4$.
21. $(2 + 3) + 4 = 2 + (3 + 4)$.
22. $(2 + 3) + 4 = 4 + (2 + 3)$.

1.7 DERIVED TRUTH TABLES

The five truth tables we have presented thus far are *basic* truth tables in the sense that each is independent of the other four. However, it is possible to *derive* other truth tables from the five basic ones. For example, from the truth tables for the conditional sentence and the conjunction, we can derive the truth table in Fig. 1.8.

p	q	$p \rightarrow q$	$q \rightarrow p$	$(p \rightarrow q) \wedge (q \rightarrow p)$
T	T	T	T	T
T	F	F	T	F
F	T	T	F	F
F	F	T	T	T

Fig. 1.8

The reader should observe from Fig. 1.8 that $(p \rightarrow q) \wedge (q \rightarrow p)$ is true whenever p and q both have the same truth value and is false whenever p and q have different truth values. In Fig. 1.7, we observed that $p \rightarrow q$ is true whenever p and q both have the same truth value and is false whenever p and q have different truth values. That is, $p \leftrightarrows q$ and $(p \rightarrow q) \wedge (q \rightarrow p)$ have the same truth value. In other words, in lieu of Definition 11, we could have stated that $p \leftrightarrows q$ is true if and only if $p \rightarrow q$ is true and $q \rightarrow p$ is true. In that case, from Fig. 1.7 and Fig. 1.8 we could *derive* the truth table in Fig. 1.9. The reader should observe from Fig. 1.9 that the truth values of $p \leftrightarrows q$ are identical with the truth values of

$(p \rightarrow q) \wedge (q \rightarrow p)$.

$p \leftrightarrows q$	$(p \rightarrow q) \wedge (q \rightarrow p)$
T	T
F	F
F	F
T	T

Fig. 1.9

Since many mathematical theorems are biconditional statements, it is advantageous to employ Fig. 1.9 in lieu of Fig. 1.7. To prove a theorem of the form $p \leftrightarrows q$, it is sufficient to prove $p \rightarrow q$ and $q \rightarrow p$. For example, to prove the theorem $\triangle ABC$ is equilateral if and only if it is equiangular, we may prove the two theorems

If $\triangle ABC$ is equiangular, then $\triangle ABC$ is equilateral

and

If $\triangle ABC$ is equilateral, then $\triangle ABC$ is equiangular.

The following examples illustrate a method of deriving truth tables.

Example 1. Derive the truth table for $\sim(p \wedge q)$.

Since p, q, $p \wedge q$, and $\sim(p \wedge q)$ are all components of the given sentence, we make a column heading for each. The truth table is shown in the accompanying figure.

p	q	$p \wedge q$	$\sim(p \wedge q)$
T	T	T	F
T	F	F	T
F	T	F	T
F	F	F	T

Example 2. Derive the truth table for $\sim p \vee \sim q$.

Since p, q, $\sim p$, $\sim q$, and $\sim p \vee \sim q$ are components of the given sentence, we make a column heading for each. The truth table is shown in the accompanying figure.

p	q	$\sim p$	$\sim q$	$\sim p \vee \sim q$
T	T	F	F	F
T	F	F	T	T
F	T	T	F	T
F	F	T	T	T

Example 3. Derive the truth table for $[p \leftrightarrows q] \leftrightarrows [(p \to q) \wedge (q \to p)]$.

Since

$$p, \quad q, \quad p \to q, \quad q \to p, \quad p \leftrightarrows q,$$
$$(p \to q) \wedge (q \to p), \quad \text{and} \quad [p \leftrightarrows q] \leftrightarrows [(p \to q) \wedge (q \to p)]$$

are all components of the given sentence, we make a column heading for each. The truth table is shown in the accompanying figure.

p	q	$p \to q$	$q \to p$	$p \leftrightarrows q$	$(p \to q) \wedge (q \to p)$	$[p \leftrightarrows q]$ $\leftrightarrows [(p \to q) \wedge (q \to p)]$
T	T	T	T	T	T	T
T	F	F	T	F	F	T
F	T	T	F	F	F	T
F	F	T	T	T	T	T

Example 4. Derive the truth table for $\sim(p \to q) \leftrightharpoons (p \wedge \sim q)$.

Since p, q, $p \to q$, $\sim q$, $\sim(p \to q)$, $p \wedge \sim q$, and $\sim(p \to q) \leftrightharpoons (p \wedge \sim q)$ are all components of the original sentence, we make a column heading for each. The truth table is shown in the accompanying figure.

p	q	$p \to q$	$\sim q$	$\sim(p \to q)$	$p \wedge \sim q$	$\sim(p \to q) \leftrightharpoons (p \wedge \sim q)$
T	T	T	F	F	F	T
T	F	F	T	T	T	T
F	T	T	F	F	F	T
F	F	T	T	F	F	T

The reader should observe that every entry in the last column of the figure in Example 3 is "T" regardless of the truth values of p and q. Similarly, every entry in the last column of the figure in Example 4 is "T" regardless of the truth values of p and q. The word *tautology* [or *logical truth*] is used to describe such compound statements as

$$\sim(p \to q) \leftrightharpoons (p \wedge \sim q) \quad \text{and} \quad [p \leftrightharpoons q] \leftrightharpoons [(p \to q) \wedge (q \to p)].$$

Definition 12. *A compound statement which is true regardless of the truth values of the component statements is called a* **tautology** [*or* **logical truth**].

We observe from Figs. 1.3, 1.4, 1.5, 1.6, and 1.7 that $\sim p$, $p \vee q$, $p \wedge q$, $p \to q$, and $p \leftrightharpoons q$ are not *logical truths*.

In mathematics we are interested in logical truths because every logical truth is a theorem. In particular, any biconditional statement which is *logically true* [i.e., which is a logical truth] is a theorem called an *equivalence*. We define the relation *is equivalent to*.

Definition 13. *The sentence p* **is equivalent to** *the sentence q* [*denoted by* "$p \Leftrightarrow q$"] *if and only if the biconditional sentence $p \leftrightharpoons q$ is a logical truth. That is, $p \Leftrightarrow q$ if and only if $p \leftrightharpoons q$ is a logical truth.*

The relation *implies* is defined in a similar manner.

Definition 14. *The sentence p* **implies** *the sentence q* [*denoted by* "$p \Rightarrow q$"] *if and only if the conditional sentence $p \to q$ is a logical truth. That is, $p \Rightarrow q$ if and only if $p \to q$ is a logical truth.*

We may refer to "$p \Rightarrow q$" as an *implication* and to "$p \Leftrightarrow q$" as an *equivalence*.

Every mathematical theorem of the form $p \to q$ is an *implication*, and the hypothesis p *implies* the conclusion q. Moreover, every mathematical theorem of the form $p \leftrightharpoons q$ is an *equivalence*, in which

p **implies** q and q **implies** p.

For example, the theorem of arithmetic

$\forall a$, *a is odd if and only if a^2 is odd*

is an *equivalence*. The theorem

If a is any counting number, then 2a is an even counting number

is an *implication*, but not an equivalence.

Example 5. Derive the truth table for $(p \rightarrow q) \leftrightarrows (\tilde{} p \vee q)$.

The truth table shown in the accompanying figure demonstrates that the conditional sentence $p \rightarrow q$ is equivalent to the disjunction $\tilde{} p \vee q$.

p	q	$\tilde{} p$	$p \rightarrow q$	$\tilde{} p \vee q$	$(p \rightarrow q) \leftrightarrows (\tilde{} p \vee q)$
T	T	F	T	T	T
T	F	F	F	F	T
F	T	T	T	T	T
F	F	T	T	T	T

Since $(p \rightarrow q) \leftrightarrows (\tilde{} p \vee q)$ is logically true, we see that

$(p \rightarrow q) \Leftrightarrow (\tilde{} p \vee q)$.

Example 6. Derive the truth table for $(p \vee q) \wedge r$.

Since $p, q, r, p \vee q$, and $(p \vee q) \wedge r$ are all components of the given sentence, we make a column heading for each. The truth table shown in the accompanying figure contains 8 rows of entries rather than 4.

p	q	r	$p \vee q$	$(p \vee q) \wedge r$
T	T	T	T	T
T	T	F	T	F
T	F	T	T	T
T	F	F	T	F
F	T	T	T	T
F	T	F	T	F
F	F	T	F	F
F	F	F	F	F

Example 7. Derive the truth table for $p \vee (q \wedge r)$.

Since p, q, r, $q \wedge r$, and $p \vee (q \wedge r)$ are all components of the given sentence, we make a column heading for each.

p	q	r	$q \wedge r$	$p \vee (q \wedge r)$
T	T	T	T	T
T	T	F	F	T
T	F	T	F	T
T	F	F	F	T
F	T	T	T	T
F	T	F	F	F
F	F	T	F	F
F	F	F	F	F

Comparison of the last column of the truth table of Example 6 with that of Example 7 proves that $(p \vee q) \wedge r$ is *not* equivalent to $p \vee (q \wedge r)$, because the truth values of $(p \vee q) \wedge r$ are not identical with the truth values of $p \vee (q \wedge r)$. Thus it is essential to punctuate with parentheses, brackets, or other marks whenever both connectives *or* and *and* are involved. If we omitted the punctuation, the expression would be ambiguous; that is, the expression $p \vee q \wedge r$ is ambiguous and hence is not a sentence. Similarly, the expression $p \wedge q \vee r$ is *not* a sentence.

The reader should observe that the sentence $p \wedge {\sim}p$ is *logically false*; that is, $p \wedge {\sim}p$ is false regardless of whether p is true or p is false. Moreover, $p \vee {\sim}p$ is *logically* true.

BASIC LAWS GOVERNING SENTENCES

Laws Involving Disjunction Only	Laws Involving Conjunction Only
$(p \vee q) \Leftrightarrow (q \vee p)$	$(p \wedge q) \Leftrightarrow (q \wedge p)$
$[(p \vee q) \vee r] \Leftrightarrow [p \vee (q \vee r)]$	$[(p \wedge q) \wedge r] \Leftrightarrow [p \wedge (q \wedge r)]$
$(p \vee f) \Leftrightarrow p$	$(p \wedge t) \Leftrightarrow p$
$(p \vee {\sim}p) \Leftrightarrow t$	$(p \wedge {\sim}p) \Leftrightarrow f$

Laws Involving Disjunction and Conjunction

$$[p \wedge (q \vee r)] \Leftrightarrow [(p \wedge q) \vee (p \wedge r)]$$
$$[p \vee (q \wedge r)] \Leftrightarrow [(p \vee q) \wedge (p \vee r)]$$

Fig. 1.10

For future reference, in Fig. 1.10 we list some of the *basic logical truths*. Since all of them are biconditional sentences, they are equivalences. As usual, p, q, and r are *any statements*. Moreover, t is a *logically true statement* and f is a *logically false statement*. Thus

$$(p \vee {\sim}p) \Leftrightarrow t$$

states that $p \vee {\sim}p$ is *logically true.* Similarly,

$$(p \wedge {\sim}p) \Leftrightarrow f$$

states that $p \wedge {\sim}p$ is *logically false.*

The basic laws listed in Fig. 1.10 and the additional laws listed in Fig. 1.11 can be proved by truth table analysis.

ADDITIONAL LAWS GOVERNING SENTENCES

$(p \vee p) \Leftrightarrow p$	(Idempotent Law)
$(p \wedge p) \Leftrightarrow p$	(Idempotent Law)
${\sim}(p \vee q) \Leftrightarrow ({\sim}p \wedge {\sim}q)$	(De Morgan's Law)
${\sim}(p \wedge q) \Leftrightarrow ({\sim}p \vee {\sim}q)$	(De Morgan's Law)
$(p \vee t) \Leftrightarrow t$	
$(p \wedge f) \Leftrightarrow f$	
${\sim}{\sim}p \Leftrightarrow p$	
${\sim}t \Leftrightarrow f$	
${\sim}f \Leftrightarrow t$	

Fig. 1.11

Since it is frequently necessary to negate $p \to q$, we recall the following equivalence from Example 4:

$$ {\sim}(p \to q) \Leftrightarrow (p \wedge {\sim}q). $$

For example, the negation of

If Dale works hard, then he prospers

is

Dale works hard and he does not prosper.

It is important to understand that $p \wedge {\sim}q$ is the negation of $p \to q$. In Section 1.9, the reader will study *proof by contradiction.* To prove that $p \to q$ is true by contradiction, we assume that p is true and q is false; i.e., we assume that $p \wedge {\sim}q$ is true. This is equivalent to assuming that $p \to q$ is false.

The reader should also recall from Example 5 that $(p \to q) \Leftrightarrow ({\sim}p \vee q)$.

EXERCISE SET 1.7

I. Derive the truth table for each of the following.

1. $p \to (p \vee q)$.

2. $q \to (p \vee q)$.

3. $(p \vee q) \to p$.

4. $(p \vee q) \to q$.

5. $p \leftrightarrows (p \vee q)$.

6. $q \leftrightarrows (p \vee q)$.

7. $(p \rightarrow q) \leftrightarrows (q \rightarrow p)$.

8. $(\sim p \rightarrow \sim q) \leftrightarrows (\sim q \rightarrow \sim p)$.

9. $(p \rightarrow q) \leftrightarrows (\sim q \rightarrow \sim p)$.

10. $(q \rightarrow p) \rightarrow (p \rightarrow q)$.

11. $(p \rightarrow q) \rightarrow (\sim p \rightarrow \sim q)$.

12. $(\sim p \vee q) \leftrightarrows \sim (p \wedge \sim q)$.

13. $\sim (p \wedge \sim q) \leftrightarrows (p \rightarrow q)$.

14. $(\sim p \rightarrow q) \leftrightarrows (p \vee q)$.

15. $\sim (p \rightleftarrows q) \leftrightarrows [(p \wedge \sim q) \vee (q \wedge \sim p)]$.

II. Decide which of the statements of Exercise I are logical truths.

III. Prove that each of the following is an *equivalence* (i.e., a logically true biconditional).

1. $(p \vee q) \leftrightarrows (q \vee p)$.

2. $(p \wedge q) \leftrightarrows (q \wedge p)$.

3. $[(p \wedge q) \wedge r] \leftrightarrows [p \wedge (q \wedge r)]$.

4. $(p \vee p) \leftrightarrows p$.

5. $(p \wedge p) \leftrightarrows p$.

6. $\sim (p \vee q) \leftrightarrows (\sim p \wedge \sim q)$.

7. $(2 + 3 = 5) \leftrightarrows [(2 + 3) + 4 = 5 + 4]$.

8. $(q \rightarrow p) \leftrightarrows (\sim p \rightarrow \sim q)$.

9. $[(p \wedge \sim q) \vee (q \wedge \sim p)] \leftrightarrows [(p \rightarrow q) \rightarrow (q \wedge \sim p)]$.

10. $\sim (p \vee q) \leftrightarrows \sim (\sim p \rightarrow q)$.

IV. Negate each of the following sentences.

1. $(3 + 4 = 8) \leftrightarrows (2 + 0 = 0)$.

2. If it doesn't rain, then John will go to town.

3. A triangle is equilateral if and only if it is equiangular.

4. Dan will do his mathematics assignment only if he stays home.

5. $4 + 5 \neq 8$ or $6 + 2 = 8$.

6. $\sim (p \vee q) \leftrightarrows (\sim p \wedge \sim q)$.

7. $(p \vee q) \rightarrow p$.

8. $(p \rightarrow q) \leftrightarrows (\sim p \vee q)$.

9. $\sim (p \rightarrow q) \leftrightarrows (p \wedge \sim q)$.

10. $[p \wedge (q \vee r)] \rightarrow [(p \wedge q) \vee (p \wedge r)]$.

1.8 CONVERSE, INVERSE, AND CONTRAPOSITIVE

In the preceding section we learned that the statement

$$p \leftrightarrows q$$

is equivalent to the statement

$$(p \rightarrow q) \wedge (q \rightarrow p).$$

For example, the statement

$\triangle ABC$ is equilateral if and only if $\triangle ABC$ is equiangular

is equivalent to the *conjunction* of the statements

If $\triangle ABC$ is equilateral, then $\triangle ABC$ is equiangular

and

If $\triangle ABC$ is equiangular, then $\triangle ABC$ is equilateral.

Each of the latter two statements is called the *converse* of the other. Thus the converse of $p \rightarrow q$ is $q \rightarrow p$. The converse of any conditional statement is that conditional statement which results from the given statement when the antecedent (hypothesis) and consequent (conclusion) are interchanged.

Definition 15. *The* **converse** *of* $p \rightarrow q$ *is* $q \rightarrow p$.

Although both conditional statements above concerning triangles are true, the converse of a true statement may be false. For example, the statement

If Mr. Jones can see, then Mr. Jones is alive

is true, whereas its converse

If Mr. Jones is alive, then Mr. Jones can see

may be false. Students frequently commit errors in mathematical proofs by assuming that the converse of a theorem is also true.

Similarly, the statement

$$\tilde{p} \rightarrow \tilde{q}$$

is not equivalent to the statement

$$p \rightarrow q.$$

The statement $\tilde{p} \rightarrow \tilde{q}$ is called the *inverse* of $p \rightarrow q$.

Definition 16. *The* **inverse** *of* $p \rightarrow q$ *is* $\tilde{p} \rightarrow \tilde{q}$.

For example, the inverse of

If Mr. Jones can see, then Mr. Jones is alive

is

If Mr. Jones cannot see, then Mr. Jones is not alive.

Although the original sentence is true, the inverse may be false.

However, we can prove that $\tilde{q} \rightarrow \tilde{p}$ is actually equivalent to $p \rightarrow q$. The statement $\tilde{q} \rightarrow \tilde{p}$ is called the *contrapositive* of $p \rightarrow q$.

Definition 17.   *The **contrapositive** of $p \rightarrow q$ is $\sim q \rightarrow \sim p$.*

For example, the contrapositive of

If Mr. Jones can see, then Mr. Jones is alive

is

If Mr. Jones is not alive, then Mr. Jones cannot see.

Although the converse of a true statement may be false and the inverse of a true statement may be false, we see that the contrapositive of a true statement is necessarily true. Hence, in proving any theorem,

we may replace any previously proved theorem by its contrapositive.

However,

we may not replace a theorem by its converse or inverse.

The relationship between a conditional statement and its contrapositive and the relationship between the inverse and converse of the conditional statement are illustrated in Figs. 1.12 and 1.13. That is, Figs. 1.12 and 1.13 illustrate the fact that the contrapositive of a given conditional statement is equivalent to the given statement, and that the converse of the given statement is equivalent to the inverse of the given statement, but *not* to the given statement.

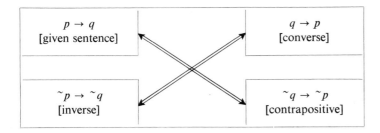

Fig. 1.12

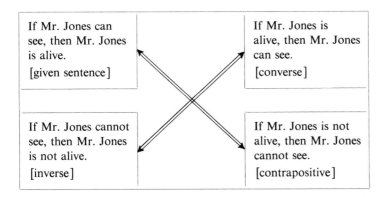

Fig. 1.13

EXERCISE SET 1.8

I. State the converse, inverse, and contrapositive of each of the following statements.

1. If Tommy earns less than $6000 per year, then Tommy earns less than $7000 per year.
2. If $\triangle ABC$ is congruent to $\triangle DEF$, then $\triangle ABC$ is similar to $\triangle DEF$.
3. If $\triangle ABC$ is equilateral, then $\triangle ABC$ is isosceles.
4. If today is Monday, then tomorrow will be Tuesday.
5. If a is an odd number, then a^2 is an odd number.
6. If $ABCD$ is a square, then $ABCD$ is a rectangle.
7. If $ABCD$ is a parallelogram, then $ABCD$ is a rectangle.
8. If $ABCD$ is a parallelogram, then $ABCD$ is a square.
9. If Johnnie is a person, then Johnnie is a girl.
10. If Kim is a boy, then Kim is a person.

II. Decide whether each statement of Exercise I is *true* or *false*.

III. Decide whether the converse of each statement of Exercise I is *true* or *false*.

IV. Decide whether the inverse of each statement of Exercise I is *true* or *false*.

V. Decide whether the contrapositive of each statement of Exercise I is *true* or *false*.

VI. Decide whether each of the following statements is *true* or *false*.

1. The contrapositive of the contrapositive of $p \rightarrow q$ is $p \rightarrow q$.
2. The inverse of the inverse of $p \rightarrow q$ is $p \rightarrow q$.
3. The converse of the converse of $p \rightarrow q$ is $p \rightarrow q$.
4. The converse of the inverse of $p \rightarrow q$ is $\tilde{~}q \rightarrow \tilde{~}p$.
5. The inverse of the converse of $p \rightarrow q$ is $\tilde{~}q \rightarrow \tilde{~}p$.
6. The contrapositive of the inverse of $p \rightarrow q$ is $q \rightarrow p$.
7. The contrapositive of the converse of $p \rightarrow q$ is $\tilde{~}p \rightarrow \tilde{~}q$.
8. The converse of the contrapositive of $p \rightarrow q$ is $\tilde{~}p \rightarrow \tilde{~}q$.
9. The inverse of the contrapositive of $p \rightarrow q$ is $q \rightarrow p$.
10. The inverse of $\tilde{~}p \rightarrow q$ is $p \rightarrow \tilde{~}q$.
11. The contrapositive of $\tilde{~}p \rightarrow \tilde{~}q$ is $q \rightarrow p$.
12. The contrapositive of $p \rightarrow \tilde{~}q$ is $q \rightarrow \tilde{~}p$.

VII. State the converse, inverse, and contrapositive of each of the following statements.

1. $(p \wedge q) \rightarrow r$.
2. $(p \wedge \tilde{~}q) \rightarrow \tilde{~}r$.
3. $(\tilde{~}p \vee q) \rightarrow (p \rightarrow q)$.
4. $(p \vee \tilde{~}q) \rightarrow (\tilde{~}p \wedge q)$.
5. $(p \vee q) \rightarrow (\tilde{~}q \vee r)$.
6. $(p \rightarrow q) \rightarrow [r \rightarrow (s \wedge p)]$.

1.9 THE NATURE OF PROOF

In order to prove a theorem of the form $p \rightarrow q$, in which p may be a compound statement, we accept p [the *hypothesis*] as true and prove that q [the *conclusion*] follows logically from p [by means of the laws of logic and the previous theorems]. For example, to prove

$$[(p \rightarrow q) \wedge p] \rightarrow q,$$

we accept the hypothesis, $(p \rightarrow q) \wedge p$, and prove that the conclusion, q, follows logically from the hypothesis [and the laws of logic].* We may arrange the argument as follows, in which H1, H2, etc., represent the hypotheses and C represents the conclusion.

> H1: $p \rightarrow q$
> H2: p [VALID]
> —————
> C : q

By truth table analysis we can prove that the above argument is *valid*; i.e., we can prove that

$$[(p \rightarrow q) \wedge p] \rightarrow q$$

is logically true. In other words, *the conclusion follows logically from the hypotheses.*

Definition 18. *Any argument in which the conjunction of the hypotheses implies the conclusion is called* **a valid argument**.

To prove that an argument is valid, we may use truth table analysis or we may reason logically from step to step until we reach the desired conclusion. For example, in the above theorem, since we are accepting the hypothesis $p \rightarrow q$ as true, and since we know that $p \rightarrow q$ is false if and only if p is true and q is false, we know that q must be true whenever p is true. But by the hypothesis H2 we know that p is true. Hence the conclusion q follows logically from the hypotheses.

The reader should satisfy himself that the following arguments are *invalid*; i.e., in each case, *the conclusion does not follow logically from the hypotheses.*

> H1: $p \rightarrow q$ H1: $p \rightarrow q$
> H2: q [INVALID]   H2: $\tilde{\ }p$ [INVALID]
> —————   —————
> C : p C : $\tilde{\ }q$
> [*Converse reasoning*]   [*Inverse reasoning*]

To prove that each of the above arguments is invalid, we may exhibit a *counterexample.* That is, we exhibit an example in which H1 and H2 are true and C is false.

———————————————————————————

*   This pattern of proof is used frequently in mathematics. In particular, if we know that r is true and we wish to prove that s is true, we frequently prove that $r \rightarrow s$ is true and then we *infer* that s is true.

The following argument, *based on the contrapositive*, is *valid*.

H1: $p \rightarrow q$
H2: $\tilde{\ }q$ [VALID]
C : $\tilde{\ }p$

[*Contrapositive reasoning*]

The reason that the above argument is valid is that the contrapositive of $p \rightarrow q$ is equivalent to $p \rightarrow q$. Thus we may replace $p \rightarrow q$ by its contrapositive, $\tilde{\ }q \rightarrow \tilde{\ }p$. The above argument may be replaced by the following argument.

H1: $\tilde{\ }q \rightarrow \tilde{\ }p$
H2: $\tilde{\ }q$
C : $\tilde{\ }p$

The immediately preceding argument is *valid* because it has the same form as the first valid argument, which we exhibit as follows.

H1: $r \rightarrow s$
H2: r
C : s

In this argument, r corresponds to $\tilde{\ }q$ and s corresponds to $\tilde{\ }p$. Hence the conclusion, $\tilde{\ }p$, follows logically from the two hypotheses $\tilde{\ }q \rightarrow \tilde{\ }p$ and $\tilde{\ }q$.

The indirect method of proof [frequently called *reductio ad absurdum* (*RAA*) for *reduction to an absurdity*, or *proof by contradiction*] is related to the *contrapositive*. In the indirect method we assume that the desired conclusion is false and hence that its negation is true. We use the negation of the desired conclusion as another hypothesis and derive a contradiction of the form $r \wedge \tilde{\ }r$. Since $r \wedge \tilde{\ }r$ is logically false, we conclude that the assumption of the negation of the desired conclusion is absurd. Hence the desired conclusion is true. The indirect method of proof is valid because the following argument is valid; the reader may prove the validity by truth table analysis.

H1: p
H2: $(p \wedge \tilde{\ }q) \rightarrow (r \wedge \tilde{\ }r)$
C : q

Thus to prove a theorem of the form $p \rightarrow q$ by the indirect method, *we assume that $p \rightarrow q$ is false. Under this assumption p is true and q is false.* Our hypotheses are now p and $\tilde{\ }q$. If we can derive a contradiction [a statement of the form $r \wedge \tilde{\ }r$], we conclude that $p \rightarrow q$ is true.

For example, if we are given the axiom

If P_1 and P_2 are any distinct points, then there is exactly one line $\mathcal{L}$ which contains P_1 and P_2

and we wish to prove the theorem

> If $\mathscr{L}_1$ and $\mathscr{L}_2$ are any distinct lines whose intersection is nonempty, then the intersection of $\mathscr{L}_1$ and $\mathscr{L}_2$ is exactly one point,

we assume that the theorem is false and derive a contradiction. Thus we assume that the hypothesis of the theorem is true and the conclusion is false. In this case,

1. $\mathscr{L}_1$ and $\mathscr{L}_2$ are distinct lines whose intersection is nonempty, and
2. the intersection of $\mathscr{L}_1$ and $\mathscr{L}_2$ contains [at least] two distinct points P_1 and P_2.

Thus the two distinct lines $\mathscr{L}_1$ and $\mathscr{L}_2$ contain the two distinct points P_1 and P_2. But, by the axiom, there is *exactly one* line which contains both P_1 and P_2. The last two statements are contradictory; i.e., their conjunction is of the form $r \wedge \sim r$. Hence the assumption is false, and thus the conclusion of the theorem is true. The reader will observe the relationship of RAA to the contrapositive. To prove $p \to q$ by RAA, we *assume* that q is *false*; that is, we assume $\sim q$. If we can prove $\sim p$ *from this assumption*, then we can conclude that $\sim q \to \sim p$ is true. But $\sim q \to \sim p$ is the *contrapositive* of $p \to q$.

Frequently in high school geometry, proofs of theorems are given in the statement–reason form indicated below.

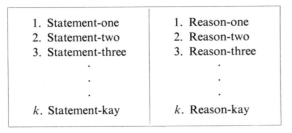

1. Statement-one	1. Reason-one
2. Statement-two	2. Reason-two
3. Statement-three	3. Reason-three
.	.
.	.
.	.
k. Statement-kay	k. Reason-kay

The last statement, statement-kay, is usually the conclusion of the theorem. Sometimes the symbol "*QED*" for "*quod erat demonstrandum*," Latin for "which was to be demonstrated," is written to indicate the end of the proof.

The particular form of the proof of a theorem is not important. The *important characteristic of any proof is its validity, its logical soundness, rather than its form.*

If we observe that a certain statement is true in many cases and do not observe any cases in which it is false, we *conjecture* that the statement is true in general. For example, if we observe that 1^2 is odd, 3^2 is odd, 5^2 is odd, 7^2 is odd, ..., then we conjecture that the square of every odd number is odd. Whenever we make a conjecture, we should attempt to *prove the conjecture* and thereby discover a *theorem*. If all attempts to prove the conjecture fail, we may then suspect that the conjecture is false and hence is not a theorem. In this case, we should attempt to *disprove* the conjecture; i.e., we should attempt to prove that the conjecture is false. If the quantifier *all* is involved, we can disprove the conjecture by exhibiting one *counterexample*. For instance, we can disprove the statement

> *All birds fly*

by exhibiting one bird which does not fly. Similarly, to disprove the statement

> *All primes are odd*

we merely exhibit the number 2, which is prime but not odd.

To prove a theorem we should know exactly what we wish to prove and then we should devise a *plan of attack*. Random manipulation of symbols seldom produces a proof. If the direct method fails, we should try the indirect method. If all methods fail, we should suspect that the statement may not be a theorem at all, but only a conjecture which is false. In this case we should try to *disprove* it by exhibiting a *counterexample*.

EXERCISE SET 1.9

I. Choose particular statements for p and q, and illustrate the following valid argument. Then employ truth table analysis to prove the validity.

> H1: $p \rightarrow q$
> H2: p
> _____
> C : q

II. By counterexample, prove that each of the following arguments is invalid.

> 1. H1: $p \rightarrow q$
>   H2: q
>   _____
>   C : p

> 2. H1: $p \rightarrow q$
>   H2: $\sim p$
>   _____
>   C : $\sim q$

III. Choose *particular* statements for p, q, and r, and illustrate the following valid argument. Then employ truth table analysis to prove the validity.

> H1: p
> H2: $(p \wedge \sim q) \rightarrow (r \wedge \sim r)$
> _____
> C : q

IV. Prove the following theorems of arithmetic.

1. If a is any odd number, then a^2 is an odd number.

2. If b is any even number, then b^2 is an even number.

3. If a^2 is an odd number, then a is an odd number.

4. If b^2 is an even number, then b is an even number.

V. Disprove each of the following statements.

1. If angle A is of the same measure as angle B, then angle A and angle B are vertical angles.

2. If $\triangle ABC$ is isosceles, then it is equilateral.

3. If $\triangle ABC$ is a right triangle, then $\triangle ABC$ is isosceles.

4. If P_1, P_2, and P_3 are three distinct points, then there is a unique circle containing (passing through) P_1, P_2, and P_3.

VI. Prove that each of the following arguments is valid. [Recall that every hypothesis is accepted as true.]

1. H1: $p \vee q$
   H2: $\sim p$
   C : q

2. H1: $p \vee \sim q$
   H2: $\sim p$
   C: $\sim q$

3. H1: $p \leftrightarrows q$
   H2: q
   C : p

4. H1: $\sim(p \wedge q)$
   H2: p
   C : $\sim q$

5. H1: $\sim p \vee \sim q$
   H2: p
   C : $\sim q$

6. H1: $\sim(p \wedge q)$
   H2: q
   C : $\sim p$

7. H1: $p \leftrightarrows q$
   H2: $p \rightarrow r$
   H3: q
   C : r

8. H1: $p \rightarrow q$
   H2: $q \rightarrow r$
   C : $p \rightarrow r$

9. H1: $p \rightarrow q$
   H2: $q \rightarrow r$
   H3: $r \rightarrow s$
   H4: $\sim s$
   C : $\sim q$

10. H1: $p \rightarrow q$
    H2: $\sim r \rightarrow \sim q$
    H3 p
    C : r

PUZZLE PROBLEMS

1. In a student's drawer there are 12 blue socks and 18 red socks. How many socks must he withdraw from the drawer (without checking the colors) to be certain that he has two socks of the same color?

2. There are 30 tennis players in a singles championship tournament. How many matches must be played to determine the winner?

3. On a prehistoric island there were two tribes, Tribe T and Tribe F. The members of Tribe F were inveterate prevaricators, and the members of Tribe T were unfailingly veracious. One day the tax collector asked the first of three inhabitants, "To which tribe do you belong?" The reply was indiscernible to the tax collector. The second inhabitant said, "He said he belongs to Tribe T. He is telling the truth." The third said, "The second is lying." Identify the tribe to which each man belongs.

4. One day the king became irritated at the court jester and said to him, "Jester, I will permit you to make one statement. If your statement is true, I'll shoot

you; if your statement is false, I'll hang you." The jester thought for a moment and then made a statement which forced the king to spare his life. What statement did the jester make?

5. Three university professors—Professor Smith, Professor Robinson, and Professor Jones—live in the Greater Boston region. A lawyer, an engineer, and a banker also live in Greater Boston. Their names (not necessarily in the order listed) are also Smith, Robinson, and Jones. To avoid confusion we agree to use only the title *Professor* for each professor and the title *Mr.* for each of the others. Professor Robinson and the banker live in Reading, Professor Jones and the lawyer live in Boston, and Professor Smith and the engineer live halfway between Reading and Boston. The banker's namesake earns exactly $20,000 per year, and the engineer earns exactly $\frac{5}{7}$ as much as the professor living nearest him. Moreover, Mr. Smith beat the lawyer at golf. What is the engineer's name?

Chapter 2

Sets

George Ferdinand Ludwig Philipp Cantor was born in St. Petersburg, Russia, on March 3, 1845. His father was a prosperous merchant and his mother was an artist. When Cantor was 11 years old, his family moved to Frankfurt, Germany, and before the age of 15 he received recognition for his great talent in mathematics. He wanted to be a mathematician, but his father was determined to force him into engineering as a more rewarding profession financially. When he was 17 years old, his father relented and permitted him to pursue a university career in mathematics. In 1867, at the age of 22, he received his Ph.D. degree from the University of Berlin.

All of Cantor's work published before he was 29 was excellent but very conservative. In none of it was there the slightest hint of the radical originator he was to become. In 1874, at the age of 29, Cantor published his first revolutionary paper on the theory of infinite sets. In his paper he undertook to establish a quite unexpected property of the set of all algebraic numbers; namely, that the set of positive integers, which is a proper subset of the set of all algebraic numbers, contains exactly as many members as (i.e., is equivalent to) the set of algebraic numbers. Since Cantor's reasoning in his theory of infinite sets is mostly nonconstructive, some of his contemporaries regarded it as mathematical insanity. Repeated attacks by critics on his theory of sets caused the hypersensitive Cantor to suffer a complete breakdown at the age of 40. Although he recovered partially, he suffered recurring breakdowns throughout the remainder of his long life. In 1918 Cantor died in a mental hospital.

At the beginning of the twentieth century Cantor's work gradually came to be accepted as a basic contribution to all mathematics and especially to the foundations of analysis. However, at about the same time, paradoxes began to appear in his theory of sets. One of the better known paradoxes was posed by Bertrand Russell, and is known as *Russell's Paradox*. Russell's Paradox relates to the question, "Is the set of all sets which are not members of themselves a member of itself?" Either answer, *yes* or *no,* is incorrect.

The flaws in Cantor's work may be the greatest contribution which Cantor's theory is destined to make to mathematics. Their existence in the foundation of the mathematics of the infinite has been the direct inspiration for the present critical movement in all deductive reasoning.

CANTOR
(1845–1918)

Chapter 2

Sets

2.1 SETS AND SUBSETS

In Chapter 1 we learned that some words in mathematics are left undefined and
other words are defined in terms of the undefined words. This procedure simplifies
our work and helps us to avoid circular definitions. Moreover, many people have
intuitive ideas of the meanings of many words which they cannot define. The
reader probably has a well-formulated intuitive idea of *set*, which we *do not define*
in this text. However, we *illustrate* the concept by means of the following examples:

1. All students in a classroom
2. All books in a classroom
3. All professors in a classroom
4. All monkeys in a classroom
5. All dishes in a kitchen cabinet
6. All silverware in a silver chest
7. All furniture in a living room
8. All golf clubs in Lionel Hebert's golf bag
9. All tools in a carpenter's tool chest
10. All instruments in a surgeon's bag.

We note that it is customary for people to refer to some of the above listed
sets as sets. Usually, we speak of the *set* of dishes, the silverware *set*, the living
room *set*, and the *set* of golf clubs. The use of the word set to refer to a *collection*,
aggregate, or *family** of objects or things is not new. However, the use of the word

---

*   In elementary school textbooks the word *group* is sometimes used as a synonym for
set. In Chapter 6 we will learn that the word *group* is used to denote another mathematical
concept.

set to refer to a collection of numbers, points, or people is relatively new in the schools. In mathematics, the word set is used to refer to any collection of numbers, things, people, or other objects. The numbers, things, people, or other objects in the set are called *members*, or *elements*, of the set.* For example, each piece of furniture in a living room set is an *element*, or *member*, of the living room set.

We agree in mathematics to consider only sets which are *well defined*.

*A set is **well defined** if and only if it is decidable whether a given object, number, or person is an element of the set.*

The sets in the above examples are well defined. However, the set of large numbers is not well defined; there is no universal agreement on what a large number is.

One way to represent a set is to *name* it by a capital letter such as *A*, *B*, or *C*, and use the name in referring to it. For example, when we write

$B = $ the set of all books in the University library,

we are *naming* the set of all books in the library by the letter *B*. This is analogous to naming a person.

A second way to represent a set is to *list* its elements in braces. For example, we can represent the set of counting numbers from 5 through 9 by *listing* the numbers 5, 6, 7, 8, and 9 in braces as follows:

$\{5, 6, 7, 8, 9\}$.

A third way to represent a set is to *describe* it, and use the description in referring to it. For example, we are *describing* $\{5, 6, 7, 8, 9\}$ when we refer to it as

the set of counting numbers from 5 through 9.

A fourth way to represent a set is to use the *set builder* notation. For example, in the set builder notation, we can represent the set $\{0, 2, 4, 6, \ldots\}$ as

$\{x : x$ is an even counting number$\}$

and say

the set of all x such that x is an even counting number.

We use the symbol "ϵ" to indicate that a certain number, object, or person is an element, or member, of a given set. For example, if

$A = \{1, 3, 5\}$,

then

$1 \in A$, $3 \in A$, $5 \in A$,   but $4 \notin A$.

If $B = \{1, 3, 5, \ldots, 35\}$, we see that $1 \in B$, $3 \in B$, $21 \in B$, $29 \in B$, etc., but $6 \notin B$, $34 \notin B$, $41 \notin B$, etc. The three dots ($\ldots$) indicate that the established pattern is to

---

*   We may say that any element of a set *belongs* to the set.

be continued. Although not all elements of B appear in the listing, as indicated by the three dots, it is understood that they are present and listed.

Definition 1. *The set X is said to be a **subset** of the set Y [denoted by "$X \subset Y$"] if and only if every element of X is an element of Y. That is, $X \subset Y$ if and only if $x \in X \Rightarrow x \in Y$.*

For example, if $A = \{1, 3, 5\}$ and $B = \{1, 3, 5, \ldots, 35\}$, then A is a subset of B. Thus we write "$A \subset B$." However, since B is *not* a subset of A, we write "$B \not\subset A$." If $C = \{1, 3, 5, \ldots\}$ and $D = \{1, 2, 3, \ldots\}$, we see that $C \subset D$; moreover, $B \subset C$, $B \subset D$, $A \subset C$, and $A \subset D$.

It follows from Definition 1 that if $X \subset Y$ and $Y \subset Z$, then $X \subset Z$.

Before we define *proper subset* we agree that *the set X is equal to the set Y [denoted by "$X = Y$"] if and only if every element of X is an element of Y and every element of Y is an element of X.** It follows from the above assumption and Definition 1 that $X = Y$ if and only if $X \subset Y$ and $Y \subset X$.

The negation of $X \subset Y$ is $X \not\subset Y$. Since $X \subset Y$ if and only if every element of X is an element of Y, it follows that $X \not\subset Y$ if and only if there exists (at least) one element of X which is not an element of Y.

Definition 2. *The set X is said to be a **proper subset** of the set Y [denoted by "$X \subsetneqq Y$"]† if and only if $X \subset Y$ and $X \neq Y$.*

For example, we observe the following relationships between the above listed sets.

$$A \subsetneqq B, \qquad B \subsetneqq C, \qquad C \subsetneqq D, \qquad A \subsetneqq C, \qquad A \subsetneqq D, \qquad B \subsetneqq D.$$

However, if $E = \{0, 2, 4, 6, 8\}$ and $F =$ the set of one-digit even counting numbers, then $E \subset F$ and $F \subset E$, but neither is a proper subset of the other because $E = F$. Any set X is a *subset* of itself but not a *proper subset* of itself.

EXERCISE SET 2.1

I.

1. Give three examples of sets which are not well defined.

2. What are four ways of specifying a set?

3. In your own words, explain what a proper subset of a given set is.

4. List six proper subsets of $\{1, 2, 3\}$.

5. List a subset of $\{1, 2, 3\}$ which is not a proper subset of $\{1, 2, 3\}$.

6. List seven subsets of $\{1, 2, 3\}$.

---

*   The assumption that $X = Y$ if and only if every element of X is an element of Y and every element of Y is an element of X is known as the *axiom of extent*.

†   Some authors use the notation "$X \subseteq Y$" to signify that X is a subset of Y and the notation "$X \subset Y$" to signify that X is a proper subset of Y. The notation "$X \subsetneqq Y$" to signify that X is a proper subset of Y emphasizes that X is a subset of Y but is not equal to Y.

II. Let $A = \{1, 4, 7, 10, \ldots\}$. By means of a sentence of the form "$a \in A$" or "$a \notin A$," tell which of the following numbers are members of A and which are not members of A.

1. 1   2. 11
3. 13   4. 22
5. 99   6. 100
7. 0   8. 301
9. 1000   10. 996

2.2 UNIVERSE, COMPLEMENT, AND EMPTY SET

It is frequently convenient or necessary to limit the set of elements which we wish to consider in a given discussion or problem. For example, in a kindergarten class the teacher may limit consideration of all numbers to the set

$$\{0, 1, 2, 3, 4, 5, 6, 7, 8, 9, \}.$$

However, in a college mathematics class the teacher may wish to consider other numbers as well. For example, so far we have considered only the counting numbers; i.e., the set from which we have chosen all numbers is $\{0, 1, 2, 3, \ldots\}$. The set to which consideration is limited in a given problem or discussion is called the *universal set* (or *universe*)* and is denoted by "*U.*" Since the reader probably has an intuitive understanding of it, we do not attempt to define *universe* but rely on the above explanation and the reader's intuition.

Since the universe (in a given discussion) contains all elements we wish to consider, it follows that every set X (in the discussion) is a subset of U; that is, $X \subset U$.

Definition 3. *The **complement** of any set X [denoted by "$\tilde{X}$" or "$U \setminus X$"] is the set of all elements of U which are not in X. That is, $\tilde{X} = \{y: y \in U \text{ and } y \notin X\}$.*

For example, if

$$U = \{1, 2, 3, 4, 5, 6, 7, 8, 9\} \quad \text{and} \quad A = \{1, 3, 5, 7, 9\},$$

then

$$\tilde{A} = \{2, 4, 6, 8\}.$$

If

$$B = \{3, 6, 9\},$$

then

$$\tilde{B} = \{1, 2, 4, 5, 7, 8\}.$$

Definition 4. *The **relative complement** of any set X with respect to any set Y [denoted by "$Y \setminus X$"] is the set of all elements of Y which are not elements of X. That is, $Y \setminus X = \{y: y \in Y \text{ and } y \notin X\}$.*

---

*   Other names for the universe are *universe of discourse* and *domain of discourse*.

For example, if

$$U = \{1, 2, 3, 4, 5, 6, 7, 8, 9\},$$
$$A = \{2, 4, 6, 8\}, \quad \text{and} \quad B = \{3, 6, 9\},$$

then

$$A \setminus B = \{2, 4, 8\} \quad \text{and} \quad B \setminus A = \{3, 9\}.$$

The reader should observe that X does not have to be a subset of Y and that Y does not have to be the universe. In this example,

$$U \setminus A = \tilde{A} = \{1, 3, 5, 7, 9\} \quad \text{and} \quad U \setminus B = \tilde{B} = \{1, 2, 4, 5, 7, 8\}.$$

From this example, we observe that $A \setminus B$ is neither $U \setminus A$ nor $U \setminus B$. Similarly, $B \setminus A$ is neither $U \setminus A$ nor $U \setminus B$.

Since $U \subset U$, it follows that $\tilde{U} = U \setminus U$. But $U \setminus U$ contains no elements. In order to consider $\tilde{U}$ to be a set, we define the *empty set*.

Definition 5. *The **empty set**, or **null set** [denoted by "$\varnothing$" or "$\{\ \}$"], is the set which contains no members.*

It follows from Definition 1 and Definition 5 that the empty set is a subset of every set. Moreover, $\tilde{\varnothing} = U \setminus \varnothing = U$ and $\tilde{U} = U \setminus U = \varnothing$. The set of all \$3 bills in United States currency is obviously empty.

EXERCISE SET 2.2

I. Let $U = \{0, 1, 2, 3, 4, \ldots\}$. Compute the complement of each of the following sets.

1. $A = \{0, 2, 4, 6, \ldots\}$
2. $A = \{1, 3, 5, 7, \ldots\}$
3. $A = \{0, 5, 10, 15, \ldots\}$
4. $A = \{1, 2, 3, 4, \ldots\}$
5. $A = \{0, 1, 2, 3, 4, \ldots\}$
6. $A = \{2, 3, 4, 5, \ldots\}$
7. $A = \{\ \}$
8. $A = \varnothing$
9. $A = \{0\}$
10. $A = \{0, 1, 3, 4,\}$

II. Let $U = \{1, 2, 3, \ldots, 20\}$. Compute $A \setminus B$, $B \setminus A$, $\tilde{A}$, and $\tilde{B}$ in each of the following.

1. $A = \{1, 3, 5, \ldots, 19\}$, $B = \{3, 6, 9, \ldots, 18\}$
2. $A = \{2, 4, 6, \ldots, 20\}$, $B = \{3, 6, 9, \ldots, 18\}$
3. $A = \{5, 10, 15, 20\}$, $B = \{10, 20\}$
4. $A = \{4, 8, 12, 16, 20\}$, $B = \{8, 16\}$
5. $A = \{1, 3, 5, \ldots, 19\}$, $B = \{2, 4, 6, \ldots, 20\}$
6. $A = \{1, 2, 3, \ldots, 10\}$, $B = \{11, 12, 13, \ldots, 20\}$
7. $A = \{4, 8, 12, 16, 20\}$, $B = \{20, 16, 12, 8, 4\}$
8. $A = U$, $B = \{5, 10, 15, 20\}$
9. $A = \varnothing$, $B = \{5, 10, 15, 20\}$
10. $A = \{5, 10, 15, 20\}$, $B = \{4, 5, 9, 10, 14, 15, 19, 20\}$

III.

1. List *all* of the subsets of $\{1, 2\}$.

2. List *all* of the subsets of $\{1, 2, 3\}$.

3. List *all* of the *proper* subsets of $\{1, 2\}$.

4. List *all* of the *proper* subsets of $\{1, 2, 3\}$.

5. How many subsets are there of a set which contains k elements?

6. How many *proper* subsets are there of a set which contains k elements?

IV. The necessity for the empty set is apparent when we consider such descriptions of sets as the following:

The set of all five-year-old college students;

The set of all surviving veterans of the War of 1812;

The set of all veterans of *both* World War II and the War of 1812;

The set of all silver quarters minted in 1969.

Frequently when one describes a set, he cannot be certain that the set contains any elements. Describe 10 sets which are empty but which may appear to be nonempty.

2.3 ONE-TO-ONE CORRESPONDENCE, INFINITE SETS, AND FINITE SETS

The reader, who probably has a well-formulated intuitive idea of the meanings of *infinite set* and *finite set*, may think of an infinite set as a set containing an unlimited number of elements, and of a finite set as a set containing a limited number of elements.   Or the reader may think of an infinite set as one whose elements cannot be counted and of a finite set as one whose elements can be counted (and have the counting process terminate).   The intuitive ideas of finite set and of infinite set are adequate for ordinary purposes, but are not quite adequate for mathematical purposes.   Therefore we give mathematical definitions of *infinite* and *finite* sets.   First we define *one-to-one correspondence* between two sets.

Definition 6.   *The set X is in* **one-to-one correspondence** *with (or is* **equivalent** *to) the set Y [denoted by "$X \approx Y$"] if and only if there is a correspondence (or pairing) between X and Y such that each element of X is paired with exactly one element of Y and, under the correspondence, each element of Y is paired with exactly one element of X.*

For example, $\{1, 2, 3, 4, 5\}$ is equivalent to $\{2, 4, 6, 8, 10\}$ and $\{1, 2, 3, 4, 5, \ldots\}$ is equivalent to $\{2, 4, 6, 8, 10, \ldots\}$.   We use the notation "$\leftrightarrow$" to show the pairing process.   If $A = \{1, 2, 3, 4, 5\}$ and $B = \{2, 4, 6, 8, 10\}$, then $A \approx B$.   One pairing is indicated in Fig. 2.1.

$$A = \{1, 2, 3, 4, 5\}$$
$$\updownarrow \; \updownarrow \; \updownarrow \; \updownarrow \; \updownarrow$$
$$B = \{2, 4, 6, 8, 10\}$$

Fig. 2.1

We now use the concept of equivalence of sets to define *infinite set.*

Definition 7. *A set is said to be **infinite** if and only if it is equivalent to some proper subset of itself.*

For example, since $\{1, 2, 3, 4, 5, \ldots\}$ is equivalent to $\{2, 4, 6, 8, 10, \ldots\}$, we see that $\{1, 2, 3, 4, 5, \ldots\}$ is an infinite set.   Similarly, $\{2, 4, 6, 8, 10, \ldots\}$ is an infinite set.   Moreover, the set of counting numbers is infinite.

Now we define *finite set* in terms of *infinite set.*

Definition 8.   *A set is said to be **finite** if and only if it is not infinite.*

Since the empty set contains no proper subset, it follows from Definition 7 that the empty set is not infinite, and therefore, by Definition 8, *the empty set is finite.*   It follows also from Definitions 7 and 8 that no finite set is equivalent to a proper subset of itself.

To prove that a given set A is infinite, it is sufficient to exhibit one proper subset of A which is equivalent to A.   Although it may seem intuitively obvious that a given set is finite, Definition 8 *does not* provide a simple method for proving that a set is finite.   The following theorem, whose proof is beyond the scope of the text, provides an alternative definition of *finite* set.

> *Theorem.* *A nonempty set K is finite if and only if there exists a nonzero counting number k such that $K \approx \{1, 2, 3, \ldots, k\}$.*

According to the above theorem, every nonempty set which is equivalent to $\{1, 2, 3, \ldots, k\}$, for some nonzero counting number k, is finite; and every other nonempty set is infinite.   Of course, the empty set is finite.   Hence the above theorem provides a simple method for determining whether a given set is finite.*
For example, the set $\{2, 4, 6, 8, 10\}$ is finite because it is equivalent to $\{1, 2, 3, 4, 5\}$.   Similarly, the set of known planets is finite because it is equivalent to

$$\{1, 2, 3, \ldots, 9\}.$$

The following examples illustrate the definitions and notation.

Example 1. The set of counting numbers is equivalent to $\{0, 10, 20, \ldots\}$.   One pairing is shown in the accompanying figure.

$$
\begin{array}{ccccccc}
\{0, & 1, & 2, & 3, & 4, \ldots, & k, \ldots\} \\
\updownarrow & \updownarrow & \updownarrow & \updownarrow & \updownarrow & \updownarrow \\
\{0, & 10, & 20, & 30, & 40, \ldots, & 10k, \ldots\}
\end{array}
$$

---

*   Definitions 7 and 8 are due to the German mathematician Richard Dedekind (1831–1916). Since the theorem is of the form $p \leftrightarrows q$, we use it as an alternative definition of finite set.

Example 2. $\{4, 12\}$ is equivalent to $\{1, 2\}$. The only two possible pairings are shown in the accompanying figure.

Example 3. $\{1, 2\}$ is *not* equivalent to $\{1, 2, 3\}$, because in every pairing of the two sets one element of $\{1, 2, 3\}$ is not paired with any element of $\{1, 2\}$. The only possible pairings are shown in the accompanying figure.

Example 4. $\{1, 5, 7, 9, 11\} \approx \{1, 2, 3, 4, 5\}$ and

$$\{1, 2, 3, 4, 5\} \approx \{12, 13, 14, 15, 16\}.$$

Also,

$$\{1, 5, 7, 9, 11\} \approx \{12, 13, 14, 15, 16\}.$$

The sets in Example 1 are *infinite*, but the sets in Examples 2, 3, and 4 are *finite*. Example 4 illustrates that if $X \approx Y$ and $Y \approx Z$, then $X \approx Z$. The reader can prove the following properties.

1. If R is any set, then $R \approx R$ (*Reflexive Property*).
2. If R and S are any sets such that $R \approx S$, then $S \approx R$ (*Symmetric Property*).
3. If R, S, and T are any sets such that $R \approx S$ and $S \approx T$, then $R \approx T$ (*Transitive Property*).*

Equivalence between sets is really a *relation* between them. That is, if $X \approx Y$, then X is *related* to Y in some way. There are other relations between sets. For example, if $X \subset Y$, then X is *related* to Y in some way other than equivalence. There are other relations in mathematics and nature. For example, if $\triangle ABC \cong \triangle A'B'C'$, then $\triangle ABC$ is *related* to $\triangle A'B'C'$. Similarly, if P has the same parents as P', then P is *related* to P'. Moreover, if $a < b$, then a is *related* to b; if $x = y$, then x is *related* to y.

We accept the word *relation* as one of the undefined terms, and we define *equivalence relation*. The symbol "**R**" denotes any relation, and the symbol "x **R** y" means that x *is related to* y (as specified by the relation **R**).

---

* The words *property*, *law*, and *principle* are practically synonymous.

For example, if **R** is the order relation $<$, then

$$x \, \mathbf{R} \, y$$

means that x is less than y.

Definition 9. *A relation* **R** *between elements of a set S obeying the following laws is called an* **equivalence relation**:

1. If r is any element of S, then $r \, \mathbf{R} \, r$ [*Reflexive Law*].
2. If r and s are any elements of S and $r \, \mathbf{R} \, s$, then $s \, \mathbf{R} \, r$ [*Symmetric Law*].
3. If r, s, and t are any elements of S and $r \, \mathbf{R} \, s$ and $s \, \mathbf{R} \, t$, then $r \, \mathbf{R} \, t$ [*Transitive Law*].

The reader should observe that equivalence of sets, congruence of triangles, and equality of numbers, persons, or objects are *equivalence relations*, but $\subset$ and $<$ do not generate equivalence relations.

EXERCISE SET 2.3

I.
1. Show two pairings of the sets A and B of Fig. 2.1 other than the pairing shown in the figure.
2. How many pairings of the sets A and B are there?

II. Decide which of the following pairs of sets are equivalent. Then write "$A \approx B$" or "$A \not\approx B$."

1. $A = \{a, x, y\}$, $B = \{a, x, y\}$
2. $A = \{1, 2, 3, 4\}$, $B = \{1, 3, 5, 7\}$
3. $A = \{0, 5, 9, 10\}$, $B = \{1, 3, 5, 7, 9\}$
4. $A = \varnothing$, $B = \varnothing$
5. $A = \{0\}$, $B = \varnothing$
6. $A = \{1, 2, 3, \ldots\}$, $B = \{5, 10, 15, \ldots\}$
7. $A = \{1, 2, 3, \ldots, 99\}$, $B = \{5, 10, 15, \ldots\}$
8. $A = \{1, 2, 3, \ldots, 99\}$, $B = \{5, 10, 15, \ldots, 495\}$
9. $A = \{1, 3, 5, 7, 9, \ldots, 99\}$, $B = \{2, 4, 6, 8, 10, \ldots, 100\}$
10. $A = \{1, 3, 5, 7, 9, \ldots, 99\}$, $B = \{0, 2, 4, 6, 8, \ldots, 100\}$

III.
1. Prove that $\{2, 4, 6, \ldots\}$ is an infinite set.
2. Prove that $\{20, 40, 60, \ldots\}$ is an infinite set.
3. Prove that $\{2, 4, 6\}$ is a finite set.
4. Prove that $\{20, 40, 60\}$ is a finite set.
5. Is the set of all people in the world an infinite set?

IV. Determine which of the following are *equivalence relations*. Name the law or laws that fail in each relation which is not an equivalence relation.

1. Let $S = \{0, 1, 2, \ldots, 100\}$. Let **R** be the relation *has the same number of digits as.*

2. Let S be the set of all human beings. Let **R** be the relation *is a sibling of.*

3. Let S be the set of all human beings. Let **R** be the relation *is a sister of.*

4. Let S be the set of all human beings. Let **R** be the relation *has the same parents as.*

5. Let $S = \{0, 1, 2, \ldots, 50\}$. Let **R** be the relation *leaves the same remainder when divided by 3.*

6. Let S be the set of all college students. Let **R** be the relation *weighs within 5 pounds of.*

7. Let S be the set of all U.S. citizens. Let **R** be the relation *lives within a block of.*

8. Let S be the set of all U.S. citizens. Let **R** be the relation *lives one block north of.*

9. Let S be a standard pack of 52 playing cards. Let **R** be the relation *is of the same suit as.*

10. Let S be a standard pack of 52 playing cards. Let **R** be the relation *is of the same denomination (face value) as.*

2.4 UNION AND INTERSECTION OF SETS

The operation and process of addition of counting numbers (e.g., $3 + 2 = 5$) are defined in terms of the *union* and *intersection* of sets.* The latter two concepts are defined in terms of *disjunction* and *conjunction* of sentences.

Definition 10. *The **union** of the sets X and Y [denoted by "$X \cup Y$"] is the set of all elements which are in X or in Y [or both]. That is, $X \cup Y = \{x : x \in X$ or $x \in Y\}$.*

Definition 11. *The **intersection** of sets X and Y [denoted by "$X \cap Y$"] is the set of all elements which are in both X and Y. That is, $X \cap Y = \{x : x \in X$ and $x \in Y\}$.*

For example, if $A = \{1, 2, 3, 4\}$ and $B = \{1, 3, 5\}$, then

$$A \cup B = \{1, 2, 3, 4, 5\} \qquad \text{and} \qquad A \cap B = \{1, 3\}.$$

If $C = \{0, 2, 4, \ldots\}$ and $D = \{1, 2, 3, \ldots\}$, then

$$C \cup D = \{0, 1, 2, 3, \ldots\} \qquad \text{and} \qquad C \cap D = \{2, 4, 6, \ldots\}.$$

However,

$$B \cup C = \{1, 3, 5, 0, 2, 4, \ldots\}$$

and

$$B \cap C = \varnothing = \{\ \}.$$

It follows from Definitions 10 and 11 that $X \cap Y \subset X \cup Y$ for any sets X and Y, even if $X = \varnothing$, or $X \cap Y = \varnothing$.

---

*   We will define addition of counting numbers in Chapter 3.

Definition 12. *Two sets are said to be **disjoint** [from each other] if and only if their intersection is the empty set. That is, the sets X and Y are disjoint if and only if $X \cap Y = \varnothing$.*

It follows from Definition 12 that every set is disjoint from the empty set. The following examples further illustrate the above definitions.

Example 1. If $A = \{$Mary, Irene, Phyllis, Suzanne$\}$ and

  $B = \{$Gail, Mark, Jude, Mary$\}$,

then

  $A \cup B = \{$Mary, Irene, Phyllis, Suzanne, Gail, Mark, Jude$\}$

and

  $A \cap B = \{$Mary$\}$.

Sets A and B are *not* disjoint.

Example 2. If $A = \{$Roy, Jerry, Al, Butch$\}$ and $B = \{$Joyce, Anita$\}$, then

  $A \cup B = \{$Roy, Jerry, Al, Butch, Joyce, Anita$\}$

and

  $A \cap B = \varnothing$.

Sets A and B are disjoint.

Example 3. If $A = \{2, 4, 6\}$ and $B = \{1, 2, 3, 4, 5, 6\}$, then

  $A \cup B = \{1, 2, 3, 4, 5, 6\} = B$

and

  $A \cap B = \{2, 4, 6\} = A$.

In general, if $A \subset B$, then $A \cup B = B$ and $A \cap B = A$.

EXERCISE SET 2.4

I.
1. $A = \{$Walter, Dorinne, Sonny$\}$ and $B = \{$Clark, Tommy, Dorinne$\}$; compute $A \cup B$ and $A \cap B$.
2. $A = \{$Carol, Merlin, Susan$\}$ and $B = \{$Beverly, Carol$\}$; compute $A \cup B$ and $A \cap B$.
3. $A = \{$John, Eleanore, Vincent, Drue$\}$ and $B = \{$David, Alicia, Leigh, Jeffrey, Jeanne, Karen$\}$; compute $A \cup B$ and $A \cap B$.
4. $A = \{$Richard, Nelson, Betty, Ruth$\}$ and $B = \{$Frem, Angelle$\}$; compute $A \cup B$ and $A \cap B$.
5. $A = \{$Vera, Emil$\}$ and $B = \{$Milton, Diana, May$\}$; compute $A \cup B$ and $A \cap B$.
6. $A = \{$Don, Sylvia, Yvonne$\}$, $B = \{$Don, Charles, Louise$\}$, and $C = \{$Jo, Erenze, Bea$\}$; compute $(A \cup B) \cup C$ and $(A \cap B) \cap C$.
7. $A = \{$Toby, Elvina$\}$, $B = \{$Toby, Gladys, Elizabeth$\}$, and $C = \{$Jennifer, Jeanette, Elizabeth$\}$; compute $(A \cup B) \cup C$ and $(A \cap B) \cap C$.

8. $A = \{$Fannie, Doris, Augustine$\}$, $B = \{$Fannie, Maurice, Mary$\}$, and $C = \{$Fannie, Doris, Bea$\}$; compute $A \cup (B \cup C)$ and $A \cap (B \cap C)$.

9. $A = \{$Anthony, Roselind$\}$, $B = \{$Lorraine, Anthony, Jacqueline$\}$, and $C = \{$Anthony, Barbara, Peter$\}$; compute $A \cup (B \cup C)$, $A \cap (B \cap C)$, $A \cup B$, $A \cap B$, and $A \cap C$.

10. $A = \{$Edmond, Sadie, Lloyd$\}$, $B = \{$Wayne, Diana$\}$, and $C = \{$Herbert, Ramona, Angie, Wayne$\}$; compute $(A \cup B) \cup C$, $A \cap (B \cap C)$, $A \cap B$, $A \cap C$, and $B \cap C$.

II. Compute $A \cup B$ and $A \cap B$ in each of the following.

1. $A = \{a, x, y\}$, $B = \{a, x, y\}$.

2. $A = \{0\}$, $B = \varnothing$.

3. $A = \{ \ \}$, $B = \varnothing$.

4. $A = \{1, 2, 3, \ldots, 99\}$, $B = \{5, 10, 15, 20, 25, \ldots, 495\}$.

5. $A = \{1, 3, 5, 7, 9, \ldots, 99\}$, $B = \{2, 4, 6, 8, \ldots, 100\}$.

6. $A = \{1, 3, 5, 7, 9, \ldots, 99\}$, $B = \{0, 2, 4, 6, \ldots, 100\}$.

7. $A = \{x: x$ is a human with blue eyes$\}$, $B = \{x: x$ is a human with red hair$\}$.

8. $A = \{x: x$ is a number less than 5$\}$, $B = \{x: x$ is a number greater than or equal to 3$\}$.

9. $A = \{x: x$ is a counting number$\}$, $B = \{x: x$ is a counting number less than 5 and greater than 4$\}$.

10. $A = \{x: x$ is a counting number less than or equal to 15 and greater than or equal to 8$\}$, $B = \{x: x$ is a counting number less than 16 and greater than 8$\}$.

2.5 VENN DIAGRAMS

We may portray sets visually by means of *Venn diagrams*.* In a Venn diagram, we usually portray the universe by a rectangular region and we portray the sets A, B, C, etc., by circular or other regions within the rectangular region. If $A \cap B = \varnothing$, we may portray $A \cap B$ by the shaded region in Fig. 2.2(a) [that is, *no shading*], and we may portray $A \cup B$ by the shaded region in Fig. 2.2(b).

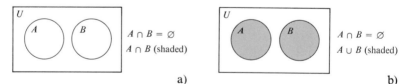

a)   b)

Fig. 2.2

---

*   The Swiss mathematician Leonhard Euler (1707–1783) first introduced the use of circular regions to portray sets and subsets. Such a diagram is called an *Euler diagram*. The British logician John Venn (1834–1883) extended the Euler diagram by using a rectangular region to portray the universal set and circular regions within the rectangular region to portray the other sets. The latter diagram is known as a *Venn diagram*.

If $A \cap B \neq \varnothing$, we may portray $A \cup B$ by the shaded region in Fig. 2.3.

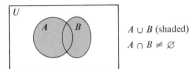

$A \cup B$ (shaded)
$A \cap B \neq \varnothing$

Fig. 2.3

If $A \cap B \neq \varnothing$, we may portray $A \cap B$ by the shaded region in Fig. 2.4.

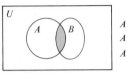

$A \cap B$ (shaded)
$A \cap B \neq \varnothing$
$A \cap B \subset A \cup B$

Fig. 2.4

We may portray $\tilde{A}$ (the complement of A) by the shaded region in Fig. 2.5.

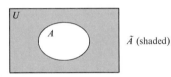

$\tilde{A}$ (shaded)

Fig. 2.5

We may portray $A \setminus B$ (the relative complement of B with respect to A) by the shaded region in Fig. 2.6.

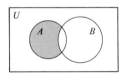

$A \setminus B$ (shaded)

Fig. 2.6

If A is a proper subset of B, we may portray $A \cap B$ by the shaded region in Fig. 2.7 and $A \cup B$ by the shaded region in Fig. 2.8.

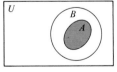

$A \cap B$ (shaded)
$A \subsetneq B$

Fig. 2.7

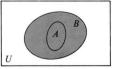

$A \cup B$ (shaded)
$A \subsetneq B$

Fig. 2.8

We may extend the definition of *union* to more than two sets. For example, it follows from Definition 10 that

$$(A \cup B) \cup C = \{x: \ (x \in A \cup B) \lor x \in C\}$$
$$= \{x: \ (x \in A \lor x \in B) \lor x \in C\}$$
$$= \{x: \ x \in A \lor (x \in B \lor x \in C)\}$$
$$(\text{since } [(p \lor q) \lor r] \Leftrightarrow [p \lor (q \lor r)]);$$

moreover,

$$A \cup (B \cup C) = \{x: \ x \in A \lor (x \in B \cup C)\}$$
$$= \{x: \ x \in A \lor (x \in B \lor x \in C)\}.$$

Hence

$$(A \cup B) \cup C = A \cup (B \cup C).$$

Since we have proved that $(A \cup B) \cup C = A \cup (B \cup C)$ for any three sets A, B, and C, we may omit the punctuation and write

$$A \cup B \cup C$$

to mean either

$$(A \cup B) \cup C$$

or

$$A \cup (B \cup C).$$

In a similar manner we can prove that $(A \cap B) \cap C = A \cap (B \cap C)$. We may portray $A \cup B \cup C$ by the shaded region in Fig. 2.9.

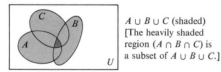

$A \cup B \cup C$ (shaded)
[The heavily shaded
region $(A \cap B \cap C)$ is
a subset of $A \cup B \cup C$.]

Fig. 2.9

Although $(A \cup B) \cup C = A \cup (B \cup C)$ and $(A \cap B) \cap C = A \cap (B \cap C)$, we can prove that

$$(A \cap B) \cup C \neq A \cap (B \cup C)$$

and

$$(A \cup B) \cap C \neq A \cup (B \cap C).$$

Hence the expressions

$$A \cup B \cap C \quad \text{and} \quad A \cap B \cup C$$

are meaningless and do not represent sets.*

The reader should draw Venn diagrams for $(A \cap B) \cup C$, $A \cap (B \cup C)$, $(A \cup B) \cap C$, and $A \cup (B \cap C)$ to illustrate that $(A \cap B) \cup C \neq A \cap (B \cup C)$ and $(A \cup B) \cap C \neq A \cup (B \cap C)$.

EXERCISE SET 2.5

I.

1. On a Venn diagram, illustrate $\widetilde{A \cap B}$ for two different sets A and B whose intersection is nonempty.
2. On a Venn diagram, illustrate $\widetilde{A \cup B}$ for two different sets A and B whose intersection is nonempty.
3. On a Venn diagram, illustrate $\tilde{A} \cup \tilde{B}$ for two different sets A and B whose intersection is nonempty.
4. On a Venn diagram, illustrate $\tilde{A} \cap \tilde{B}$ for two different sets A and B whose intersection is nonempty.

II. A survey taken at a college with an enrollment of 5000 students revealed the following information:

a) 350 students are enrolled in Spanish,

b) 300 students are enrolled in German,

c) 400 students are enrolled in French,

d) 100 students are enrolled in both Spanish and German,

e) 80 students are enrolled in both French and German,

f) 80 students are enrolled in both Spanish and French,

g) 30 students are enrolled in all three languages (Spanish, French, and German).

1. How many students are not enrolled in any foreign language (French, German, or Spanish)?
2. How many students are enrolled in Spanish only?
3. How many students are enrolled in French only?
4. How many students are enrolled in German only?
5. How many students are enrolled in both German and Spanish, but not in French?
6. How many students are enrolled in German and French but not in Spanish?
7. How many students are enrolled in Spanish and French but not in German?

[*Hint:* Draw a Venn diagram with three regions, representing Spanish, French, and German students. Start with (g) and work back.]

---

*   The reader should review the similar notes in Section 1.7 concerning the expressions $p \wedge q \vee r$ and $p \vee q \wedge r$.

III. Using the accompanying Venn diagram, name the regions (in terms of A, B, C, $\tilde{A}$, $A \cup B$, etc.) identified below.

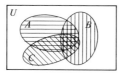

1. The unshaded region.
2. The triply shaded region.
3. The horizontally shaded region.
4. The vertically shaded region.
5. The diagonally shaded region.
6. The region with both vertical and horizontal shading but with no diagonal shading.
7. The region with both vertical and diagonal shading but with no horizontal shading.
8. The region with both horizontal and diagonal shading but with no vertical shading.
9. The region with both diagonal and vertical shading or with diagonal shading.
10. The region with either horizontal or vertical shading and with diagonal shading.

2.6 BOOLEAN ALGEBRA*

The system consisting of sets and the set operations which we defined in Sections 2.2 and 2.4 obeys certain abstract laws common to several other systems (e.g., the system of compound statements in Section 1.7). The reader can illustrate the *set laws* by means of Venn diagrams and prove them by means of the basic logical truths (which can be proved by means of truth tables). Some of the laws we state resemble the basic laws of algebra, with which the reader is familiar. A system consisting of any nonempty set considered as the universe, its subsets, the set operations $\cup$ and $\cap$, and the rules governing the combinations of subsets is known as a *Boolean algebra*, because the British mathematician George Boole (1815–1864) was the first person to study sets and their operations as an algebraic system.

The system consisting of the statements in Fig. 1.10 (with the usual definitions of the connectives) is a Boolean algebra, as the following analogy indicates.

$\sim p$	$\tilde{A}$
$p \vee q$	$A \cup B$
$p \wedge q$	$A \cap B$
$p \rightarrow q$	$A \subset B$
$p \leftrightarrows q$	$A = B$

---

*   Section 2.6 may be omitted without loss of continuity.

The basic laws of Boolean algebra are listed in Fig. 2.10. The reader should observe that some laws involve only one set operation and other laws involve more than one set operation. As usual, A, B, and C are any sets which are subsets of U; and U and $\emptyset$ are the universal set and the empty set, respectively.

BASIC LAWS GOVERNING SETS

Laws Involving Union Only	Laws Involving Intersection Only
Commutative Law for Union: If A and B are any subsets of U, then $$A \cup B = B \cup A.$$	*Commutative Law for Intersection:* If A and B are any subsets of U, then $$A \cap B = B \cap A.$$
Associative Law for Union: If A, B, and C are any subsets of U, then $$(A \cup B) \cup C = A \cup (B \cup C).$$	*Associative Law for Intersection:* If A, B, and C are any subsets of U, then $$(A \cap B) \cap C = A \cap (B \cap C).$$
Identity Law for Union: The universe U contains the unique subset $\emptyset$ such that $$A \cup \emptyset = A$$ for all subsets A of U.	*Identity Law for Intersection:* The universe U contains the unique subset U such that $$A \cap U = A$$ for all subsets A of U.
Complement Law for Union: If A is any subset of U, then there exists a unique subset $\tilde{A}$ of U such that $$A \cup \tilde{A} = U.$$	*Complement Law for Intersection:* If A is any subset of U, then there exists a unique subset $\tilde{A}$ of U such that $$A \cap \tilde{A} = \emptyset.$$

Laws Involving Union and Intersection

Distributive Law for Intersection over Union:
If A, B, and C are any subsets of U, then

$$A \cap (B \cup C) = (A \cap B) \cup (A \cap C).$$

Distributive Law for Union over Intersection:
If A, B, and C are any subsets of U, then

$$A \cup (B \cap C) = (A \cup B) \cap (A \cup C).$$

Fig. 2.10

The two statements $(p \lor f) \leftrightarrows p$ and $(p \land t) \leftrightarrows p$, in which f is a *logically false statement* and t is a *logically true statement*, correspond to the set laws $A \cup \varnothing = A$ and $A \cap U = A$. The reader should complete the analogy by pairing the remaining statements of Figs. 1.10 and 1.11 with the corresponding laws of Figs. 2.10 and 2.11.

The laws listed in Fig. 2.11 are consequences of the basic laws listed in Fig. 2.10. The reader can *assume* the laws in Fig. 2.10 and *prove* the laws in Fig. 2.11 as theorems, without resorting to truth table analysis or the *logical truths* of Section 1.7; or the reader can prove all of the basic laws of Fig. 2.10 and the laws of Fig. 2.11 by use of the *logical truths* of Section 1.7.*

ADDITIONAL LAWS GOVERNING SETS

Idempotent Laws:
If A is any subset of U, then
$$A \cup A = A$$
and
$$A \cap A = A.$$

De Morgan's Laws:
If A and B are any subsets of U, then
$$\widetilde{A \cup B} = \tilde{A} \cap \tilde{B}$$
and
$$\widetilde{A \cap B} = \tilde{A} \cup \tilde{B}.$$

Universal Law for Union:
If A is any subset of U, then
$$A \cup U = U.$$

Annihilation Law for Intersection:
If A is any subset of U, then
$$A \cap \varnothing = \varnothing.$$

Complement Laws:
1. If A is any subset of U, then
$$\tilde{\tilde{A}} = A.$$
2. $\tilde{U} = \varnothing.$
3. $\tilde{\varnothing} = U.$

Fig. 2.11

---

*   In mathematics we can assume any noncontradictory postulates which satisfy certain conditions, and we can prove the theorems which are consequences of the postulates. Frequently, for the sake of convenience, we assume more postulates than necessary. By assuming certain theorems as postulates, we can avoid difficult and tedious proofs.

EXERCISE SET 2.6

I. Let U be the set of counting numbers, $A = \{0, 2, 4, 6, 8, 10\}$, $B = \{1, 2, 3, 4, 5, 6, 7, 8, 9, 10\}$, and $C = \{1, 3, 4, 5\}$. Compute each of the following.

1. $A \cap B$	2. $B \cap C$	3. $A \cup C$
4. $B \cup C$	5. $(B \cup C) \cup A$	6. $(A \cup C) \cup B$
7. $A \cap (B \cup C)$	8. $A \cup (B \cap C)$	9. $\widetilde{A \cup B}$
10. $\widetilde{A \cap B}$	11. $\widetilde{A \cup U}$	12. $\tilde{A} \cup B$
13. $\tilde{B} \cap C$	14. $\widetilde{A \cap B} \cap C$	15. $\tilde{C}$

II. Let A, B, and C be any subsets of U. State the truth value of each of the following

1. $A \cap (B \cup C) = (A \cap B) \cup C$.   2. $A \cup (B \cap C) = (A \cup B) \cap C$.

3. $\widetilde{A \cup B} \cap C = \tilde{A} \cap \tilde{B} \cap C$.   4. $\widetilde{A \cap B} \cup C = \tilde{A} \cup \tilde{B} \cup C$.

5. $\widetilde{A \cup B \cup C} = \tilde{A} \cap \tilde{B} \cap \tilde{C}$.   6. $\widetilde{A \cap B \cap C} = \tilde{A} \cup \tilde{B} \cup \tilde{C}$.

7. $B \cap (A \cup C) = (C \cup A) \cap B$.   8. $B \cup (A \cap C) = (C \cap A) \cup B$.

9. $\widetilde{A \cup B} = A \cap B$.   10. $\widetilde{A \cap B} = \tilde{A} \cup B$.

III. Prove each of the following.

1. If A and B are any subsets of U, then
$$A \setminus B = A \cap \tilde{B}.$$

2. If A is any subset of U, then
 a) $A \setminus U = \emptyset$,
 b) $A \setminus \emptyset = A$,
 c) $A \setminus A = \emptyset$.

3. Refer to a standard dictionary for standard meanings of *idempotent*, *annihilation*, and *complement*. Compare the standard meanings with the corresponding laws governing sets.

2.7 CARTESIAN PRODUCT OF SETS*

So far we have considered only sets whose elements are numbers, persons, or objects. For example $\{1, 2, 3\}$ is a set of numbers; $\{$Roy, Joyce$\}$ is a set of persons; and $\{$ball, bat, glove$\}$ is a set of objects. In mathematics we frequently study sets whose elements are ordered pairs. For example,

$$\{(\text{Roy, ball}), \quad (\text{Joyce, bat})\}$$

is a set of ordered pairs—not a set of persons or objects. In

$$\{(\text{Roy, ball}), \quad (\text{Joyce, bat})\},$$

Roy is *paired* with the ball, and Joyce is *paired* with the bat (perhaps Roy is

---

*   Section 2.7 may be omitted in a course which terminates prior to Chapter 7. The concepts in Section 2.7 are needed in Chapters 7 and 8.

holding the ball and Joyce is holding the bat). It should be intuitively clear that
(Roy, ball) is not necessarily equal to (ball, Roy); i.e., the *order* of appearance of
the components of the *ordered pairs* is important.* In the following definition of
Cartesian product† it is understood that $(a, b) = (x, y)$ if and only if $a = x$ and
$b = y$.

Definition 13. *The* **Cartesian product** *of the sets X and Y [denoted by "X × Y"*
and read "X cross Y"] is the set of all ordered pairs (x, y) such that $x \in X$ and
$y \in Y$. That is,

$$X \times Y = \{(x, y): x \in X \text{ and } y \in Y\}.$$

In the ordered pair (x, y), x is called the **first coordinate** *and y is called the* **second**
coordinate.

The reader should observe that $(x, y) = (y, x)$ if and only if $x = y$. For
example,

$$(5, 3 + 2) = (3 + 2, 5)$$

but

$$(5, 1) \neq (1, 5).$$

The following examples illustrate the *Cartesian product*.

Example 1. If $A = \{1, 2, 3\}$ and $B = \{3, 4\}$, then

$$A \times B = \{(1, 3), (1, 4), (2, 3), (2, 4), (3, 3), (3, 4)\}$$

and

$$B \times A = \{(3, 1), (3, 2), (3, 3), (4, 1), (4, 2), (4, 3)\}.$$

Although $A \times B \neq B \times A$, each contains 6 elements (which are ordered pairs).
We observe that A contains 3 elements, B contains 2 elements, and $3 \times 2 = 6$.

Example 2. If $A = \{1, 2, 3\}$ and $B = \{1, 3, 5, \ldots\}$, then

$$A \times B = \{(1, 1), (1, 3), (1, 5), \ldots$$
$$(2, 1), (2, 3), (2, 5), \ldots$$
$$(3, 1), (3, 3), (3, 5), \ldots\}$$

and

$$B \times A = \{(1, 1), (1, 2), (1, 3), (3, 1), (3, 2), (3, 3), (5, 1), (5, 2), (5, 3), \ldots\}.$$

Although $A \times B \neq B \times A$, both are infinite sets.

---

*   If the ordered pair (Roy, ball) indicates that Roy is holding the ball, then (ball,
Roy) indicates that the ball is holding Roy. Certainly (Roy, ball) ≠ (ball, Roy).

†   The *Cartesian product* is named for the famous French mathematician René
Descartes (1596–1650).

Example 3. If A is any set, then

$$A \times \varnothing = \varnothing,$$
$$\varnothing \times A = \varnothing,$$

and thus

$$A \times \varnothing = \varnothing \times A.$$

Example 4. If $A = \{1, 3\}$ and $B = \{1, 3\}$, then

$$A \times B = \{(1, 1), (1, 3), (3, 1), (3, 3)\}$$

and

$$B \times A = \{(1, 1), (1, 3), (3, 1), (3, 3)\}.$$

The above examples illustrate that

$A \times B = B \times A$ *if and only if* $A = B$ *or* $A = \varnothing$ *or* $B = \varnothing$ *and*
$A \times B \approx B \times A$ *for any two sets A and B.*

In Example 4, $A \times B = B \times A$, because $A = B$. In Example 3, $A \times B = B \times A$, because $B = \varnothing$. However, in Example 2, $A \times B \neq B \times A$. That is, there exist sets A and B such that $A \times B \neq B \times A$. The fact that the Cartesian product operation is not commutative should not be surprising. After all, subtraction is not commutative. That is, $a - b = b - a$ if and only if $a = b$; in all other cases, $a - b \neq b - a$.*

The ordered pair (a, b) should not be confused with the set $\{a, b\}$; $(5, 1) \neq (1, 5)$ and $\{(5, 1)\} \neq \{(1, 5)\}$, but $\{5, 1\} = \{1, 5\}$. Moreover, the Cartesian product $A \times B$ should not be confused with the intersection $A \cap B$ or the union $A \cup B$. The Cartesian product of A and B is a set of ordered pairs. The elements of $A \times B$ are elements of *neither* A nor B. However, the elements of $A \cap B$ are elements of *both* A and B, and the elements of $A \cup B$ are elements of *either* A or B.

Example 5. If $A = \{5\}$ and $B = \{1, 5\}$, then

$$A \times B = \{(5, 1), (5, 5)\}$$
$$B \times A = \{(1, 5), (5, 5)\},$$
$$A \cap B = \{5\},$$
$$A \cup B = \{1, 5\},$$
$$(A \times B) \cap (B \times A) = \{(5, 5)\},$$
$$(A \times B) \cup (B \times A) = \{(5, 1), (1, 5), (5, 5)\},$$
$$A \cap (A \times B) = \varnothing,$$

and

$$B \cap (A \times B) = \varnothing.$$

---

*   A similar statement is true for $a \div b$.

Moreover,

$$5 \in A, \quad 5 \in B, \quad 1 \notin A, \quad 1 \in B, \quad 5 \notin A \times B, \quad 1 \notin A \times B,$$

$$5 \notin B \times A, \quad 1 \notin B \times A, \quad 1 \notin (1, 5), \quad 1 \notin \{(1, 5)\}, \quad (1, 5) \notin (1, 5),$$

$$(1, 5) \notin \{1, 5\}, \quad (1, 5) \in \{(1, 5)\}, \quad \varnothing \subset A, \quad \varnothing \subset B,$$

$$\varnothing \subset A \times B, \quad \varnothing \times \varnothing \subset A \times B, \quad \varnothing \times A \subset A \times B,$$

$$\varnothing \times B \subset A \times B.$$

We have defined *equivalence relation* in terms of the undefined term *relation*, and we have illustrated the concept *relation* by means of examples. Although we have not defined *relation*, the examples help us to understand what a relation is. As we mentioned in Chapter 1, in mathematics (as in life) we frequently leave certain terms undefined, but we understand their meanings from usage or illustrations. For example, it is not necessary to define the word *chair*; most children know what a chair is.

Although we did not define *relation*, we can define it if we wish. Recalling that the members of an ordered pair (*a*, *b*) are related in some way, we can define *relation* in terms of ordered pairs. For example, the members of the ordered pair (Cain, Adam) are related in the sense that Cain *is the son of* Adam, whereas the members of the ordered pair (Adam, Cain) are related in the sense that Adam *is the father of* Cain. Since the relationships are not the same, we say that (Cain, Adam) is not the same ordered pair as (Adam, Cain). Moreover, the ordered pair (Eve, Adam) expresses another relationship—one different from that expressed by the ordered pair (Cain, Adam) and different from that expressed by the ordered pair (Adam, Cain).

Since every ordered pair is an element of some Cartesian product, we can define a *relation* from one set to a second set as a subset of the Cartesian product of the two sets. Some authors choose the following definition of *relation*.

*Any subset of X × Y is called a **relation** from X to Y.*

Although the above definition has many advantages, especially in more advanced mathematics, we prefer to consider *relation* as undefined. The reason for the word *subset* in the above definition is that there may exist some elements of *X* which are not related to some elements of *Y*. For example, although (Cain, Adam) is a member of the son–father relation, (Eve, Adam) is not because Eve is the wife of Adam.

EXERCISE SET 2.7

I. Let $A = \{1, 2\}$, $B = \{3, 5, 7\}$, $X = \{1, 2, 3\}$, $Y = \{1, 3, 5, 7\}$. Observe that $A \subset X$ and $B \subset Y$.

1. Compute $A \times B$ and $X \times Y$, and prove that $A \times B \subset X \times Y$.

2. Compute $B \times A$ and $Y \times X$, and prove that $B \times A \subset Y \times X$.

II. Let $A = \{x: x \text{ is a counting number and } 5 < x < 15\}$ and $B = \{y: y \text{ is a counting number and } 9 < y < 11\}$.* Compute $A \times B$ and $B \times A$.

III.
1. Compute the Cartesian product of $\{0, 1, 2\}$ and $\{0, 1, 2, \ldots\}$.
2. Compute the Cartesian product of $\{0, 1, 2, \ldots\}$ and $\{0, 1, 2\}$.

IV.
1. How would you define

    $A \times B \times C$?

2. Would you define

    $A \times B \times C$ so that $(A \times B) \times C = A \times (B \times C)$?

V. In each of the following, $A \times B$ is indicated. List the elements of A and the elements of B.
1. $A \times B = \{(1, 2), (2, 2), (3, 2), (4, 2), (5, 2)\}$
2. $A \times B = \{(2, 1), (2, 2), (2, 3), (2, 4), (2, 5)\}$
3. $A \times B = \{(0, 1), (0, 2), (0, 3), \ldots\}$
4. $A \times B = \{(1, 0), (2, 0), (3, 0), \ldots\}$
5. $A \times B = \{(0, 1)\}$
6. $A \times B = \{(1, 1)\}$

VI. For each part of Exercise V, list the elements [ordered pairs (a, b)] of $A \times B$ which are related in the sense $a \leq b$. Could each subset of $A \times B$ be considered a relation from A to B? Is each relation from A to B the *is less than or equal to* relation?

VII. In each of the following, prove that $A \times B \approx B \times A$.
1. $A = \{1, 2, 3\}$, $B = \{2, 4, 6, 8\}$
2. $A = \{1, 3, 5, 7\}$, $B = \{2, 4, 6\}$
3. $A = \{0\}$, $B = \{0, 3\}$
4. $A = \{1\}$, $B = \{1, 2\}$
5. $A = \emptyset$, $B = \{5, 7, 9\}$
6. $A = \{2, 4, 6, 8\}$, $B = \emptyset$
7. $A = \{2, 1\}$, $B = \{1, 2\}$
8. $A = \{3, 2, 1\}$, $B = \{2, 1, 3\}$

PUZZLE PROBLEMS

1. There are 28 bones (pieces) in a domino set that runs to double-six. There are 55 bones in a domino set that runs to double-nine. How many bones are there in a domino set that runs to double-twelve?

---

* The symbol "$a < b$" means that a is less than b, and the symbol "$a \leq b$" means that a is less than or equal to b.

2. Ten volumes of an encyclopedia are placed in order on a bookcase. Each cover is $\frac{1}{8}$ in. thick and each set of pages in each volume is $1\frac{3}{4}$ in. thick. A bookworm eats its way (in a straight line perpendicular to the cover of each volume) from the first sheet of Volume 1 to the last sheet of Volume 10. How far does the bookworm travel?

3. A wooden block in the shape of a cube with a three-foot edge is painted blue on all six faces. A carpenter cuts the block into 27 cube-shaped blocks each with a one-foot edge.

   Consider each block with no blue face. How many elements does the set of all such blocks contain?

   Consider each block with exactly one blue face. How many elements does the set of all such blocks contain?

   Consider each block with exactly two blue faces. How many elements does the set of all such blocks contain?

   Consider each block with exactly three blue faces. How many elements does the set of all such blocks contain?

   Consider each block with exactly four blue faces. How many elements does the set of all such blocks contain?

Numeration Systems

Gottfried Wilhelm Leibniz was born in Leipzig, Germany, on July 1, 1646. His father was a professor of philosophy whose family had worked three generations for the government of Saxony. Leibniz spent his early years in an atmosphere of scholarship and politics. He attended school in Leipzig, but he was very largely self-taught through incessant reading in his father's library.

Leibniz showed conspicuous genius in many fields—law, religion, politics, history, mathematics, logic, and philosophy. At 15 years of age he entered the University of Leipzig as a law student, and he received his bachelor's degree at the age of 17. By the age of 20, he was thoroughly prepared for his doctor's degree, but the University of Leipzig refused to grant him that degree because of his youth. Leibniz was so discouraged that he left his native town and proceeded to the University of Altdorf in Nuremberg, Germany, which granted him a doctor's degree immediately for his brilliant essay on a new method of teaching law.

During his lifetime Leibniz developed two very important branches of mathematics—calculus and combinatorial analysis. Sir Isaac Newton, a contemporary of Leibniz, was an agent for the expression of the spirit of his time, but Leibniz was more. In his dream of a *universal characteristic* (now called *symbolic logic*), Leibniz was two centuries ahead of his time. He had great insight and capability in both combinatorial and analytical methods. Some historians credit him with the development of the first calculating machine and with the use of numeration systems with bases other than 10. In his machine he used the binary system. He predicted the use of other numeration systems in more advanced machines. Today Leibniz's reputation as a mathematician is higher than it was during his lifetime, and it is still rising.

Had Leibniz devoted his exceptional abilities entirely to mathematics, it might be a completely different subject today. However, since Leibniz desired prestige and money, he entered into the service of several royal families and served as librarian, historian, and general brains for each family. By the age of 68, Leibniz had begun to deteriorate both mentally and physically, and he died in 1716 at the age of 70.

LEIBNIZ
(1646–1716)

Chapter 3

Numeration Systems

3.1 ADDITION AND MULTIPLICATION OF COUNTING NUMBERS*

The concepts of sets and counting numbers are very closely related; counting objects is really counting the members of some set. For example, when a child counts the fingers on one hand (or the toes on one foot), he is counting the elements of a set containing *five* members. When he counts the school days in a typical week, he is counting the elements of a set containing *five* members. He realizes that the *physical* properties of the three sets are not identical but the *number* property of each of the three different kinds of sets is *five*; i.e., each set has *five* elements. The number of elements in a given set does not depend on the other properties of the set but only on the abstract nature of the set. In fact, the number property of a set is an abstract concept associated with the set of all sets equivalent to it. When a child thinks of the number *five*, he probably thinks of several different sets, each set consisting of *five* members.

Each set containing exactly *five* elements is equivalent to every set containing exactly *five* elements. That is, there is a one-to-one correspondence between any two sets each of which consists of exactly *five* elements. Since $\{1, 2, 3, 4, 5\}$ contains exactly *five* elements, we can establish a one-to-one correspondence between it and any other set of *five* elements whenever we wish to count the elements of the latter set. For example, to count the elements of $\{8, 2, 6, 9, 0\}$ we may establish the one-to-one correspondence in Fig. 3.1.

$$\{8, 2, 6, 9, 0\}$$
$$\updownarrow \;\updownarrow \;\updownarrow \;\updownarrow \;\updownarrow$$
$$\{1, 2, 3, 4, 5\}$$

Fig. 3.1

---

* Section 3.1 should *not* be omitted. However, Sections 3.2 through 3.7 may be omitted without loss of continuity.

Since $\{1, 2, 3, 4, 5\} \approx \{8, 2, 6, 9, 0\}$ and $\{1, 2, 3, 4, 5\}$ has *five* elements, we conclude that $\{8, 2, 6, 9, 0\}$ has *five* elements.

To count the elements of any nonempty finite set K, we establish a one-to-one correspondence between K and $\{1, 2, 3, \ldots, k\}$ and then conclude that K has k elements. Whenever a person counts a set of k objects one by one, he is really establishing a one-to-one correspondence between the set and $\{1, 2, 3, \ldots, k\}$. We agree that counting is a process which associates a counting number with each finite set; hence each *counting number k* is an abstract concept associated with every set equivalent to $\{1, 2, 3, \ldots, k\}$. For example, the counting number *five* is associated with every set equivalent to $\{1, 2, 3, 4, 5\}$. We associate the counting number 0 with *the empty set*. We formalize the above discussion in the following definition.

Definition 1

a) *The **number of elements** in the nonempty finite set K is equal to the counting number k [denoted by "$n(K) = k$"] if and only if $K \approx \{1, 2, 3, \ldots, k\}$.*

b) *The **number of elements** in the empty set [denoted by "$n(\varnothing)$"] is zero; that is,* $n(\varnothing) = 0$.

For example, if $K = \{2, 4, 6\}$, then $K \approx \{1, 2, 3\}$ and hence $n(K) = 3$.

It follows from Definition 1 and the fact that equivalence between sets is an equivalence relation that $n(A) = n(B)$ if and only if $A \approx B$ for any finite sets A and B.

The following examples illustrate Definition 1 and motivate Definition 2.

Example 1. If $A = \{1, 4, 8, 0\}$ and $B = \{2, 5, 8\}$, then

$$A \cup B = \{1, 4, 8, 0, 2, 5\} \quad \text{and} \quad A \cap B = \{8\} \neq \varnothing.$$

Moreover, $n(A) = 4$, $n(B) = 3$, and $n(A \cup B) = 6$. Thus

$$n(A \cup B) \neq 7. \quad [A \text{ and } B \text{ are } not \text{ disjoint.}]$$

Example 2. If $A = \{1, 4, 8, 0\}$ and $B = \{2, 5, 9\}$, then

$$A \cup B = \{1, 4, 8, 0, 2, 5, 9\} \quad \text{and} \quad A \cap B = \varnothing.$$

Moreover, $n(A) = 4$, $n(B) = 3$, and $n(A \cup B) = 7$. Thus

$$n(A) + n(B) = n(A \cup B). \quad [A \text{ and } B \text{ are disjoint.}]$$

Example 3. If $A = \{2, 4, 6\}$ and $B = \varnothing$, then

$$A \cup B = \{2, 4, 6\} \quad \text{and} \quad A \cap B = \varnothing.$$

Moreover, $n(A) = 3$, $n(B) = 0$, and $n(A \cup B) = 3$. Thus

$$n(A) + n(B) = n(A \cup B). \quad [A \text{ and } B \text{ are disjoint.}]$$

Example 4. If $a = 3$ and $b = 2$, then there exist disjoint sets $A = \{1, 3, 5\}$ and $B = \{2, 4\}$ such that $n(A) = a$ and $n(B) = b$. Thus

$$A \cup B = \{1, 3, 5, 2, 4\} = \{1, 2, 3, 4, 5\}.$$

Hence $n(A \cup B) = 5$. Moreover, if $A' = \{6, 7, 8\}$ and $B' = \{2, 5\}$, then

$$A' \approx A, \quad B' \approx B, \quad A' \cup B' = \{6, 7, 8, 2, 5\},$$
$$A' \cap B' = \varnothing, \quad \text{and} \quad A' \cup B' \approx A \cup B.$$

Thus

$$n(A' \cup B') = n(A \cup B) = 5.$$

In the above examples we were able to exhibit appropriate sets corresponding to the given counting numbers. We assume the following general statement, which guarantees the existence of the sets in Definitions 2 and 3.

If x and y are any counting numbers, then there exist disjoint finite sets X and Y such that $n(X) = x$ *and* $n(Y) = y$.

Definition 2. *The **sum** of the counting numbers x and y [denoted by "x + y"] is the counting number* $n(X \cup Y)$ *such that* $n(X) = x$, $n(Y) = y$, *and* $X \cap Y = \varnothing$. *That is,* $x + y = n(X) + n(Y) = n(X \cup Y)$.

The reader may prove that if $X' \approx X$, $Y' \approx Y$, $X' \cap Y' = \varnothing$, and $X \cap Y = \varnothing$, then

$$(X' \cup Y') \approx (X \cup Y).$$

Thus the *sum* $x + y$ is *well defined*.

The process of computing the sum of two numbers is called *addition*. To *add* two numbers is to compute the sum. According to Definition 2 we can add any two counting numbers. For this reason we say that addition is a *binary operation* and that $+$ is a *binary operator*. If we wish to add more than two numbers, we must agree on the manner in which we will add them. For example, we may add the numbers 2, 3, and 7 as follows:

$$(2 + 3) + 7 = 5 + 7 = 12.$$

Or we may add them as follows:

$$2 + (3 + 7) = 2 + 10 = 12.$$

Although the two procedures are different, the result of each addition is 12. For this reason, we may add 2, 3, and 7 in any way, and we may write

$$2 + 3 + 7$$

without parentheses. We may express the sum of more than three numbers in a similar manner. For example, we may write

$$a + b + c + d$$

to mean

$$[(a + b) + c] + d.$$

The following examples motivate Definition 3.

Example 5. If $A = \{1, 3\}$ and $B = \{0, 2, 4\}$, then

$$A \times B = \{(1, 0), (1, 2), (1, 4), (3, 0), (3, 2), (3, 4)\}.$$

Thus

$$\mathbf{n}(A \times B) = \mathbf{n}(\{(1, 0), (1, 2), (1, 4), (3, 0), (3, 2), (3, 4)\})$$
$$= \mathbf{n}(\{(1, 0)\ (1, 2), (1, 4)\} \cup \{(3, 0), (3, 2), (3, 4)\})$$
$$= \mathbf{n}(\{(1, 0), (1, 2), (1, 4)\}) + \mathbf{n}(\{(3, 0), (3, 2), (3, 4)\})$$
$$= 3 + 3$$
$$= 6.$$

Similarly,

$$\mathbf{n}(B \times A) = \mathbf{n}(\{(0, 1), (0, 3)\}) + \mathbf{n}(\{(2, 1), (2, 3)\})$$
$$+ \mathbf{n}(\{(4, 1), (4, 3)\})$$
$$= 2 + 2 + 2$$
$$= 6.$$

Example 6. If $A = \emptyset$ and $B = \{2, 3\}$, then

$$A \times B = \emptyset.$$

Thus

$$\mathbf{n}(A \times B) = 0.$$

Similarly,

$$\mathbf{n}(B \times A) = 0.$$

Example 7. If $A = \{1, 2, 4, 8\}$ and $B = \{4\}$, then

$$A \times B = \{(1, 4), (2, 4), (4, 4), (8, 4)\}$$
$$= \{(1, 4)\} \cup \{(2, 4)\} \cup \{(4, 4)\} \cup \{(8, 4)\}.$$

Thus

$$\mathbf{n}(A \times B) = \mathbf{n}(\{(1, 4)\}) + \mathbf{n}(\{(2, 4)\}) + \mathbf{n}(\{(4, 4)\}) + \mathbf{n}(\{(8, 4)\})$$
$$= 1 + 1 + 1 + 1 = 4.$$

Definition 3. The **product** of the counting numbers a and b [denoted by "$a \times b$" or "$a \cdot b$" or "ab" or "$a(b)$" or "$(a)(b)$" or "$(a)b$"] is the counting number $\mathbf{n}(A \times B)$ such that $\mathbf{n}(A) = a$ and $\mathbf{n}(B) = b$. That is, $ab = \mathbf{n}(A \times B)$.

The reader may prove that if $A' \approx A$ and $B' \approx B$, then $A' \times B' \approx A \times B$. Thus the *product ab* is *well defined*.

When we compute the product of a and b, we *multiply* them. The computation is called *multiplication*. Multiplication is a *binary operation* and $\times$ is a *binary operator*. As in addition, we may write

$$a \times b \times c$$

to mean either

$$(a \times b) \times c$$

or

$$a \times (b \times c).$$

We may employ Definitions 2 and 3 and the set laws to prove the following laws governing addition and multiplication of counting numbers.

Closure Laws

If a and b are any counting numbers, then the sum $a + b$ is a *unique* counting number.

If a and b are any counting numbers, then the product ab is a *unique* counting number.

Associative Laws

If a, b, and c are any counting numbers, then

$$(a + b) + c = a + (b + c).$$

If a, b, and c are any counting numbers, then

$$(ab)c = a(bc).$$

Identity Laws

There exists a unique counting number *zero* (denoted by "0" and called the *additive identity*) such that $a + 0 = a$ for every counting number a.

There exists a unique counting number *one* (denoted by "1" and called the *multiplicative identity*) such that $a \times 1 = a$ for every counting number a.

Commutative Laws

If a and b are any counting numbers, then $a + b = b + a$.

If a and b are any counting numbers, then $ab = ba$.

Cancellation Laws

If a, b, and c are any counting numbers such that $a + b = a + c$, then $b = c$; moreover, if $b = c$, then $a + b = a + c$.

If a, b, and c are any counting numbers such that $ab = ac$ and $a \neq 0$, then $b = c$; moreover, if $b = c$, then $ab = ac$.

Multiplication Law of Zero

If a and b are any counting numbers, then $ab = 0$ if and only if $a = 0$ or $b = 0$.

Distributive Law

If a, b, and c are any counting numbers, then $a(b + c) = ab + ac$.

The closure laws are immediate consequences of the definitions of *sum* and *product*. We may prove the commutative law for multiplication as follows:

$$ab = \mathbf{n}(A \times B)$$

$$= \mathbf{n}(B \times A) \qquad [\text{since } A \times B \approx B \times A]$$

$$= ba.$$

To prove the distributive law, we would first let A, B, and C be sets such that $\mathbf{n}(A) = a$, $\mathbf{n}(B) = b$, $\mathbf{n}(C) = c$, and $B \cap C = \varnothing$ and prove that

$$A \times (B \cup C) = (A \times B) \cup (A \times C).$$

Then we would proceed as follows:

$$a(b + c) = \mathbf{n}[A \times (B \cup C)]$$

$$= \mathbf{n}[(A \times B) \cup (A \times C)]$$

$$= \mathbf{n}(A \times B) + \mathbf{n}(A \times C)$$

$$= ab + ac.$$

The reader may prove the other laws, or he may accept them as axioms. The proofs may require unusual ingenuity and perseverance.

It is probably intuitively clear that 0 is less than 1, 1 is less than 2, 2 is less than 3, etc. In the following definition we define the order relation *is less than*.

Definition 4

a) *The counting number a is **less than** the counting number b [denoted by "$a < b$"] if and only if there exists a nonzero counting number k such that $a + k = b$.*

b) *The counting number a is **less than or equal to** the counting number b [denoted by "$a \le b$"] if and only if $a < b$ or $a = b$.* *

Since $0 + 4 = 4$, it follows that $0 < 4$. In fact, if a is any counting number except 0, then $0 < a$. Similarly, $5 < 8$ and $8 < 10$. The following laws governing the order relation *is less than* are probably familiar to the reader. The proofs, which are not difficult, are omitted.

Trichotomy Law for $<$

If a and b are any counting numbers, then *exactly* one of the following is true:

1. $a < b$,
2. $a = b$,
3. $b < a$.

---

*   We may read "$a < b$" either as "a *is less than* b" or as "b *is greater than a.*" We may use "$b > a$" to convey the same idea. We use the notation "$a \le b$" in a similar manner.

Additive Law for $<$

If a, b, and c are any counting numbers, then $a < b$ if and only if $a + c < b + c$.

Multiplicative Law for $<$

If a and b are any counting numbers and c is any nonzero counting number, then $a < b$ if and only if $ac < bc$.

Transitive Law for $<$

If a, b, and c are any counting numbers such that $a < b$ and $b < c$, then $a < c$.

EXERCISE SET 3.1

I. The *well-ordering principle* is stated as follows: *If A is any nonempty subset of the set of counting numbers, then there is exactly one element in A which is the least element of A.*

Illustrate the well-ordering principle for each of the following sets.

1. $A = \{10, 5, 2, 0, 3, 4, 9\}$ 2. $B = \{1, 3, 5, 7, \ldots\}$

3. $A \cup B$ 4. $A \cap B$

II. The *Archimedean principle** is stated as follows: *If a is any nonzero counting number and b is any counting number, then there exists a counting number k such that ak > b.*

Illustrate the Archimedean principle for each of the following pairs of counting numbers and then determine whether k is unique.

1. $a = 6$, $b = 21$ 2. $a = 3$, $b = 1$

3. $a = 2$, $b = 60$ 4. $a = 5$, $b = 510$

5. $a = 17$, $b = 283$ 6. $a = 30$, $b = 420$

7. $a = 700$, $b = 800$ 8. $a = 15$, $b = 0$

9. $a = 1$, $b = 99$ 10. $a = 2$, $b = 99$

III. Compute $\mathbf{n}(A \times B)$ and $\mathbf{n}(B \times A)$ for each of the following pairs of sets.

1. $A = \{2, 4\}$, $B = \{0\}$

2. $A = \{0, 1, 2\}$, $B = \{2, 4, 6, 8\}$

3. $A = \{2, 4\}$, $B = \{ \ \}$

4. $A = \{1, 3, 4\}$, $B = \{2, 4, 6, 8, 10\}$

IV. Identify the law(s) or definition(s) which make(s) each of the following statements true.

1. $4 + 3 = 3 + 4$ 2. $2 \times 6 = 6 \times 2$

3. $5 + (7 + 6) = (7 + 6) + 5$ 4. $5 + (7 + 6) = (5 + 7) + 6$

5. $5 \times (7 + 6) = (5 \times 7) + (5 \times 6)$ 6. $(4 \times 8) \times 2 = 2 \times (4 \times 8)$

7. $2 \times (8 + 4) = (2 \times 8) + (2 \times 4)$ 8. $6 + (8 + 9) = (6 + 8) + 9$

---

*   The Archimedean principle is named for the famous Greek mathematician Archimedes of Syracuse (*circa* 287 B.C.–212 B.C.).

9. $(4 + 5) + (0 + 6) = 9 + 6$ 10. $(3 \times 1)(4 \times 2) = 8 \times 3$

11. $(3 \times 6)(2 \times 5) = 10 \times 18$ 12. $4 \times 1 = 4$

V. By Definition 2, verify each of the following.

1. $4 + 3 = 7$ 2. $2 + 2 = 4$

3. $5 + 1 = 6$ 4. $6 + 0 = 6$

5. $3 + 4 = 7$ 6. $7 + 3 = 10$

7. $4 + 5 = 9$ 8. $0 + 7 = 7$

9. $0 + 0 = 0$ 10. $1 + 3 = 4$

VI. By Definition 3, verify each of the following.

1. $4 \times 3 = 12$ 2. $2 \times 2 = 4$

3. $5 \times 1 = 5$ 4. $6 \times 0 = 0$

5. $2 \times 3 = 6$ 6. $3 \times 2 = 6$

7. $1 \times 9 = 9$ 8. $0 \times 7 = 0$

9. $0 \times 0 = 0$ 10. $4 \times 2 = 8$

VII. State the law which guarantees the truth of each of the following equations [the universal quantifier is implied]. Observe that the punctuation and order do not affect the sum of three counting numbers.

1. $(a + b) + c = (b + a) + c$ 2. $(b + a) + c = b + (a + c)$

3. $b + (a + c) = b + (c + a)$ 4. $b + (c + a) = (b + c) + a$

5. $(b + c) + a = (c + b) + a$ 6. $(c + b) + a = c + (b + a)$

7. $c + (b + a) = c + (a + b)$ 8. $c + (a + b) = (c + a) + b$

9. $(c + a) + b = (a + c) + b$ 10. $(a + c) + b = a + (c + b)$

11. $a + (c + b) = a + (b + c)$

VIII. State the law which guarantees the truth of each of the following equations [the universal quantifier is implied].

1. $(ab)c = (ba)c$ 2. $(ba)c = b(ac)$

3. $b(ac) = b(ca)$ 4. $b(ca) = (bc)a$

5. $(bc)a = (cb)a$ 6. $(cb)a = c(ba)$

7. $c(ba) = c(ab)$ 8. $c(ab) = (ca)b$

9. $(ca)b = (ac)b$ 10. $(ac)b = a(cb)$

11. $a(cb) = a(bc)$

IX. Employ the distributive law to prove each of the following.

1. $(4 + 6) \times 4 = 40$ 2. $12 = 2 \times 4 + 2 \times 2$

3. $32a = 4(3a) + 5(4a)$ 4. $3t(2 + 4) = 18t$

X. Use Definition 4 to decide whether each of the following is *true* or *false*.

1. $4 < 6$ 2. $5 < 2$

3. $4 > 1$ 4. $6 > 8$

5. $7 < 8$ 6. $0 < 4$

7. $6 < 6$ 8. $1 > 4$

9. $0 < 0$ 10. $3 + 5 < 4 + 3$

3.2 ANCIENT NUMERATION SYSTEMS

As early as 3000 years ago Egypt had prosperous cities, markets, business establishments, and government offices. The commercial and government accounting records required the use of large numbers. Consequently, the Egyptians developed a set of *numerals* (symbols for numbers) to express numbers from one to a million.

The Egyptians denoted the number *one* by the symbol "|" (a stroke), *two* by "‖", and *nine* by nine strokes. They invented other symbols for larger numbers. Each Egyptian symbol and the number it represents are listed in Fig. 3.2(a). To express numbers other than those indicated in Fig. 3.2(a), the Egyptians combined symbols as illustrated in Fig. 3.2(b).

Egyptian Symbol	Number
| (stroke)	one
∩ (heelbone)	ten
৭ (scroll)	hundred
⚘ (lotus flower)	thousand
⁄ (bent line)	ten thousand
◠ (fish)	hundred thousand
⚇ (amazed man)	million

a)

Number	Egyptian Symbol
thirteen	∩ |||
thirty-seven	∩∩∩ |||||||
one hundred twenty-three	৭ ∩∩ |||
three hundred thousand five hundred sixty-nine	◠◠◠ ৭৭৭৭৭ ∩∩∩∩∩ |||||||||

b)   **Fig. 3.2**

It is easy to see that the Egyptian symbol representing a number like 999,999 is awkward. Moreover, there is no symbol to represent any number larger than 9,999,999. In today's world of macroeconomics and space travel, we would have to invent new symbols to represent the larger numbers whose names are in the average person's vocabulary.

The Egyptians had no symbol for the counting number *zero*, and they did not employ the place value* concept. Fortunately, the repetition in the Egyptian system enabled them to write numerals by combining and repeating the basic symbols of the system.

In the history of mankind there have been many *numeration systems* (sometimes called *notational systems*) as cumbersome as the Egyptian system. Fortunately, most of them are now obsolete. The familiar Roman numeration system uses capital letters as symbols to represent certain numbers, as shown in Fig. 3.3(a). These symbols are usually called *Roman numerals*. To express numbers other than those listed in Fig. 3.3(a), the Romans combined symbols as shown in Fig. 3.3(b).

Roman Numeral	Number
I	one
V	five
X	ten
L	fifty
C	one hundred
D	five hundred
M	one thousand

a)

Number	Roman Numeral
two	II
three	III
four	IV
six	VI
nine	IX
eleven	XI
thirty	XXX
forty	XL
seventy-six	LXXVI
ninety	XC
four hundred	CD
nine hundred	CM

b)   **Fig. 3.3**

As in the Egyptian system, there is no symbol for *zero* in the Roman system. The reader should observe a distinct difference between the Egyptian system and the Roman system. In the Roman system, the order of appearance of the individual

---

*   *Place value* will be discussed in Section 3.3.

symbols in a numeral is important, whereas in the Egyptian system the order is unimportant. For example, in the Roman system the symbol "IX" represents the number *nine*, but the symbol "XI" represents the number *eleven*. In the Egyptian system, we could represent *eleven* by either "∩|" or "|∩"; i.e., the Egyptian system does not employ the subtractive process.

　　Neither the Roman system nor the Egyptian system is suitable for book-keeping purposes. Although addition is not difficult, it is tedious in both systems. However, multiplication is so difficult and time-consuming that it would be impossible to keep up-to-date records in either system today.*

EXERCISE SET 3.2

　I. Represent each of the following counting numbers in the Roman system and in the Egyptian system.

1. 26	2. 39	3. 407
4. 987	5. 999	6. 573
7. 101	8. 202	9. 749
10. 751	11. 1971	12. 1969

　II. The statement

　　　$13(11 + 27) = (13 \times 11) + (13 \times 27)$

　　　is an example of the distributive property.

　1. Express the above example in the Egyptian system.

　2. Express the above example in the Roman system.

3.3 HINDU-ARABIC NUMERATION SYSTEM

In its present form, the Hindu-Arabic numeration system uses the *ten* symbols

　　0, 1, 2, 3, 4, 5, 6, 7, 8, 9

called *digits*, to express (in writing) any counting number by a symbol called a *numeral*. Each digit of the numeral representing a number has both a *face value* and a *place value*. For example, we express the counting number *thirteen* by the symbol "13." The numeral "13" consists of two *digits*, "1" and "3." The *face value* of "1" is *one*, and the *face value* of "3" is *three*. However, the *place value* of "1" is *ten*, and the *place value* of "3" is *one*. That is, the numeral "13" for the number *thirteen* indicates that thirteen is the sum of one *ten* and three *ones*. Similarly, the numeral "258" indicates that the number 258 is the sum of two

---

*　Actually, the Romans did not use their letter numerals in either addition or multiplication; they did their computations on counting boards and used their numerals to record the results. Modern data processing and record keeping even in the Hindu-Arabic numeration system are so complex that high-speed electronic digital computers are essential today.

hundreds, five *tens*, and eight *ones*. The face value of "2" is *two* but its place value is *one hundred*; the face value of "5" is *five*, but its place value is *ten*; and the face value of "8" is *eight*, but its place value is *one*.

Since the reader is familiar with the numerals of the Hindu-Arabic numeration system and can express any counting number by a numeral of the system, our purpose is to *analyze* the system and verify the usual rules or devices (called algorithms) for adding and multiplying two or more counting numbers. We assume that the reader knows all additional facts through $9 + 9$ and all multiplication facts through 9×9, and we confine our attention to the addition (or multiplication) of two counting numbers, one of which is represented by a numeral consisting of (at least) two digits. For example, we will analyze and verify the algorithm for adding and multiplying such numbers as 6 and 72, 508 and 33, etc.

To simplify the language we agree, for example, that

a is a three-digit number

means

the Hindu-Arabic numeral for the number a is a three-digit numeral.

Moreover, since there are *ten* distinct symbols in the Hindu-Arabic numeration system, we agree to refer to the Hindu-Arabic numeration system as the *base ten (numeration) system* or the *decimal (numeration) system*, and we say that the *base* of the system is *ten*.

Each digit of a numeral in the decimal system is traditionally named for its place value. For example, the digit whose place value is one thousand is traditionally called the *thousands digit*. The face value, place value, and name of each digit of "74709" are shown in Fig. 3.4.

Digit	7	4	7	0	9
Face Value	seven	four	seven	zero	nine
Place Value	ten thousand	one thousand	one hundred	ten	one
Traditional Name	ten thousands digit	thousands digit	hundreds digit	tens digit	units digit

Fig. 3.4

To represent a counting number of more than ten digits, it is necessary to *repeat* at least one digit. For example, in the eleven-digit numeral

53,218,764,904

"4" is repeated. However, the place values of the two "4's" are different.

We observe the following facts regarding the Hindu-Arabic numeration system:

1. Every counting number can be represented by a numeral consisting of no more than *ten different* digits (0, 1, 2, 3, 4, 5, 6, 7, 8, 9).

2. No counting number can be represented by two different numerals.

3. Each digit of every numeral has a unique face value and a unique place value.

4. The place value of each digit (except the units digit) of any numeral is ten times the place value of the digit on its right.

The above properties of the decimal system make it superior to the ancient numeration systems. In particular, the reader should observe that the invention of new symbols (for very large numbers) is not necessary in the decimal system; regardless of its magnitude, every counting number can be represented by a numeral consisting of only ten distinct symbols. If it were not for place value and the digit "0," the system would have few advantages over the ancient systems.*

EXERCISE SET 3.3

I. Construct a table like the one in Fig. 3.4 for each of the following numerals.

1. 2753

2. 27,530

3. 207,507

4. 777,333

5. 1,009,901

6. 99,999,999

II. What is the largest counting number which can be represented by each of the following?

1. a one-digit numeral

2. a two-digit numeral

3. a three-digit numeral

4. a four-digit numeral

5. a five-digit numeral

6. a six-digit numeral

III. What is the smallest counting number which can be represented by each of the following?

1. a one-digit numeral

2. a two-digit numeral

3. a three-digit numeral

4. a four-digit numeral

5. a five-digit numeral

6. a six-digit numeral

---

*   The Hindus probably invented the numeration system known as the *Hindu-Arabic numeration system* sometime before 200 B.C. However, the digit "0" did not appear until 800 A.D. The Arabs adopted the system by 800 A.D. and took it to Europe in the *tenth* century.

3.4 EXPONENTIAL NOTATION

We recall that each digit of a numeral expressed in the decimal system has both a face value and a place value and that the place value of any digit except the units digit is ten times the place value of the digit on its right. For example, the place value of the thousands digit is ten times the place value of the hundreds digit, the place value of the hundreds digit is ten times the place value of the tens digit, and the place value of the tens digit is ten times the place value of the units digit. Thus the place value of the thousands digit is $10 \times 10 \times 10$ times the place value of the units digit. We introduce the *exponential notation* "10^3" to represent $10 \times 10 \times 10$. That is, $10^3 = 10 \times 10 \times 10$. Similarly,

$$10^5 = 10 \times 10 \times 10 \times 10 \times 10 \quad \text{and} \quad 3^4 = 3 \times 3 \times 3 \times 3.$$

Definition 5

a) $a^m = \underbrace{a \times a \times \cdots \times a}_{m \text{ factors}}$, *for any counting number a and any counting number m greater than 1;*

b) $a^1 = a$, *for any counting number a;*
c) $a^0 = 1$, *for any nonzero counting number a;*
d) a^m *is called an **exponential** form of a number, a is called the **base**, and m is called the **exponent**.*

For example, an exponential form of 1000 is 10^3, the exponent is 3, and the base is 10. We may express 64 in the following exponential forms:

8^2 (base is 8, exponent is 2),
4^3 (base is 4, exponent is 3),
2^6 (base is 2, exponent is 6).

The reader will observe that *the exponential form of a number depends on the base or the exponent.*

The exponential form "a^m" is read variously as follows:

the mth power of a,

a to the mth power,

or

a to the m.

However, "a^2" is usually read *a squared*, and "a^3" is usually read *a cubed.*[*]
Because of Definition 5, we observe that the place value of the thousands digit is 10^3 times the place value of the units digit. Since the place value of the ten thousands digit is 10 times the place value of the thousands digit, it follows that the place value of the ten thousands digit is 10^4 times the place value of the units digit.

---

[*]   In order to avoid confusion, we may read "$(a + b)^2$" as *the square of $a + b$,* and we may read "$a + b^2$" as *$a + $ the square of b.*

The following examples illustrate how we may use the exponential notation to express a counting number in a form which emphasizes place value.   The reader is reminded that $10^0 = 1$.

Example 1

$$654 = 600 + 50 + 4$$
$$= 6(100) + 5(10) + 4(1)$$
$$= 6(10^2) + 5(10^1) + 4(10^0).$$

Example 2

$$6547 = 6000 + 500 + 40 + 7$$
$$= 6(1000) + 5(100) + 4(10) + 7(1)$$
$$= 6(10^3) + 5(10^2) + 4(10^1) + 7(10^0).$$

Example 3

$$605{,}407 = 600{,}000 + 5000 + 400 + 7$$
$$= 6(100{,}000) + 0(10{,}000) + 5(1000) + 4(100) + 0(10) + 7(1)$$
$$= 6(10^5) + 0(10^4) + 5(10^3) + 4(10^2) + 0(10^1) + 7(10^0).$$

Example 4

$$65{,}000 = 60{,}000 + 5000$$
$$= 6(10{,}000) + 5(1000) + 0(100) + 0(10) + 0(1)$$
$$= 6(10^4) + 5(10^3) + 0(10^2) + 0(10^1) + 0(10^0).$$

The form in the last line of each of the above examples is called the *polynomial form* (or the *expanded form*), and the number is said to be expressed in *expanded notation*. For example, the expanded notation for 654 is

$$6(10^2) + 5(10^1) + 4(10^0).$$

Since $a^3 = a \times a \times a$ and $a^2 = a \times a$, it follows that

$$a^3 \times a^2 = (a \times a \times a) \times (a \times a) = a^5.$$

Similarly, $a^2 \times a^1 = a^3$ and $a^5 \times a^0 = a^5$. In general,

$$a^m \times a^k = \underbrace{a \times a \times \cdots \times a}_{m \text{ factors}} \times \underbrace{a \times a \times \cdots \times a}_{k \text{ factors}} = \underbrace{a \times a \times \cdots \times a}_{m+k \text{ factors}} = a^{m+k}.$$

The reader should observe that we do *not multiply* the exponents m and k but we *add* them.

EXERCISE SET 3.4

I. Express each of the following in *expanded notation*.

1. 54   2. 612

3. 4,216   4. 519

5. 20,101   6. 40,020

7. 1,268,721 8. 200,100,001

9. 66,006,600 10. 601,020,109

II. Express each of the following counting numbers in *standard form* [for example, $2^4 = 16$ and $2^4 + 5^0 = 17$].

1. 2^3 2. 5^2

3. 8^0 4. 5^0

5. 1^{22} 6. $(5^0)^{22}$

7. 12^3 8. 10^4

9. $2^3 + 3^2$ 10. $2^2 + 3^3$

11. $(2 + 3)^3$ 12. $(3 + 2)^2$

13. $4^0 + 1^0$ 14. $(4 + 1)^0$

15. $(5 + 5)^4$ 16. $(2 + 1)^5$

17. $2^5 + 1^5$ 18. $2 + 1^5$

19. $2(7 + 3)^4$ 20. $[2(7 + 3)]^4$

III. Express each of the following in *exponential form* [for example, $5^2 \times 5^4 = 5^6$].

1. $3^2 \times 3$ 2. $2^4 \times 2^3 \times 2$

3. $5^4 \times 5^3$ 4. $6^4 \times 6^5$

5. $10^k \times 10^m$ 6. $2^4 \times 2^5 \times 2^0$

7. $18^{20} \times 18^{11}$ 8. $a \times a^3 \times a^4$

9. $a^0 \times a \times a^2$ 10. $10^3 \times 10^2 \times 10$

11. $10^4 \times 10^2 \times 10^3$ 12. $5^k \times 5^m \times 5^4$

IV. We may represent every counting number in terms of sets of powers of 10. For example, we may represent 234 as 2 sets of *one hundred* elements each, 3 sets of *ten* elements each, and 4 sets of *one* element each. Represent each of the following counting numbers in terms of sets of powers of 10.

1. 29 2. 38

3. 92 4. 83

5. 289 6. 892

7. 950 8. 590

9. 4023 10. 7203

3.5 ADDITION ALGORITHM IN THE DECIMAL SYSTEM

We now analyze the familiar *addition algorithm* (rule for adding counting numbers) which is taught in the elementary schools. According to the algorithm we can add 53 and 45 as follows.

$$\begin{array}{r} 53 \\ +45 \\ \hline 98 \end{array} \qquad \begin{array}{l} [3 + 5 = 8] \\ [5 + 4 = 9] \end{array}$$

According to the algorithm, we add the units digits [3 and 5] to obtain the units digit [8] of the sum, and we add the two tens digits [5 and 4] to obtain the tens digit [9] of the sum. The only addition facts we need are those involving the sums of one-digit numbers, which we can compute from Definition 2. Hence the algorithm enables us to compute $53 + 45$ without forming the union of a 53-member set and a 45-member set and counting the elements in the union.

The analysis and justification of the addition algorithm involve the exponential notation, the notation of the decimal system, and the laws of Section 3.1. We express each number in expanded notation and apply the appropriate laws as follows:

$$53 + 45 = [5(10^1) + 3(10^0)] + [4(10^1) + 5(10^0)]$$
$$= [5(10^1) + 4(10^1)] + [3(10^0) + 5(10^0)]$$
$$= [5 + 4] (10^1) + [3 + 5] (10^0)$$
$$= 9(10^1) + 8(10^0)$$
$$= 98.$$

In the computation of the sum of 53 and 45 by the addition algorithm, each *partial sum* [$3 + 5 = 8$ and $5 + 4 = 9$] is a one-digit number. However, if one of the partial sums is a two-digit number, the algorithm involves a so-called *carry*. For example, according to the algorithm we may add 37 and 45 as follows.

$$\begin{array}{r} \overset{1}{3}7 \\ +45 \\ \hline 82 \end{array} \qquad \begin{array}{l} [7 + 5 = 12, \text{ put down 2, and carry 1}] \\ [3 + 4 = 7,\ 7 + 1 \text{ (carried)} = 8] \end{array}$$

The analysis and justification are as follows:

$$37 + 45 = [3(10^1) + 7(10^0)] + [4(10^1) + 5(10^0)]$$
$$= [3(10^1) + 4(10^1)] + [7(10^0) + 5(10^0)]$$
$$= [3 + 4] (10^1) + [7 + 5] (10^0)$$
$$= [3 + 4] (10^1) + [12] (10^0)$$
$$= [3 + 4] (10^1) + [10 + 2] (10^0)$$
$$= [3 + 4] (10^1) + [10(10^0) + 2(10^0)]$$
$$= [3 + 4] (10^1) + [10^1 + 2(10^0)]$$
$$= [3 + 4] (10^1) + [1(10^1) + 2(10^0)]*$$
$$= [3 + 4 + 1] (10)^1 + 2(10^0)*$$
$$= 8(10^1) + 2(10^0)$$
$$= 82.$$

---

*   The "1" *carried* is shown in boldface type.

The reader should observe that the number *carried* is not *one* but *ten*. The *face value* of the digit carried is *one* but the *place value* is *ten*. The sum of 7 and 5 $[7 + 5 = 12]$ is expressed as $10 + 2$, and then the *ten* is carried.

We may illustrate the *carry* procedure with money. If a man has \$37 [3 ten-dollar bills and 7 one-dollar bills] and his wife has \$45 [4 ten-dollar bills and 5 one-dollar bills], together they have \$82 [7 ten-dollar bills and 12 one-dollar bills]. If they *exchange* 10 of the one-dollar bills for 1 ten-dollar bill, they still have \$82 [8 ten-dollar bills and 2 one-dollar bills]. The *carry* is really an *exchange*— 10 *ones* are exchanged for 1 *ten*, and 2 *ones* are retained.

Frequently it is necessary to *carry* more than once. For example, we may compute the sum of 268 and 437 as follows.

$$
\begin{array}{l}
\overset{1\,1}{268} \quad [8 + 7 = 15, \text{ put down 5, and carry 1}]\\
\underline{+437} \quad [6 + 3 = 9, 9 + 1 \text{ (carried)} = 10, \text{ put down 0, and carry 1}]\\
705 \quad [2 + 4 = 6, 6 + 1 \text{ (carried)} = 7]
\end{array}
$$

The analysis and justification are as follows:

$$
\begin{aligned}
268 + 437 &= [2(10^2) + 6(10^1) + 8(10^0)] + [4(10^2) + 3(10^1) + 7(10^0)]\\
&= [2(10^2) + 4(10^2)] + [6(10^1) + 3(10^1)] + [8(10^0) + 7(10^0)]\\
&= [2 + 4] (10^2) + [6 + 3] (10^1) + [8 + 7] (10^0)\\
&= [2 + 4] (10^2) + [6 + 3] (10^1) + [15] (10^0)\\
&= [2 + 4] (10^2) + [6 + 3] (10^1) + [10 + 5] (10^0)\\
&= [2 + 4] (10^2) + [6 + 3 + 1] (10^1) + 5(10^0)\\
&= [2 + 4] (10^2) + [10] (10^1) + 5(10^0)\\
&= [2 + 4] (10^2) + [10 + 0] (10^1) + 5(10^0)\\
&= [2 + 4 + 1] (10^2) + 0(10^1) + 5(10^0)\\
&= 7(10^2) + 0(10^1) + 5(10^0)\\
&= 705.
\end{aligned}
$$

Although the three examples do not constitute proof of the validity of the addition algorithm in general, they do suggest the method of proof. Since the general proof is somewhat tedious, we do not include it. The reader should observe that the method suggested by the above examples is valid also for the sum of three or more counting numbers.

EXERCISE SET 3.5

Justify the addition algorithm in each of the following. State the reason or reasons for each step.

1. 82	2. 28	3. 28	4. 82	5. 82
13	31	13	9	29

6. 28	7. 147	8. 698	9. 80	10. 90
92	884	304	79	68
			22	33

11. 87	12. 85
23	34
14	19
5	3

3.6 MULTIPLICATION ALGORITHM IN THE DECIMAL SYSTEM

Now we analyze the familiar *multiplication algorithm* which is taught in the elementary schools. According to the algorithm we can multiply 29 by 3 as follows.

$$
\begin{array}{r}
29 \\
\times 3 \\
\hline
87
\end{array}
\qquad
\begin{array}{l}
[3 \times 9 = 27, \text{ put down 7, and carry 2}] \\
[3 \times 2 = 6,\, 6 + 2\ (\text{carried}) = 8]
\end{array}
$$

The analysis and justification are as follows:

$$
\begin{aligned}
3 \times 29 &= 3 \times [2(10^1) + 9(10^0)] \\
&= 3 \times [2(10^1)] + 3 \times [9(10^0)] \\
&= [3 \times 2] (10^1) + [3 \times 9] (10^0) \\
&= [3 \times 2] (10^1) + [27] (10^0) \\
&= [3 \times 2] (10^1) + [2(10^1) + 7(10^0)] (10^0) \\
&= [3 \times 2] (10^1) + [2(10^1) (10^0) + 7(10^0) (10^0)] \\
&= [3 \times 2] (10^1) + [2(10^1) + 7(10^0)] \\
&= [3 \times 2 + 2] (10^1) + 7(10^0)* \\
&= [6 + 2] (10^1) + 7(10^0) \\
&= 8(10^1) + 7(10^0) \\
&= 87.
\end{aligned}
$$

As in the addition algorithm, the number *carried* is not 2 but 2 *tens*. Again, the reader may think of *exchanging* the 27 ones for 2 *tens* and 7 *ones* and then adding the 2 *tens* to the 3×2 tens.

We can easily extend the above analysis to computing the product of *any* counting number and *any* one-digit counting number. For example, we can justify that

$$3 \times 297 = 891, \qquad 5 \times 297 = 1485, \qquad \text{and} \qquad 8 \times 297 = 2376.$$

---

*   Here we adopt the usual convention that $3 \times 2 + 2 = 6 + 2$ rather than 3×4. However, $3 \times (2 + 2) = 3 \times 4$. Whenever parentheses are omitted in an expression involving multiplication and addition, the multiplication takes precedence over the addition.

We can employ the preceding analysis to facilitate the analysis of the algorithm for multiplying any two counting numbers. For example, we may compute the product of 297 and 358 as follows.

$$
\begin{array}{r}
297 \\
\times\, 358 \\
\hline
2376 \\
1485 \\
891 \\
\hline
106326
\end{array}
$$

The analysis and justification are as follows:

$$
\begin{aligned}
297 \times 358 &= 297 \times [3(10^2) + 5(10^1) + 8(10^0)] \\
&= 297 \times [3(10^2)] + 297 \times [5(10^1)] + 297 \times [8(10^0)] \\
&= [297 \times 3](10^2) + [297 \times 5](10^1) + [297 \times 8](10^0) \\
&= 891(10^2) + 1485(10^1) + 2376(10^0) \\
&= 89,100 + 14,850 + 2376 \\
&= 106,326.
\end{aligned}
$$

The above analysis clearly shows why we *shift* the second *partial product* one place to the left and the third *partial product* two places to the left. The second partial product is really 14,850 rather than 1485, and the third partial product is really 89,100 rather than 891. Many adults who have been using the algorithm since childhood have never known the reason for *shifting* partial products. The following algorithm, which is being taught in many contemporary elementary schools, does not require *shifting* but displays the partial products as they really are.

$$
\begin{array}{r}
297 \\
\times\, 358 \\
\hline
2376 \\
14850 \\
89100 \\
\hline
106326
\end{array}
$$

EXERCISE SET 3.6

I. Employ the expanded notation to express each of the following in the customary decimal form.

[*Hint*: $72 \times 10^2 = [7(10^1) + 2(10^0)] \times 10^2 = 7 \times 10^1 \times 10^2 + 2 \times 10^0 \times 10^2 = 7 \times 10^3 + 2 \times 10^2 = 7(10^3) + 2(10^2) + 0(10^1) + 0(10^0) = 7200.$]

1. 79×10^2 2. 93×10^2

3. 872×10^2 4. 287×10^2

5. 6×10^4

6. 9×10^4

7. 97×10^4

8. 76×10^4

9. 207×10^5

10. 809×10^5

II. Analyze and justify the multiplication in the computation of each of the following products.

1. 83×29

2. 38×92

3. 125×73

4. 251×37

5. 806×53

6. 607×72

7. 950×702

8. 905×720

9. 819×198

10. 981×189

3.7 QUINARY NUMERATION SYSTEM

In the Hindu-Arabic numeration system we can express any counting number by employing only the ten digits

0, 1, 2, 3, 4, 5, 6, 7, 8, 9

and the concept of place value. The reader will recall that we frequently refer to the Hindu-Arabic numeration system as the *decimal* (or *base ten*) system. The word *decimal* is used because it pertains to the number *ten*. The choice of *ten* as a base for the Hindu-Arabic numeration system was probably due to the fact that man has *ten* fingers (and *ten* toes). If man had been born with only one hand (i.e., with *five* fingers), the numeration system might well be of base *five* rather than *ten*. If man had decided to use both hands and both feet for counting, he might have developed a numeration system based on *twenty*.*

By now the reader probably realizes that there is nothing sacred about the decimal system. Any other system which employs the place value concept may serve our purposes just as well. For example, we could employ a numeration system based on *five*, *twelve*, *twenty*, or even *two*. In fact, for some purposes, a base other than *ten* may be superior to *ten*.

Some reasons for investigating numeration systems with bases other than *ten* are the following.

1. A study of other numeration systems provides better understanding of the decimal system.

2. A study of other numeration systems (which are foreign to one who knows only the decimal system) presents problems similar to those children experience when they first study the decimal system (which is strange to them).

3. A study of other numeration systems provides a better understanding of the basic principles of electronic digital computers. (Every digital computer operates in base *two*. To locate information stored in its memory banks, a

---

*   In fact, the Mayas of Yucatan used a modified base twenty system to represent time intervals between dates on the calendar.

computer may use either base *eight* or base *sixteen*; the newer computers use base *sixteen* because it decreases processing time and therefore increases efficiency.)

4. A study of other numeration systems is interesting and enlightening.

Now we are ready to investigate the base *five* system, which is sometimes called the *quinary* numeration system. In the quinary system there are *five* distinct digits to represent the numbers *zero, one, two, three,* and *four.* We may choose any five different digits we desire, but after we have chosen them, we must be consistent in our usage of them and preserve the place value feature of the Hindu-Arabic numeration system. For example, we may choose the digits

0, *a, b, c,* and *d*

to represent the counting numbers

zero, one, two, three, and *four,*

respectively. Because of the place value concept, the numeral

c0b

would represent the counting number *seventy-seven.* To prove that *c0b* = seventy-seven, we use the expanded notation in *base five* as follows:

$$c0b = c(\text{five}^b) + 0(\text{five}^a) + b(\text{five}^0)$$

$$= \text{three}(\text{five}^{\text{two}}) + \text{zero}(\text{five}^{\text{one}}) + \text{two}(\text{five}^{\text{zero}})$$

$$= \text{three}(\text{five} \times \text{five}) + \text{zero}(\text{five}) + \text{two}(\text{one})$$

$$= \text{three}(\text{twenty-five}) + \text{zero}(\text{five}) + \text{two}(\text{one})$$

$$= \text{seventy-five} + \text{zero} + \text{two}$$

$$= \text{seventy-seven}.$$

Instead of choosing the digits

0, *a, b, c,* and *d*

we can choose the familiar digits

0, 1, 2, 3, and 4

to represent the numbers

zero, one, two, three, and *four,*

respectively. If we do, then we must be extremely careful not to confuse a *quinary* numeral with a *decimal* numeral. For example, the *quinary* numeral

123   (read *one-two-three*)

represents the counting number

thirty-eight,

whereas the *decimal* numeral

123

represents the counting number

one hundred twenty-three.

If we use a different set of symbols, we avoid that confusion, but we lose the advantage of recognizing the digits immediately. We follow the custom of most authors and employ the familiar digits

0, 1, 2, 3, and 4

to represent the five counting numbers

zero, one, two, three, and *four,*

respectively, and we read each *single digit* as if it were a digit in the decimal system. Thus the *quinary* numeral

1403210

is read

one-four-zero-three-two-one-zero.

The reader should observe that it is *incorrect* to read it as *one million, four hundred three thousand, two hundred ten,* which is the way to read the *decimal* numeral

1,403,210.

The reader is familiar with the *odometer** of a standard automobile. The odometer consists of six drums (or discs) which rotate about their axes. On the face of each drum are the *ten* digits

0, 1, 2, 3, 4, 5, 6, 7, 8, and 9,

as indicated in Fig. 3.5.

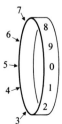   **Fig. 3.5**

---

*   The *mileage meter*, not the speedometer.

For this discussion we ignore tenths of miles and consider only the *five* drums indicating *units, tens, hundreds, thousands,* and *ten thousands* of miles. After the automobile has been driven *nine* miles, the digit "9" on the right drum appears in the window and the digit "0" on each of the other drums appears in the window, as shown in Fig. 3.6.

Fig. 3.6

As the car is driven one more mile, the right drum rotates so that "0" appears in the right window. This action causes the adjacent drum to rotate so that "1" appears in that window, as shown in Fig. 3.7. We say that the car has been driven *ten* miles and indicate *ten* by "10."

Fig. 3.7

As the car is driven more, the drums rotate accordingly. At ninety-nine miles, "9" appears in the right window and also in the adjacent window. Then after one more mile, the right drum rotates so that "0" appears in the window, and the adjacent drum rotates so that "0" appears in the corresponding window. This action causes the center drum to rotate so that "1" appears in the center window. The transition from *ninety-nine* (99) miles to *one hundred* (100) miles is shown in Fig. 3.8.

Fig. 3.8

The odometer described above is based on the *decimal* system. An odometer based on the *quinary* system would differ from the one based on the decimal system in the markings of the drums. On the face of each drum of a *quinary* odometer are the *five* digits

0, 1, 2, 3, and 4,

as indicated in Fig. 3.9.

Again we ignore fractions of miles and consider only *five* drums. One complete rotation of the right drum now indicates *five* miles rather than *ten* miles.

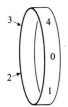

Fig. 3.9

Thus the drums from right to left in the *quinary* odometer indicate *units, fives, twenty-fives, one hundred twenty-fives,* and *six hundred twenty-fives,* rather than *units, tens, hundreds, thousands,* and *ten thousands* in the *decimal* odometer.

After the car has been driven *four* miles, the digit "4" on the right drum appears in the window, and the digit "0" on each of the other drums appears in the window, as shown in Fig. 3.10.

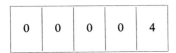

Fig. 3.10

As the car is driven one more mile, the right drum rotates so that "0" appears in the right window. This action causes the adjacent drum to rotate so that "1" appears in that window, as shown in Fig. 3.11. We say that the car has been driven *five* miles and indicate *five* by "10." We must be careful to read "10" as *one-zero* or *one-zero base five,* rather than *ten.*

Fig. 3.11

As the car is driven more, the drums rotate accordingly. At *twenty-four* miles the *quinary* odometer reads "00044." After one more mile, the right drum rotates so that "0" appears in the window, and the adjacent drum rotates so that "0" appears in the corresponding window. This action causes the center drum to rotate so that "1" appears in the center window. The transition from twenty-four (44) miles to twenty-five (100) miles is shown in Fig. 3.12.

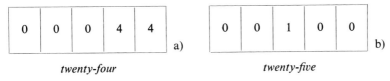

a)
twenty-four

b)
twenty-five

Fig. 3.12

The reader can use the quinary odometer to verify the entries in Fig. 3.13, which permit us to count and add in the quinary system.

Decimal Notation	0	1	2	3	4	5	6	7	8	9	10	11	12	13	14	15
Quinary Notation	0	1	2	3	4	10	11	12	13	14	20	21	22	23	24	30

Decimal Notation	16	17	18	19	20	21	22	23	24	25	26	27	28	29	30
Quinary Notation	31	32	33	34	40	41	42	43	44	100	101	102	103	104	110

Fig. 3.13

In order to compute sums like 243 + 104 (in the *quinary* system) we need an addition table for sums through 4 + 4; that is, we need the basic addition facts in *quinary* notation. The addition table is shown in Fig. 3.14.

Quinary Addition Table

+	0	1	2	3	4
0	0	1	2	3	4
1	1	2	3	4	10
2	2	3	4	10	11
3	3	4	10	11	12
4	4	10	11	12	13

Fig. 3.14

Employing the addition facts in Fig. 3.14, we can compute the sum of any two counting numbers in quinary notation. For example, 243 + 104 = 402. The computation by the usual addition algorithm may be expressed in the following format, in which the *carries* are indicated by the small "1's."

$$
\begin{array}{r}
{}^{1\,1} \\
243 \\
+134 \\
\hline
432
\end{array}
$$

We may justify the quinary addition algorithm in a manner similar to that in which we justified the decimal addition algorithm. The reader should supply the details and reasons for the following analysis.

$$243 + 134 = [2(\text{five}^2) + 4(\text{five}^1) + 3(\text{five}^0)]$$
$$+ [1(\text{five}^2) + 3(\text{five}^1) + 4(\text{five}^0)]$$
$$= [2 + 1](\text{five}^2) + [4 + 3](\text{five}^1) + [3 + 4](\text{five}^0)$$
$$= [2 + 1](10^2) + [4 + 3](10^1) + [12](10^0)$$
$$= [2 + 1](10^2) + [4 + 3](10^1) + [10 + 2](10^0)$$
$$= [2 + 1](10^2) + [4 + 3 + 1](10^1) + [2](10^0)$$
$$= [2 + 1](10^2) + [10 + 3](10^1) + 2(10^0)$$
$$= [2 + 1 + 1](10^2) + 3(10^1) + 2(10^0)$$
$$= 4(10^2) + 3(10^1) + 2(10^0)$$
$$= 432.$$

The reader is cautioned that all numerals in the above analysis are *quinary* numerals and that 10 is equal to *five* rather than *ten*. Whenever there is danger of ambiguity, we may indicate that the base is *five* by the subscript "5" (in decimal notation) or by the word *five*. For example,

$$432_5 = 432_{\text{five}} = 4(\text{five}^2) + 3(\text{five}) + 2.$$

The multiplication table in Fig. 3.15 can be constructed from the addition table in Fig. 3.14. For example,

$$2 \times 4 = 4 + 4 = 13,$$

and

$$3 \times 2 = 2 + 2 + 2$$
$$= (2 + 2) + 2$$
$$= 4 + 2$$
$$= 11.$$

Quinary Multiplication Table

×	0	1	2	3	4
0	0	0	0	0	0
1	0	1	2	3	4
2	0	2	4	11	13
3	0	3	11	14	22
4	0	4	13	22	31

Fig. 3.15

Employing the multiplication facts in Fig. 3.15 and the addition facts in Fig. 3.14, we can compute the product of any two counting numbers in quinary notation. For example, $123 \times 24 = 4112$. The computation by the multiplication algorithm may be expressed in the following format, in which the *carries* are indicated by the small numerals.

$$
\begin{array}{l}
_{1\,1} \leftarrow carries \text{ of second partial product} \\
_{2\,2} \leftarrow carries \text{ of first partial product} \\
123 \\
\times 24 \\
\hline
1102 \\
301 \\
\hline
4112
\end{array}
$$

The reader may justify the quinary multiplication algorithm in a manner similar to that in which we justified the decimal multiplication algorithm. Just as a student of French should think *in French* when he is conversing in French, we should perform all additions and multiplications in *base five* when we are calculating in base five. If we convert the quinary numerals to decimal numerals, compute in decimal numerals, and then convert the resulting decimal numerals to quinary numerals, we do not attain maximum understanding of the quinary system. To do so is analogous to conversing in French through an interpreter who translates from French to English, receives the reply in English, and translates the reply from English to French.

EXERCISE SET 3.7

I. Each of the following sets is expressed in the decimal system. Express each set in the *quinary* system.

1. $\{10, 15, 20, 25, 30\}$ 2. $\{4, 8, 12, 16, 20\}$
3. $\{18, 19, 20, 21, 22, 23, 24, 25, 26, 27\}$
4. $\{12, 13, 14, 15, 16, 17, 18, 19, 20, 21\}$
5. $\{121, 322\}$ 6. $\{420, 133\}$
7. $\{236, 237, 238\}$ 8. $\{199, 200, 201\}$
9. $\{2010\}$ 10. $\{1241\}$

II. Express each of the following in expanded notation [for example, $243_5 = 2(\text{five}^2) + 4(\text{five}^1) + 3(\text{five}^0) = 2(10^2) + 4(10^1) + 3(10^0)$].

1. 32_5 2. 41_5
3. 242_5 4. 342_5
5. 401_5 6. 203_5
7. 2134_5 8. 32321_5
9. 423020_5 10. 203210_5

III. Each number in Exercise II is expressed in base five. Express each in expanded decimal notation [for example, $243_5 = 2(5^2) + 4(5^1) + 3(5^0)$].

IV. Express each number of Exercise II in decimal notation [for example,

$243_5 = 2(5^2) + 4(5^1) + 3(5^0) = 2(25) + 4(5) + 3(1) = 50 + 20 + 3 = 73$

(base ten)].

V. Compute each of the following sums [for example, $3_5 + 4_5 = 12_5$].

1. $3_5 + 42_5$ 2. $12_5 + 13_5$
3. $4_5 + 34_5$ 4. $20_5 + 11_5$
5. $223_5 + 314_5$ 6. $414_5 + 213_5$
7. $2012_5 + 3122_5$ 8. $4321_5 + 4030_5$
9. $2024_5 + 4444_5$ 10. $1214_5 + 3101_5$

VI. Compute each of the following products [for example, $3_5 \times 4_5 = 22_5$].

1. $3_5 \times 42_5$ 2. $12_5 \times 13_5$
3. $4_5 \times 34_5$ 4. $20_5 \times 11_5$
5. $223_5 \times 314_5$ 6. $414_5 \times 213_5$

VII.

1. What is the largest number that can be expressed as a four-digit quinary numeral?
2. What is the smallest number that can be expressed as a four-digit quinary numeral?
3. What is the largest number that can be expressed as a two-digit quinary numeral?
4. What is the smallest number that can be expressed as a two-digit quinary numeral?
5. What is the smallest number that can be expressed as a five-digit quinary numeral?
6. What is the largest number that can be expressed as a five-digit quinary numeral?

VIII. We can illustrate the *carry* procedure in the quinary system by means of *pennies*, *nickels* and *quarters*. For example, since $243 = 2(\text{five}^2) + 4(\text{five}^1) + 3(\text{five}^0)$, we can regard "243" as representing 2 quarters + 4 nickels + 3 pennies. Justify each of the following additions by means of pennies, nickels, and quarters. [*Hint:* Follow the procedure in Section 3.5].

1.   124   2.   232   3.   333   4.   322
    + 112   + 121   + 123   + 123

IX. The *binary* system is a numeration system whose base is *two*. Let the numerals "0" and "1" represent the *two* digits in the binary system. Complete the accompanying tables, and use the addition and multiplication facts to compute the following sums and products.

+	0	1
0		1
1		

Binary Addition Table

×	0	1
0		
1		

Binary Multiplication Table

1.	101	2.	1010	3.	110	4.	1010
	$+111$		$+110$		$\times 101$		$\times 110$

5.	111	6.	111	7.	101	8.	100
	$+1101$		$+100$		$\times 101$		$\times 101$

9.	1000	10.	10101	11.	111	12.	111
	$+11101$		$+1010$		$\times 111$		$\times 101$

X. Express each number of Exercise IX in the decimal system, compute the sums and products in the decimal system, and compare the results with those of Exercise IX.

XI. The *duodecimal* system is a numeration system whose base is *twelve*. Let the numerals

$0, 1, 2, 3, 4, 5, 6, 7, 8, 9, t$, and e

represent the *twelve* digits in the duodecimal system. Complete the accompanying tables, and use the addition and multiplication facts to compute the following sums and products.

1.	15	2.	34	3.	$3t$	4.	78
	$+26$		$+68$		$\times 56$		$\times 25$

5.	$t00$	6.	$t0t$	7.	ett	8.	180
	$+t0e$		$+tee$		$\times t0$		$\times t6$

9.	283	10.	444	11.	$1t7$	12.	eee
	$+138$		$+808$		$\times 10t$		$\times 48$

Duodecimal Addition Table

+	0	1	2	3	4	5	6	7	8	9	t	e
0	0	1	2	3	4	5	6	7	8	9	t	e
1		2	3	4	5	6	7	8	9	t	e	10
2			4	5	6	7	8	9	t	e	10	11
3												
4												
5												
6												
7												
8												
9												
t												
e											$1t$	

Duodecimal Multiplication Table

×	0	1	2	3	4	5	6	7	8	9	t	e
0	0	0	0	0	0	0	0	0	0	0	0	0
1		1	2	3	4	5	6	7	8	9	t	e
2			4	6	8	t	10	12	14	16	18	1t
3												
4												
5												
6												
7												
8												
9												
t												
e												t1

XII. The *hexadecimal* system is a numeration system whose base is *sixteen*. Let the numerals

0, 1, 2, 3, 4, 5, 6, 7, 8, 9, □, ⚀, ⚁, ⚂, ⚃, and ⚅

represent the *sixteen* digits in the hexadecimal system. Complete the accompanying hexadecimal table, and use the addition facts to compute the following sums.

Hexadecimal Addition Table

+	0	1	2	3	4	5	6	7	8	9	□	⚀	⚁	⚂	⚃	⚅
0	0	1	2	3	4											
1	1	2	3	4												
2	2	3	4	5												
3	3	4	5	6												
4	4	5	6													
5	5	6														
6																
7																
8																
9	9	□	⚀	⚁	⚂	⚃	⚅	10	11	12	13					
□																
⚀																
⚁																
⚂																
⚃																
⚅																1⚃

1.   9 4 3   2.   8 7 6   3. [·][·][∴]   4. 3 [∷] 9
   + 4 4 0   + 7 5 8   + [∷][·][∷]   + 4 5 [∴]

5.   9 [·][∴]   6.   9 0 9   7. [∴] 0 [·]   8. 9 9 [·]
   + 2 [∴] 9   + [·] 0 [·]   + [·][·][·]   + [·] 9 9

XIII. We may convert a *decimal* numeral to a *quinary* numeral by expressing it as a sum of powers of five. For example,

$$317_{10} = [125 + 125 + 25 + 25 + 5 + 5 + 5 + 1 + 1] \quad \text{(base \textit{ten})}$$
$$= [2 \times 125 + 2 \times 25 + 3 \times 5 + 2 \times 1] \quad \text{(base \textit{ten})}$$
$$= [2(5^3) + 2(5^2) + 3(5^1) + 2(5^0)] \quad \text{(base \textit{ten})}$$
$$= [2(10^3) + 2(10^2) + 3(10^1) + 2(10^0)] \quad \text{(base \textit{five})}$$
$$= 2232_5.$$

Employ the procedure illustrated above to convert each of the following decimal numerals to the corresponding quinary numeral.

1. 507   2. 537
3. 609   4. 639
5. 912   6. 962
7. 3125   8. 3124
9. 16,724   10. 16,725

XIV. Employ the procedure of Exercise XIII to convert each of the following decimal numerals to the corresponding numeral whose base is indicated.

1. 63   (to binary system)
2. 65   (to binary system)
3. 143   (to duodecimal system)
4. 145   (to duodecimal system)
5. 143   (to quinary system)
6. 145   (to quinary system)
7. 65,535 (to hexadecimal system)
8. 65,537 (to hexadecimal system)
9. 101   (to binary system)
10. 110   (to binary system)

XV. To the question, "How tall are you?" a person five feet nine inches tall is likely to respond, "Five-nine." Usage makes it clear that he does not mean 59 inches but 69 inches, because he is really replying in a duodecimal numeral, in which the place value of 5 is *twelve* and the place value of 9 is *one*. Thus

$$59_{12} = 5 \text{ \textit{twelves}} + 9 \text{ \textit{ones}}$$
$$= 6 \text{ \textit{tens}} + 9 \text{ \textit{ones}}$$
$$= 69_{10} = 69 \text{ in.}$$

State the height *in inches* of a person who states that his height is each of the following.

1. five-seven
2. five-ten
3. five-eleven
4. six-zero
5. six-two
6. six-three
7. six-six
8. six-eleven
9. six-ten
10. seven-two

PUZZLE PROBLEMS

1. Three hens can lay three eggs in three days. At the same rate, how many eggs can six hens lay in six days?
2. A brick weighs $\frac{3}{4}$ pound more than three-fourths of a brick. How much does a whole brick weigh?
3. Donna drove 60 miles from A to B at an average speed of 40 miles per hour and returned from B to A at an average speed of 60 miles per hour. What was her average speed for the round trip?
4. Darrell drove 15 miles of a 30-mile trip at a speed of 30 miles per hour. At what rate must he drive the remaining 15 miles to average 60 miles per hour for the 30-mile trip?

Karl Friedrich Gauss was born in Brunswick, Germany, on April 30, 1777. He is generally conceded to be one of the three greatest mathematicians of all time. Archimedes, Newton, and Gauss created tidal waves in both pure and applied mathematics.

Although he is often called the "Prince of Mathematicians," Gauss came from a modest family. His father was a gardener, canal tender, and bricklayer, and his mother was the daughter of a stonecutter.

Gauss was the most precocious child in the history of mathematics. It is well documented that he taught himself to read before the age of three. One day his father was preparing a payroll for his workers, unaware that young Karl—not yet quite three—was looking over his shoulder. As the father was coming to the end of his lengthy computations, he was startled to hear the little boy say, "Father, the reckoning is wrong; it should be ————." A check of the computations showed that young Gauss was correct. A photographic memory and a prodigious power for involved mental calculations remained with him all his life.

Gauss was fortunate during his earliest school days (age 10) to encounter a young assistant schoolmaster, Johann Martin Bartels (age 17), who had a strong passion for mathematics. They studied together, helping each other with difficulties and clarifying the proofs in their algebra and rudimentary analysis textbooks.

At the age of 12, Gauss was already questioning the foundation of Euclidean geometry; and by 16 he already had a glimpse of hyperbolic geometry, a geometry in which Euclid's famous fifth postulate is replaced by a contradictory one.

The years spent as an undergraduate at the University of Göttingen (1795–1798) were probably the most prolific in Gauss's life. While at Göttingen he wrote in Latin most of *Disquisitiones Arithmeticae*, a treatise on the theory of numbers. In 1798 he entered the University of Helmstedt, and he completed the treatise there. Unfortunately, because of difficulties encountered by the publisher, it was not published until 1801. The first of Gauss's masterpieces, considered by some to be his greatest, was his farewell to pure mathematics as an exclusive interest. After publication of the book, Gauss broadened his interests to include astronomy, geodesy, and electromagnetism. However, arithmetic remained his first love, and he regretted in later life that he never had time to write the second volume of *Disquisitiones Arithmeticae,* which he had planned while he was a young man.

One example of the ingenuity of Gauss is his invention in 1833 of the electric telegraph that he and a fellow worker used in sending messages. However, Gauss cared little for the possible practical use of his invention. Like Archimedes, he preferred mathematics to all the kingdoms of the earth.

It is impossible to list the many achievements of the Prince of Mathematics without writing a book about Gauss. In sharp contrast to his towering accomplishments, he was a man of simple tastes, and he cared little for the acclaim of others. His mind remained clear and powerful, and he was active and inventive until his death in Göttingen on February 23, 1855.

Chapter 4

Introduction to the Theory of Numbers

4.1 DIVISORS, MULTIPLES, AND DIVISION

Since the operation of *subtraction* is needed in the development of the theory of numbers, we define the *difference* in the *subtraction* of certain counting numbers.

Definition 1. *The **difference** [denoted by "$x - y$"] in the subtraction of the counting number y from the counting number x [provided $y \leq x$] is the counting number z if and only if $x = y + z$. [That is, $x - y = z$ if and only if $x = y + z$.]*

The reader should observe that we have not defined $x - y$ if $x < y$. The difference $x - y$ exists if and only if $x \geq y$. The reason for the restriction is that the universe [i.e., the only set of numbers we are considering] is the set of counting numbers [i.e., $\{0, 1, 2, \ldots\}$].* Since we can *subtract* y from x by determining that counting number z such that the *sum* of y and z is x, we frequently refer to subtraction as the *inverse* of addition. Moreover, we may prove that the difference is unique as follows:

> If $x - y = z_1$ and $x - y = z_2$,
>
> then $x = y + z_1$ and $x = y + z_2$;
>
> thus $y + z_1 = y + z_2$;
>
> hence $z_1 = z_2$.

To illustrate Definition 1, we *subtract* 6 from 13; i.e., we compute the *difference* $13 - 6$. Since $13 - 6 = z$ if and only if $13 = 6 + z$, we determine the counting number z such that $13 = 6 + z$. By trial (if necessary) we see that $z = 7$; i.e., $13 = 6 + 7$ and hence $13 - 6 = 7$.

When a child first learns to subtract, he reasons as above. Later, he learns certain basic subtraction facts which simplify his calculations. If he tries to subtract 7 from 5, he seeks that counting number z such that $5 - 7 = z$; that is, he tries

---

*   Later, when we extend the universe, we can extend the definition of subtraction.

to *solve the equation* $5 = 7 + z$.* He soon realizes (by trial, if necessary) that there is no counting number z such that $5 = 7 + z$. Thus he concludes that he cannot subtract 7 from 5.

Now we are prepared to define the relation *divides* and prove some basic theorems. Throughout the chapter each variable represents any counting number, unless we specify otherwise. That is, the universal quantifier is implied unless specified otherwise.

Definition 2. *The counting number y **divides** the counting number x [denoted by* "$y \mid x$"] *if and only if there exists a counting number k such that $x = yk$; y is called a **divisor** [or **factor**] of x, x is called a **multiple** of y, and is said to be **divisible** by y.*

The following examples illustrate Definition 2.

Example 1. $3 \mid 21$ because $21 = 3 \times 7$ ($x = 21$, $y = 3$, $k = 7$), 3 is a divisor of 21, 3 is a factor of 21, 21 is a multiple of 3, and 21 is divisible by 3.

Example 2. $5 \mid 0$ because $0 = 5 \times 0$ ($x = 0$, $y = 5$, $k = 0$), 5 is a divisor of 0, 5 is a factor of 0, 0 is a multiple of 5, and 0 is divisible by 5.

Example 3. $0 \mid 0$ because $0 = 0 \times 0 = 1 \times 0 = 2 \times 0$, etc. ($x = 0$, $y = 0$, $k = 0$ or $k = 1$ or $k = 2$, etc.), 0 is a divisor of 0, 0 is a factor of 0, 0 is a multiple of 0, and 0 is divisible by 0.

Example 4. $0 \nmid 3$ because if 0 did divide 3, then there would exist a counting number k such that $3 = 0 \times k$. However, $0 \times k = 0$ for every counting number k. Hence $3 \neq 0 \times k$, and thus 0 does not divide any counting number except 0.

Example 5. $2 \nmid 9$ because $9 \neq 2 \times 0$, $9 \neq 2 \times 1$, $9 \neq 2 \times 2$, $9 \neq 2 \times 3$, $9 \neq 2 \times 4$, $9 \neq 2 \times 5$, etc. Since $2 \times 4 < 9 < 2 \times 5$, we can be certain that there is no counting number k such that $9 = 2k$.

The counting number k in Example 3 is *not unique*; that is, $\{k: 0 = k \times 0\}$ contains more than one element (in fact, it is an infinite set). Any counting number k satisfies the conditions of Definition 2. However, the counting number k in Example 2 is unique; i.e., there is only one counting number which satisfies the conditions of Definition 2. If y divides x, Definition 2 guarantees the existence of *at least one* counting number k such that $x = yk$; however, it does not guarantee the existence of *only one* counting number k such that $x = yk$. The following theorem guarantees that if $y \neq 0$, then k is unique. The proof is *indirect*.

> **Theorem 1.** *If x is any counting number, if y is any nonzero counting number, and if y divides x, then there exists a unique counting number k such that $x = yk$.*

---

*   We use the word *equation* in the traditional sense; that is, an *equation* is a statement of equality expressed by means of the *equals sign*.

Before we prove Theorem 1, we restate it in the *valid argument* form of Section 1.9, which exhibits the hypotheses and conclusion.

H1: x is a counting number.
H2: y is a nonzero counting number.
H3: $y \mid x$.

C : ∃ a *unique* counting number k such that $x = yk$.

Proof. We negate the conclusion; that is, we introduce an additional hypothesis, H4.

H4: There are two distinct counting numbers, k_1 and k_2, such that $x = yk_1$ and $x = yk_2$, or there is no counting number k such that $x = yk$.

However, because of H3 and Definition 1, we derive the intermediate conclusion C1.

C1: There exists a counting number k such that $x = yk$.

Because of H4 and C1, we derive the intermediate conclusion C2.

C2: There exist two distinct counting numbers, k_1 and k_2, such that $x = yk_1$ and $x = yk_2$.

Because of C2 and the transitive law for equality, we derive C3.

C3: $yk_1 = yk_2$.

Because of C3 and the cancellation law, we derive C4.

C4: $k_1 = k_2$.

Because of C2 and C4, we derive C5.

C5: $k_1 \neq k_2$ and $k_1 = k_2$.

Because of C5 and RAA, we derive C.

C: There exists a unique counting number k such that $x = yk$.   (QED)

The reader should observe that H4 is an additional hypothesis which negates (or contradicts) the conclusion C, and C5 is a conclusion of the form $r \wedge \sim r$. According to the indirect method of proof in Section 1.9, whenever we negate the conclusion of a theorem and derive the contradiction $r \wedge \sim r$, we can assert that the conclusion follows logically from the hypotheses.

The usual proof in a mathematics text, which is more informal than the above proof, may appear in paragraph form without specifically stated reasons and without specifically labeled hypotheses and conclusion. For example, Theorem 1 and its proof may appear in the following form.

Theorem 1. *If x is any counting number, if y is any nonzero counting number, and if y divides x, then there exists a unique counting number k such that x = yk.*

Proof. By Definition 1, there exists at least one counting number k such that $x = yk$. Assume that there exist two distinct counting numbers, k_1 and k_2, such that $x = yk_1$ and $x = yk_2$. Then $yk_1 = yk_2$. Hence $k_1 = k_2$. Thus the assumption is false. Therefore there is one and only one counting number k such that $x = yk$. (QED)

Since $3 \mid 21$ (because $21 = 3 \times 7$), it follows that $7 \mid 21$ (because $21 = 7 \times 3$). Similarly, $5 \mid 65$ and $13 \mid 65$. Whenever y divides x and $y \neq 0$, we can define x *divided by* y to be the unique counting number k of Theorem 1.

Definition 3. *The **quotient** [denoted by "$x \div y$" or "x/y" and read **x divided by y** or **x over y**] in the division of the counting number x by the nonzero counting number y [provided $y \mid x$] is the unique counting number k such that $x = yk$. [That is, $x \div y = k$ if and only if $x = yk$ and $y \neq 0$.]*

For example, $21 \div 3 = 7$, $21 \div 7 = 3$, $65 \div 5 = 13$, and $65 \div 13 = 5$. However, $21 \div 5$, $65 \div 7$, $0 \div 0$, and $3 \div 0$ are not defined. The reason that $0 \div 0$ is not defined is that k is not unique; however, $3 \div 0$ is not defined because there is no integer k satisfying the conditions of Definition 3.

Later the definition of *division* will be generalized so that $a \div b$ will be defined for any counting number a and any nonzero counting number b, even if b does not divide a. In the meantime, the reader should not confuse *divides* (which is a *relation*) with *divided by* (which is an *operation*). Although $35 \div 7$ is the number 5, and we say "$35 \div 7 = 5$," we must be careful not to say "$7 \mid 35 = 5$." The former ($35 \div 7$) is a *number*, but the latter ($7 \mid 35$) is a *statement*.

The following theorems are useful and interesting in mathematics and further clarify the relation *divides*.

Theorem 2. *If x, y, and z are any counting numbers such that $z \mid y$ and $y \mid x$, then $z \mid x$.*

Proof. Now $z \mid y$ and $y \mid x$ [by hypothesis]. Thus there exist counting numbers k_1 and k_2 such that $y = zk_1$ and $x = yk_2$ [by Definition 2]. Then

$$x = yk_2$$
$$= (zk_1)k_2 \qquad [\text{since } y = zk_1]$$
$$= z(k_1 k_2) \qquad [\text{by associative law for multiplication}]$$
$$= zk \qquad [\text{by closure law for multiplication}].$$

Thus

$$z \mid x \qquad [\text{by Definition 2}]. \quad (\text{QED})$$

Theorem 3. *If x, y, and z are any counting numbers such that $z \mid x$ and $z \mid y$, then $z \mid (x + y)$.*

Proof. Now $z \mid x$ and $z \mid y$ [by hypothesis]. Thus there exist counting numbers k_1 and k_2 such that $x = zk_1$ and $y = zk_2$ [by Definition 2]. Then

$$x + y = zk_1 + zk_2$$

$$= z(k_1 + k_2) \qquad \text{[by distributive law]}$$

$$= zk \qquad \text{[by closure law for addition]}.$$

Thus

$$z \mid (x + y) \qquad \text{[by Definition 2]. \quad (QED)}$$

Theorem 4. *If x, y, and z are any counting numbers such that $z \mid x$, $z \mid y$, and $x \geq y$, then $z \mid (x - y)$.*

Proof. Now $z \mid x$ and $z \mid y$. Thus there exist counting numbers k_1 and k_2 such that $x = zk_1$ and $y = zk_2$. Then

$$x - y = zk_1 - zk_2$$

$$= z(k_1 - k_2)*$$

$$= zk \qquad \text{[since } k_1 \geq k_2\text{]}.$$

Thus

$$z \mid (x - y). \quad \text{(QED)}$$

Theorem 2 asserts that the relation *divides* obeys the transitive law. Moreover, since any counting number divides itself, *divides* obeys the reflexive law. However, since 3 divides 9 but 9 does not divide 3, we see that *divides* does not obey the symmetric law. Hence *divides* is not an equivalence relation.

Theorems 2, 3, and 4 justify the simple test for divisibility by 4; namely, a counting number represented by two or more digits is divisible by 4 if and only if the number represented by the two terminal digits is divisible by 4. For example, 538,728 is divisible by 4 because 28 is divisible by 4. However, 538,729 is not divisible by 4 because 29 is not divisible by 4. We know by Theorem 2 that 538,700 is divisible by 4 because $4 \mid 100$ and $100 \mid 538,700$. Since $4 \mid 538,700$ and $4 \mid 28$, it follows from Theorem 3 that $4 \mid (538,700 + 28)$; i.e., $4 \mid 538,728$. Now $4 \nmid 29$ and $4 \mid 538,700$.

If we assume that $4 \mid 538,729$, then $4 \mid (538,729 - 538,700)$ [by Theorem 4]. Hence $4 \mid 29$. But $4 \nmid 29$. Thus $4 \mid 29$ and $4 \nmid 29$. By RAA, the assumption is false; i.e., $4 \nmid 538,729$.

---

*   The reader may prove that $zk_1 - zk_2 = z(k_1 - k_2)$. The proof depends on the distributive law and the definition of subtraction.

EXERCISE SET 4.1

I. Decide whether y divides x in each of the following.

1. $x = 5,\quad y = 30$ 2. $x = 17,\quad y = 51$

3. $x = 30,\quad y = 5$ 4. $x = 51,\quad y = 17$

5. $x = 0,\quad y = 5$ 6. $x = 14,\quad y = 3$

7. $x = 0,\quad y = 0$ 8. $x = 7,\quad y = 7$

9. $x = 7796,\ y = 4$ 10. $x = 7798,\ y = 4$

II.

1. Explain why $0 \div 0$ is not defined.
2. Explain why $5 \div 0$ is not defined.
3. Explain why $17 \div 3$ is not defined.
4. Explain why $21 \div 3$ is defined.

III. List ten *multiples* of each of the following.

1. 5   2. 7

3. 2   4. 1

5. 8   6. 9

7. 10   8. 20

9. 400   10. 100

IV. List all *factors* (*divisors*) of each of the following.

1. 121   2. 169

3. 54   4. 56

5. 55   6. 91

7. 2621   8. 3001

9. 4987   10. 4999

V. Prove each of the following.

1. Any counting number a divides itself.
2. Every counting number is divisible by 1.
3. There exists a counting number z such that every counting number greater than z divides z.
4. If $zk_1 \geq zk_2$, then $zk_1 - zk_2 = z(k_1 - k_2)$.
5. If $z \mid y$, $y \mid x$, and $x \mid w$, then $z \mid w$.
6. If $z \mid y$, $z \mid x$, and $z \mid w$, then $z \mid (w + x + y)$.
7. If $z \mid y$, then $z \mid xy$.
8. If $z \mid y$ and $z \mid (x + y)$, then $z \mid x$.

VI.

1. Explain why $5 - 7$ is not defined.
2. Explain why $0 - 3$ is not defined.

3. Let $a = b + c$. Compute b in terms of a and c.

4. Let $a = 3 + t$. Compute t in terms of a and 3. Can a be less than 3?

5. Let $x = 2a + b$. Compute b in terms of x and a.

4.2 PRIMES AND COMPOSITES

Recalling that y divides x if and only if there exists k such that $x = yk$, we see that the only counting numbers which divide 7 are 1 and 7. Similarly, the only divisors of 5 are 1 and 5. However, the divisors of 6 are 1, 2, 3, and 6, and the divisors of 9 are 1, 3, and 9. On the other hand, the only divisor of 1 is 1 itself. Moreover, every counting number greater than 1 has at least two divisors, 1 has exactly one divisor, and 0 has infinitely many divisors. In the following definition we classify the nonzero counting numbers according to the number of divisors each has.

Definition 4

   a) *Any counting number p which has exactly two divisors is called a **prime number** [or **prime**]*.

   b) *Any nonzero counting number c which has more than two divisors is called a* **composite number** [or **composite**].

   c) *Any counting number u which has exactly one divisor is called a* **unit**.

For example, the primes less than 20 are 2, 3, 5, 7, 11, 13, 17 and 19; the composites less than 20 are 4, 6, 8, 9, 10, 12, 14, 15, 16, and 18; and the *only* unit is 1. Although the only divisors of the prime p are 1 and p, every composite c has a divisor d such that $1 < d < c$. Of course, the only divisor of the unit 1 is 1 itself.*

The reader may wonder how many primes there are. Later in the chapter we will prove that the set of primes is infinite. In the meantime, we develop a procedure [known as the *sieve of Eratosthenes*] for listing the set of all primes less than any specified counting number. Although we develop the sieve for the counting number 60, the method is general and usable for any counting number.

First we list the nonzero counting numbers 1, 2, 3, . . ., 60 as in Fig. 4.1.

Next, with a hole punch or other device, we delete 1† to indicate that 1 is not a prime. Since 2 is a prime, we do not delete 2. Since every multiple of 2 (except 2) is composite, we delete 4, 6, 8, . . ., 60. The list appears in Fig. 4.2.

---

*   Later, after the introduction of negative integers, we can classify the negative integers as primes, composites, and units. In such event, $^-5$ is a prime, $^-6$ is a composite, and $^-1$ is a unit; however, every prime will then have exactly *four* divisors [two positive divisors and two negative divisors], and each unit will then have exactly two divisors [1 and $^-1$].

†   We really delete the *numeral* "1" to indicate that the *number* 1 is not a prime. If we delete the numerals from a card or sheet of paper by punching holes, the card or paper resembles a *sieve*. Perhaps the *sieve of Eratosthenes* derived its name from this consideration.

1	2	3	4	5	6	7	8	9	10
11	12	13	14	15	16	17	18	19	20
21	22	23	24	25	26	27	28	29	30
31	32	33	34	35	36	37	38	39	40
41	42	43	44	45	46	47	48	49	50
51	52	53	54	55	56	57	58	59	60

Fig. 4.1

1	2	3	4	5	6	7	8	9	10
11	12	13	14	15	16	17	18	19	20
21	22	23	24	25	26	27	28	29	30
31	32	33	34	35	36	37	38	39	40
41	42	43	44	45	46	47	48	49	50
51	52	53	54	55	56	57	58	59	60

Fig. 4.2

We observe from Fig. 4.2 that 3 remains in the list. Since every multiple of 3 (except 3) is composite, we delete 6, 9, 12, . . . , 60.* The list appears in Fig. 4.3.

1	2	3	4	5	6	7	8	9	10
11	12	13	14	15	16	17	18	19	20
21	22	23	24	25	26	27	28	29	30
31	32	33	34	35	36	37	38	39	40
41	42	43	44	45	46	47	48	49	50
51	52	53	54	55	56	57	58	59	60

Fig. 4.3

We observe from Fig. 4.3 that 5 remains in the list. Since every multiple of 5 (except 5) is composite, we delete 10, 15, 20, . . . , 60. The list appears in Fig. 4.4.

1	2	3	4	5	6	7	8	9	10
11	12	13	14	15	16	17	18	19	20
21	22	23	24	25	26	27	28	29	30
31	32	33	34	35	36	37	38	39	40
41	42	43	44	45	46	47	48	49	50
51	52	53	54	55	56	57	58	59	60

Fig. 4.4

---

*   We have already deleted the even multiples of 3 as multiples of 2.

We observe from Fig. 4.4 that 7 remains in the list. Since every multiple of 7 (except 7) is composite, we delete 14, 21, 28, ..., 56. The list appears in Fig. 4.5.

1	2	3	4	5	6	7	8	9	10
11	12	13	14	15	16	17	18	19	20
21	22	23	24	25	26	27	28	29	30
31	32	33	34	35	36	37	38	39	40
41	42	43	44	45	46	47	48	49	50
51	52	53	54	55	56	57	58	59	60

Fig. 4.5

We observe from Fig. 4.5 that 11 remains in the list. Since every multiple of 11 (except 11) is composite, we should delete 22, 33, 44, and 55. However, since we have already deleted the multiples of 11 as multiples of smaller primes, we can terminate the procedure. The numbers which have not been deleted are primes. That is, the primes less than 60 are 2, 3, 5, 7, 11, 13, 17, 19, 23, 29, 31, 37, 41, 43, 47, 53, and 59.

We terminated the deletion procedure after we deleted the multiples of 7. We are certain that the remaining numbers are primes because $7^2 \leq 60$ and $11^2 > 60$ and there is no prime between 7 and 11; i.e., 7 is the largest prime whose square does not exceed 60. In general, to list the primes less than k, we can terminate the procedure after we have deleted all composite multiples of the largest prime p whose square does not exceed k. For example, to list the primes less than 175, we can terminate the deletion procedure after we have deleted the composite multiples of 13, because $13^2 \leq 175$ and $17^2 > 175$. Similarly, to compute the primes less than 400, we can terminate the procedure after we have deleted the composite multiples of 19, because $19^2 \leq 400$ and $23^2 > 400$.

EXERCISE SET 4.2

I. Classify each of the following as *prime, composite,* or *unit.*

1. 3657
2. 2757
3. 3659
4. 2749
5. 2895
6. 8280
7. 4999
8. 4957
9. 1101
10. 1111

II. Employ the sieve of Eratosthenes to list all primes less than each of the following counting numbers.

1. 80
2. 85
3. 95
4. 90
5. 100
6. 101

7. 102   8. 103
9. 104   10. 105

III. List the *prime* divisors of each of the following counting numbers.
  1. 75   2. 55
  3. 80   4. 40
  5. 22   6. 33
  7. 44   8. 66
  9. 101   10. 103

IV. List *all* divisors of each counting number in Exercise III.

V. In computing all primes less than a given counting number k (by the sieve of Eratosthenes), we can terminate the procedure after we have deleted all composite multiples of the largest prime p whose square does not exceed k.

  1. Explain why the procedure is valid.
  2. What is the largest prime whose square does not exceed 500?
  3. What is the largest prime whose square does not exceed 525?
  4. What is the largest prime whose square does not exceed 529?
  5. What is the largest prime whose square does not exceed 625?
  6. What is the smallest prime whose square does exceed 500?
  7. What is the smallest prime whose square does exceed 525?
  8. What is the smallest prime whose square does exceed 529?
  9. What is the smallest prime whose square does exceed 625?
  10. What is the smallest prime whose square does exceed 700?

VI.

  1. State definitions of *prime, composite,* and *unit* which are equivalent to those in Definition 4.
  2. Explain why 0 is not a prime, not a composite, and not a unit.

4.3 FACTORIZATION

We learned in Section 4.1 that the counting number y is a *factor* (or *divisor*) of the counting number x if and only if there exists a counting number k such that $x = yk$. For example, 3 is a factor of 15 because $15 = 3 \times 5$, and 4 is a factor of 36 because $36 = 4 \times 9$. Similarly, 12 is a factor of 36 because $36 = 12 \times 3$. In each case we say that the given counting number has been *factored*. Thus 36 has been factored in two ways, and 15 has been factored uniquely as a product of *prime* factors. If we factor the composite factors of 36 as products of prime factors, then the *factorization* of 36 as a product of prime factors is unique. Thus the *unique prime factorization* of 36 is $2 \times 2 \times 3 \times 3$. Similarly, the unique prime factorization of 42 is $2 \times 3 \times 7$. In the following definition we define the above terms.

Definition 5

a) *The counting number x is said to be **factored** if and only if it is expressed as a product of factors. The product of factors is called a **factorization of x**.*

b) *The counting number x is said to be **factored into prime factors** if and only if it is expressed as a product of prime factors. The product of prime factors is called a **prime factorization of x**.*

c) *To **factor** a counting number x is to express it as a product of factors.*

For example, since

$$42 = 2 \times 21 = 6 \times 7 = 21 \times 2$$

$$= 7 \times 6 = 2 \times 3 \times 7 = 3 \times 7 \times 2 = 2 \times 7 \times 3,$$

etc., each expressed product is a factorization of 42. Obviously, there is no *unique* factorization of 42. However, if we permit only *prime* factors and ignore the *order* in which the factors occur, then there is *exactly one* factorization of 42. In other words, the *unique prime factorization* of 42 is $2 \times 3 \times 7$. Similarly, the unique prime factorization of 330 is $2 \times 3 \times 5 \times 11$.

The following theorem, which is known as the *unique prime factorization theorem*,* guarantees that the prime factorization of any composite number is unique (except for the order in which the factors occur). We omit the proof; the reader may assume the theorem as an axiom.†

> **Theorem 5** (***Unique Prime Factorization Theorem***). *Every composite number can be factored uniquely as a product of prime factors (except for the order of the factors).*

Because of Theorem 5, we may speak of *the* prime factorization of any given composite number.

The following examples illustrate Theorem 5.

Example 1. The unique prime factorization of 910 is $2 \times 5 \times 7 \times 13$ because

$$910 = 2 \times 455$$

$$= 2 \times 5 \times 91$$

$$= 2 \times 5 \times 7 \times 13.$$

Example 2. The unique prime factorization of 18,200 is

$$2 \times 2 \times 2 \times 5 \times 5 \times 7 \times 13$$

---

*   The unique prime factorization theorem is also known as the *fundamental theorem of arithmetic*.

†   The proof depends on other theorems which we have not included.

because

$$18,200 = 2 \times 9100$$
$$= 2 \times 2 \times 4550$$
$$= 2 \times 2 \times 2 \times 2275$$
$$= 2 \times 2 \times 2 \times 5 \times 455$$
$$= 2 \times 2 \times 2 \times 5 \times 5 \times 91$$
$$= 2 \times 2 \times 2 \times 5 \times 5 \times 7 \times 13.$$

It is not necessary to extract the primes in any given order. However, for convenience we extract the prime factors in the order 2, 3, 5, 7, 11, 13, ... [The prime factors in the prime factorization of a given composite are not necessarily distinct.] That is, we first determine whether 2 is a factor, then 3, then 5, etc., and we indicate the number of times each is a factor by expressing it accordingly.

The reader should observe that Theorem 5 applies to composite numbers and that every composite number is a counting number. In fact, the definitions we have stated are based on the assumption that the universe is the set of counting numbers.

If the universe is *not* the set of counting numbers and if the definition of *prime* is modified slightly to conform to the different universe, then there may be more than one prime factorization of a given composite in U. For example, if $U = \{1, 5, 9, 13, 17, \ldots\}$ and any element p of U [except 1] is a *prime* [in U] if and only if the only divisors of p [in U] are 1 and p, then there is no unique prime factorization in U. The first 20 primes in U are listed in Fig. 4.6.

5, 9, 13, 17, 21, 29, 33, 37, 41, 49, 53, 57, 61, 69, 73, 77, 89, 93, 97, 101

Fig. 4.6

The first 10 composites of U are listed in Fig. 4.7.

25, 45, 65, 81, 85, 105, 117, 125, 145, 153

Fig. 4.7

Although 21 is not a prime in the set of counting numbers [since $21 = 3 \times 7$], it is a prime in U because the only divisors of 21 [in U] are 1 and 21 [3 and 7 are not in U]. On the other hand, 25 is composite in U because $25 = 5 \times 5$ and 5 is in U. Similarly, since $45 = 5 \times 9$ [and both 5 and 9 are primes in U], we see that 45 is composite in U. Moreover, the only prime factorization of 45 [in U] is 5×9, and the only prime factorization of 25 [in U] is 5×5. In fact, each composite in Fig. 4.7 has a unique prime factorization in U. Thus it appears from the prime factorizations of the composites in Fig. 4.7 that every composite in U can be factored uniquely as a product of prime factors of U. However, 693 [which is an element of U] has *two* different prime factorizations in U; namely, $693 = 9 \times 77$ and $693 = 21 \times 33$. That is, there is no unique prime factorization in U.

The above discussion highlights two main points: (1) definitions and theorems stated for a particular universal set may not be applicable to a different universal set; (2) the truth of a statement in several cases does not imply the truth of the statement in all cases.

EXERCISE SET 4.3

I. Express the unique prime factorization of each of the following composite numbers.

1. 30   2. 35
3. 105   4. 221
5. 143   6. 187
7. 144   8. 168
9. 15,400   10. 38,500

II. Let D_x be the set of all divisors of x. In each of the following, compute D_a, D_b, and $D_a \cap D_b$. [For example, $D_{20} = \{1, 2, 4, 5, 10, 20\}$, $D_{30} = \{1, 2, 3, 5, 6, 10, 15, 30\}$, and $D_{20} \cap D_{30} = \{1, 2, 5, 10\}$.]

1. $a = 20, b = 15$ 2. $a = 20, b = 25$
3. $a = 35, b = 25$ 4. $a = 35, b = 49$
5. $a = 21, b = 49$ 6. $a = 21, b = 9$
7. $a = 21, b = 10$ 8. $a = 15, b = 14$
9. $a = 7,\ b = 12$ 10. $a = 7,\ b = 11$

III. What is the largest element of $D_a \cap D_b$ in each part of Exercise II?

IV. Let M_x be the set of all nonzero multiples of x. In each of the following, compute M_a, M_b, and $M_a \cap M_b$. [For example, $M_{20} = \{20, 40, 60, \ldots\}$, $M_{30} = \{30, 60, 90, \ldots\}$, and $M_{20} \cap M_{30} = \{60, 120, 180, \ldots\}$.]

1. $a = 10, b = 15$ 2. $a = 10, b = 25$
3. $a = 20, b = 25$ 4. $a = 20, b = 15$
5. $a = 14, b = 10$ 6. $a = 14, b = 21$
7. $a = 10, b = 14$ 8. $a = 21, b = 14$
9. $a = 50, b = 75$ 10. $a = 20, b = 45$

V. What is the smallest element of $M_a \cap M_b$ in each part of Exercise IV?

4.4 GREATEST COMMON DIVISOR AND LEAST COMMON MULTIPLE

We have learned that every prime number p has exactly two divisors, 1 and p, every composite number has more than two divisors, and the unit 1 has only one divisor—itself. If we denote the set of all divisors of any nonzero counting number x by "D_x," then

$$D_{20} = \{1, 2, 4, 5, 10, 20\} \quad \text{and} \quad D_{30} = \{1, 2, 3, 5, 6, 10, 15, 30\}.$$

The intersection of D_{20} and D_{30} is the set of all divisors of *both* 20 and 30; that is, $D_{20} \cap D_{30}$ is the set of *common divisors* of 20 and 30. Since $D_{20} \cap D_{30} = \{1, 2, 5, 10\}$, we see that 1, 2, 5, and 10 are common divisors of 20 and 30; i.e., 1, 2, 5, and 10 divide *both* 20 and 30. Since the set of all divisors of any nonzero counting number x is a finite set, it follows that $D_a \cap D_b$ [the set of all common divisors of any nonzero counting numbers a and b] is a finite set. Since every finite set contains a largest element, it follows that $D_a \cap D_b$ contains a greatest element, which we call *the greatest common divisor* of a and b.

Definition 6

a) *Any divisor of both of the nonzero counting numbers a and b is called **a common divisor** of a and b.*

b) *The largest element in the set of all common divisors of the nonzero counting numbers a and b is called **the greatest common divisor of a and b** [denoted by "GCD of a and b"].*

c) *Any two counting numbers whose greatest common divisor is 1 are said to be **relatively prime** (with respect to each other).*

For example, common divisors of 20 and 30 are 1, 2, 5, and 10; the greatest common divisor of 20 and 30 is 10 [the largest element of $\{1, 2, 5, 10\}$]. Similarly, the GCD of 5 and 8 is 1; i.e., 5 and 8 are relatively prime. The reader should observe that relatively prime numbers are not necessarily prime. For example, 4 and 9 are relatively prime, but neither 4 nor 9 is prime; 5 and 9 are relatively prime, but 9 is not prime; 5 and 7 are relatively prime, and both are prime.

When we reduce a fraction* to lowest terms, we divide numerator and denominator by their GCD. For example, $\frac{20}{30} = \frac{2}{3}$ because the GCD of 20 and 30 is 10.

If we denote the set of all nonzero multiples of any nonzero counting number x by "M_x," then

$$M_9 = \{9, 18, 27, 36, \ldots\},$$

$$M_6 = \{6, 12, 18, 24, 30, 36, \ldots\},$$

and

$$M_9 \cap M_6 = \{18, 36, 54, \ldots\}.$$

---

* Although we have not discussed fractions, we assume that the reader is familiar with the simple arithmetic of fractions.

That is, $M_9 \cap M_6$ is the set of *common multiples* of 9 and 6.*

Although $M_a \cap M_b$ [the set of all common multiples of *a* and *b*] is an infinite set, it contains a least element, which we call *the least common multiple of a and b.†*

Definition 7

  a) *Any nonzero counting number which is a multiple of both counting numbers a and b is called a common multiple of a and b.*

  b) *The smallest element in the set of all common multiples of the counting numbers a and b is called the least common multiple of a and b* [*denoted by "LCM of a and b"*].

For example, common multiples of 9 and 6 are 18, 36, 54, ... ; the least common multiple of 9 and 6 is 18 [the smallest element of $\{18, 36, 54, \ldots\}$]. Similarly, the LCM of 9 and 5 is 45, and the LCM of 12 and 6 is 12. If *a* and *b* are relatively prime, then the LCM of *a* and *b* is *ab*.

When we add fractions whose denominators are different, we compute the *least common denominator*, which is merely the LCM of the denominators.

Although we may compute the GCD and the LCM of two numbers *a* and *b* by choosing the largest member of $D_a \cap D_b$ and the smallest member of $M_a \cap M_b$, respectively, we can frequently compute them by inspection, especially if *a* and *b* are small or relatively prime. For example, inspection reveals that the GCD and LCM of 4 and 6 are 2 and 12, respectively; inspection reveals that the GCD of 5 and 6 is 1 and hence that the LCM is 30 [i.e., 5×6]. If *a* and *b* are large, computation of the GCD and the LCM by inspection may not be so simple. Hence we consider a systematic procedure based on the unique prime factorization theorem.

To illustrate the procedure, we compute the GCD [and, later, the LCM] of 60 and 40. First we factor 60 and 40 as follows:

$$60 = 2 \times 2 \times 3 \times 5 = 2^2 \times 3 \times 5 = 2^2 \times 3^1 \times 5^1,$$

$$40 = 2 \times 2 \times 2 \times 5 = 2^3 \times 5 = 2^3 \times 3^0 \times 5^1.$$

Since the GCD of 60 and 40 divides *both* 60 and 40, it cannot contain the factor 2^3, because 2^3 is not a factor of 60. However, 2^2 is a factor of 60 and also a factor of 40; moreover, 2^2 is the largest power of 2 which is a factor of both 60 and 40. Hence 2^2 is the largest power of 2 which is a factor of the GCD of 60 and 40.‡ Similarly, 3^0 is the largest power of 3 which is a factor of the GCD

---

*   Actually, since 0 is a multiple of every number, it is a common multiple of any two numbers. However, since we are interested only in nonzero multiples, we exclude 0 from consideration.

†   The existence of the least element in any nonempty subset of the set of counting numbers is guaranteed by the *well-ordering principle*.

‡   Every common divisor of *a* and *b* divides the GCD of *a* and *b*. The proof is beyond the scope of the text.

of 60 and 40, and 5^1 is the largest power of 5 which is a factor of the GCD of 60 and 40.   Hence $2^2 \times 3^0 \times 5^1$ is the largest number which divides both 60 and 40; i.e., $2^2 \times 3^0 \times 5^1$ is the GCD of 60 and 40.

We further illustrate the procedure by computing the GCD of 29,575 and 14,625.

$$29,575 = 5 \times 5 \times 7 \times 13 \times 13 \qquad = 3^0 \times 5^2 \times 7^1 \times 13^2,$$

$$14,625 = 3 \times 3 \times 5 \times 5 \times 5 \times 13 = 3^2 \times 5^3 \times 7^0 \times 13^1.$$

Choosing the *smaller* of the two exponents in each prime factor above, we see that the GCD is $3^0 \times 5^2 \times 7^0 \times 13^1$; i.e., the GCD of 29,575 and 14,625 is 325.

Now we compute the LCM of 60 and 40 by the procedure based on the unique prime factorization theorem.   The prime factorizations of 60 and 40 are as follows:

$$60 = 2^2 \times 3^1 \times 5^1,$$

$$40 = 2^3 \times 3^0 \times 5^1.$$

Since the LCM of 60 and 40 is divisible by *both* 60 and 40, it is divisible by every *factor* of 60 and every *factor* of 40.   Hence it is divisible by $2^3, 3^1,$ and 5^1. Moreover, the LCM of 60 and 40 is the smallest nonzero counting number which is divisible by $2^3, 3^1,$ and 5^1, and hence by $2^3 \times 3^1 \times 5^1$.   Therefore the LCM of 60 and 40 is $2^3 \times 3^1 \times 5^1$.

We further illustrate the procedure by computing the LCM of 29,575 and 14,625.

$$29,575 = 3^0 \times 5^2 \times 7^1 \times 13^2,$$

$$14,625 = 3^2 \times 5^3 \times 7^0 \times 13^1.$$

Choosing the *larger* of the two exponents in each prime factor above, we see that the LCM is $3^2 \times 5^3 \times 7^1 \times 13^2$; i.e., the LCM of 29,575 and 14,625 is 1,330,875.

The above procedures for computing the GCD and the LCM of a and b from the prime factorizations of a and b are general and may be formulated as theorems whose proofs are not difficult.   However, since the notation is somewhat tedious, we do not state and prove the theorems, but we rely on the reader to formulate his statements of the procedures.

It is easy to generalize the definitions of *greatest common divisor* and *least common multiple*.   The above procedures are valid in the computations of the GCD and the LCM of three or more numbers.   For example, to compute the GCD and the LCM of 24, 45, and 84, we factor 24, 45, and 84 and choose the appropriate powers of the prime factors.

$$24 = 2^3 \times 3^1 \times 5^0 \times 7^0,$$

$$45 = 2^0 \times 3^2 \times 5^1 \times 7^0,$$

$$84 = 2^2 \times 3^1 \times 5^0 \times 7^1.$$

Choosing the *smallest* of the three exponents in each prime factor above, we see that the GCD of 24, 45, and 84 is $2^0 \times 3^1 \times 5^0 \times 7^0$. Choosing the *largest* of the three exponents in each prime factor above, we see that the LCM of 24, 45, and 84 is $2^3 \times 3^2 \times 5^1 \times 7^1$.

EXERCISE SET 4.4

  I. Compute the *greatest common divisor* of each of the following pairs or triples of numbers.

    1. 45 and 84   2. 24 and 84

    3. 84 and 360   4. 24 and 360

    5. 122 and 142   6. 121 and 143

    7. 34, 117, and 420   8. 102, 117, and 60

    9. 68, 234, and 300   10. 68, 234, and 420

  II. Compute the *least common multiple* of each pair or triple of numbers in Exercise I.

 III.

    1. Illustrate that the product of the GCD and the LCM of *a* and *b* is equal to *ab*.

    2. Assume that the product of the GCD and the LCM of *a* and *b* is equal to *ab*. Prove that if *a* and *b* are relatively prime, then the LCM of *a* and *b* is equal to *ab*.

 IV.

    1. Formulate a definition for the GCD of *a*, *b*, and *c*.

    2. Formulate a definition for the LCM of *a*, *b*, and *c*.

    3. Formulate a definition for the GCD of *a*, *b*, *c*, and *d*.

    4. Formulate a definition for the LCM of *a*, *b*, *c*, and *d*.

4.5 SOME SOLVED AND SOME UNSOLVED PROBLEMS

Since the set of composites is infinite and every composite number is the product of primes, it seems reasonable to assert that the set of primes is infinite. However, we have already observed that there are false statements which seem reasonable. Consequently we should attempt to prove any *conjecture** we make [from observation, experience, or intuition] and discover a *theorem*. After we have proved a given *conjecture*, it is no longer a conjecture but a *theorem*. For example, if we observe that 1^2 is odd, 3^2 is odd, 5^2 is odd, etc., we *conjecture* that the square of every odd number is odd, and then we try to prove that the conjecture is true. If we are successful in our attempt, then we can *assert* as a *theorem* that the square of every odd number is odd.

    We now prove the following theorem which we conjectured above and which Euclid proved in approximately 300 B.C. The proof is indirect.

---

*   A *conjecture* is a statement which seems to be true [from serious evidence] but which has not been proved.

Theorem 6. *The set of primes is infinite.*

Proof. We assume that the set P of primes is *not* infinite. Then the set is finite; i.e., there exists a largest prime p_k such that

$$P = \{p_1, p_2, \ldots, p_k\},$$

in which

$$p_1 = 2, \qquad p_2 = 3, \qquad p_3 = 5, \qquad p_4 = 7, \qquad p_5 = 11, \quad \text{etc.}$$

Letting

$$q = 1 + p_1 \times p_2 \times \cdots \times p_k,$$

we observe that q is greater than the largest prime p_k. Hence q cannot be prime. Since $q > 1$ and q is not prime, it follows that q is composite. Then q is divisible by some prime p. If p is any one of the primes in P, then p divides $p_1 p_2 \cdots p_k$ and p divides q. Hence p divides $(q - p_1 p_2 \cdots p_k)$. But $q - p_1 p_2 \cdots p_k = 1$. Hence q divides 1. But the only nonzero divisor of 1 is 1. Thus q does not divide 1. The statement

q divides 1 *and q does not divide* 1

is contradictory. Hence the assumption is false. Therefore the set of primes is infinite. (QED)

Now we consider some of the interesting problems of number theory which have fascinated mathematician and nonmathematician for centuries. Since they belong to the set of unsolved problems in mathematics, the reader may suspect that they are difficult to state or understand. Although the *proofs* have evaded the greatest mathematicians, the *statements* are comprehensible to a secondary school student.

Any ordered pair of consecutive primes which differ by 2 is called a *twin prime pair*. For example, (17, 19) is a twin prime pair. Similarly, (29, 31) is a twin prime pair, but (13, 17) is not a twin prime pair. Since the set of primes is infinite, it seems reasonable to conjecture that the set of twin prime pairs is infinite. In fact, all empirical evidence indicates that the set of twin prime pairs is infinite.* However, no one has ever been able to *prove* or *disprove* the conjecture. Hence the following question remains unanswered: *Is the set of twin prime pairs infinite?*

Charles Christian Goldbach (1690–1764), a rather obscure mathematician, conjectured that every even number greater than 2 is the sum of two primes. For example, $4 = 2 + 2$, $6 = 3 + 3$, $8 = 3 + 5$, and $10 = 3 + 7 = 5 + 5$. Although the above conjecture, known as *Goldbach's conjecture*, has been verified empirically at least to the hundred thousands, no one has ever been able to prove or disprove the conjecture. Hence the following question remains unanswered: *Is every even number greater than 2 the sum of two primes?*

---

*   More than 100,000 twin prime pairs are known.

The great French mathematician Pierre de Fermat (1601–1665) conjectured that there are no nonzero counting numbers x, y, and z such that $x^m + y^m = z^m$ if $m > 2$. Although in 1637 Fermat wrote in the margin of one of his books, "And I have assuredly found an admirable proof of this, but the margin is too narrow to contain it," sustained efforts by some of the greatest mathematicians have failed to produce a proof of Fermat's conjecture, which is known as *Fermat's Last Theorem*. The reader is cautioned, however, that Fermat's Last Theorem is really a conjecture. Hence the following question remains unanswered: *Are there any nonzero counting numbers x, y, and z such that $x^m + y^m = z^m$ if $m > 2$?*[*]

Any counting number c which is the sum of its divisors [less than c] is called a *perfect number*. For example, 6 is a perfect number because the divisors of 6 are 1, 2, 3, and 6 and $6 = 1 + 2 + 3$. Similarly, 28 is a perfect number because the divisors of 28 are 1, 2, 4, 7, 14, and 28 and $28 = 1 + 2 + 4 + 7 + 14$. The first six perfect numbers are as follows:

6
28
496
8128
33,550,336
8,589,869,056.

Although Euclid defined *perfect numbers* and the ancient Greeks studied perfect numbers, there are still some unanswered questions concerning perfect numbers. The reader will observe that the first six perfect numbers are even. Are all perfect numbers even? If there are any odd perfect numbers, they are larger than a trillion. We have proved that the set of primes is infinite. Is the set of perfect numbers infinite? No one has ever answered either of the above questions. Although we believe that the answers are in the affirmative, the following questions remain unanswered: *Are all perfect numbers even? Is the set of perfect numbers infinite?*

Although the above questions concerning perfect numbers are unanswered, there are some known facts about perfect numbers. For example, the following theorem, *in which p is prime*, provides a method for generating perfect numbers. We omit the proof.

Theorem 7

a) *The number $2^{p-1}(2^p - 1)$, in which p is a prime, is perfect if and only if $2^p - 1$ is a prime.*

b) *Every even perfect number can be expressed as $2^{p-1}(2^p - 1)$, in which p is a prime and $2^p - 1$ is a prime.*

---

[*]   Many cases have been investigated; e.g., if m is a prime which does not divide x, y, or z, the answer is *no* for m not exceeding 253, 747, 889.

Although applications of number theory to the physical world are not as numerous as those of other branches of mathematics, the study of number theory has provided the inspiration and stimulus necessary to the development of other branches of mathematics. For example, attempts to prove Fermat's Last Theorem kindled the investigation and study of the theory of algebraic numbers; the latter theory generated the development of such important concepts as *ideals* in abstract algebra; the concepts of abstract algebra have influenced the development of modern physics.

Karl Friedrich Gauss (1777–1855), one of the world's greatest mathematicians and one of the developers of non-Euclidean geometry, called number theory *the queen of mathematics.**

EXERCISE SET 4.5

  I. List the twin prime pairs (p, q) such that $q < 200$.

 II. Verify Goldbach's conjecture for every even number less than 101.

III. Employ Theorem 7 to generate the first six perfect numbers.

 IV. Explain the difficulties inherent in any attempt to *verify* [not *prove*] Fermat's Last Theorem in even the simple case $x^3 + y^3 = z^3$.

PUZZLE PROBLEMS

  1. Explain the rationale in the following trick.
     a) Choose any positive integer.
     b) Add its successor (the next largest integer) to it.
     c) Add 9.
     d) Divide by 2.
     e) Subtract the original number.
     f) The result is 5.

  2. Observe that $(571,428 \times 5) \div 4$ is equal to 714,285. Moreover, we can obtain the numeral "714,285" from the numeral "571,428" by moving the first digit "5" from the hundred-thousands place to the units place. What is the smallest positive integer k such that we can obtain $(k \times 4) \div 5$ from k by moving the left digit of the decimal representation of k to the units place?

---

*   Mathematics is affectionately known as *the queen of the sciences.*

Chapter 5

Fields—Infinite and Finite

Julius Wilhelm Richard Dedekind was born in Brunswick, Germany, on October 6, 1831. Dedekind, who was born in the birthplace of Gauss, was one of the last students of Gauss.

Dedekind was the youngest of four children of Julius Dedekind, a professor of law. During the first 9 years of his formal education he showed no signs of unusual mathematical talent; in fact, he considered mathematics to be merely a servant of science. However, by the age of 17 he had turned to the study of mathematics in preference to the study of the other sciences because he found the logic of mathematics to be more straightforward and believable. In 1848, shortly after his preference for mathematics began to manifest itself, he entered Caroline College, the same college that Gauss had attended as a youth. Two years later he entered the University of Göttingen, where he received a thorough preparation in the mathematics required for a state teacher's certificate. In later years Dedekind regretted that the mathematical instruction he received at Göttingen was insufficient to prepare him for a career in mathematics. He spent two years of self study to prepare for his doctorate. In 1852 Gauss awarded him the Ph.D. for a short dissertation on Eulerian integrals. Although the dissertation was a useful piece of work, it was not a masterpiece and it gave no evidence of Dedekind's genius.

Dedekind was one of the first to appreciate the basic importance of the concept of a *group* in algebra and arithmetic. The concept of *field* was implicit in work by Galois and Abel, but in 1879 Dedekind gave what was probably the first explicit definition of a *field*. He is probably best known, however, for his theory of irrational numbers and for his development of *ideals*.

For eight years after he received his Ph.D., Dedekind pursued a career as instructor of mathematics at Göttingen and at the Zürich Polytechnic Institute. In 1862 he returned to Brunswick as a professor at the technical high school, and he remained there for 50 years. It seems inconceivable that Dedekind occupied such a relatively obscure position for 50 years while men of much less talent and accomplishment occupied such important and influential university positions.

Dedekind remained active in the field of mathematics until his death in 1916 at the age of 85.

DEDEKIND
(1831–1916)

Chapter 5

Fields—Infinite and Finite

5.1 THE REAL NUMBER SYSTEM

We have defined *addition* and *multiplication* of any two counting numbers and have stated some laws which the operations obey. For example, we have learned that

$$3 + 2 = 2 + 3, \qquad 0 + 7 = 7,$$

and

$$5 \times (4 + 3) = 5 \times 4 + 5 \times 3.$$

It is really imprecise to say that the *set* of counting numbers or the *operations* of addition and multiplication obey the laws listed in Section 3.1. It is really the *system* of counting numbers which obeys those laws. A *system* is any nonempty set with one or more binary* operations defined. For example, denoting the *set* of counting numbers by "C_0" and the *system* of counting numbers by "$(C_0, +, \times)$," we may state that the system $(C_0, +, \times)$ obeys the closure laws, the associative laws, the identity laws, the commutative laws, the cancellation laws, the multiplication law of zero, and the distributive law. However, there are laws which $(C_0, +, \times)$ does not obey but which some other number systems obey.

We can solve simple equations such as $2 + x = 5, 2 + x = 2$, and $2x = 10$ in $(C_0, +, \times)$. However, we cannot solve

$$5 + x = 2$$

in $(C_0, +, \times)$. In order to make such equations solvable, we invent new numbers $^-1, {}^-2, {}^-3, \ldots$ with the property that

$$^-1 + 1 = 1 + {}^-1 = 0, \qquad {}^-2 + 2 = 2 + {}^-2 = 0,$$

$$^-3 + 3 = 3 + {}^-3 = 0, \ldots;$$

---

* A *binary operator* operates on an ordered pair of numbers to produce a single number.

we call the new numbers *negative integers*, and we denote the set of negative integers by the symbol "I^-." We form the *union* of C_0 and I^-, denote it by "I," and call I the *set of integers*. Thus

$$C_0 = \{0, 1, 2, 3, \ldots\},$$
$$I^- = \{^-1, ^-2, ^-3, \ldots\} = \{\ldots, ^-3, ^-2, ^-1\},$$

and

$$I = C_0 \cup I^- = \{\ldots, ^-3, ^-2, ^-1, 0, 1, 2, 3, \ldots\}.$$

The equation $5 + x = 2$ is solvable in $(I, +, \times)$; the solution is $^-3$, as the following computation indicates:*

$$5 + x = 2,$$
$$^-5 + (5 + x) = ^-5 + 2,$$
$$^-5 + (5 + x) = (^-3 + ^-2) + 2,$$
$$(^-5 + 5) + x = ^-3 + (^-2 + 2),$$
$$0 + x = ^-3 + 0,$$
$$x = ^-3.$$

All simple equations of the form $a + x = b$ are solvable in the system of integers. The solution, which is an integer, may be a counting number or a negative integer. We denote the set of nonzero counting numbers by the symbol "I^+" and call each nonzero counting number a *positive integer*. For emphasis, we may designate any positive integer a by "^+a." Thus

$$I^+ = \{1, 2, 3, \ldots\} = \{^+1, ^+2, ^+3, \ldots\}.$$

Every integer is a negative integer, zero, or a positive integer. That is,

$$I = I^- \cup \{0\} \cup I^+.$$

We may compute the *sum* of any two integers as in the following examples:

$$5 + 0 = 5, \quad\quad 5 + 3 = 8,$$
$$5 + ^-5 = 0, \quad\quad ^-5 + 5 = 0,$$
$$^-3 + 0 = ^-3, \quad\quad 0 + ^-3 = ^-3,$$
$$^-8 + ^-3 = ^-11, \quad\quad ^-3 + ^-8 = ^-11,$$
$$8 + ^-3 = (5 + 3) + ^-3 = 5 + (3 + ^-3) = 5 + 0 = 5,$$
$$^-3 + 8 = ^-3 + (3 + 5) = (^-3 + 3) + 5 = 0 + 5 = 5,$$
$$^-8 + 3 = (^-5 + ^-3) + 3 = ^-5 + (^-3 + 3) = ^-5 + 0 = ^-5,$$
$$3 + ^-8 = 3 + (^-3 + ^-5) = (3 + ^-3) + ^-5 = 0 + ^-5 = ^-5.$$

---

*   We assume that the reader is familiar with addition and multiplication of integers. We are interested in the reasons for development of the set of integers and other sets.

In Section 4.1 we defined *subtraction* for certain pairs of counting numbers. Now we can generalize the definition so that the *difference $a - b$ exists* [in I] for every integer a and every integer b:

$$a - b = c \text{ if and only if } a = b + c.$$

Thus we may subtract any integer from any integer; the difference is an integer. For example, $7 - 5 = 2, 5 - 8 = {}^-3, {}^-5 - 4 = {}^-9, {}^-5 - {}^-3 = {}^-2,$ ${}^-5 - {}^-8 = 3, {}^-7 - 0 = {}^-7, 0 - 5 = {}^-5,$ and $0 - {}^-6 = 6$.

The *additive inverse* of any integer a is that unique integer x such that $a + x = 0$. Hence the additive inverse of a is ${}^-a$. For example, the additive inverse of 5 is ${}^-5$, the additive inverse of ${}^-7$ is 7, and the additive inverse of 0 is 0. Since $a + {}^-a = 0$ and ${}^-({}^-a) + {}^-a = 0$, it follows that ${}^-({}^-a) = a$. For example, ${}^-({}^-5) = 5$.

It can be proved that $a - b = a + {}^-b$ for any integers a and b. For example,

$$5 - 3 = 5 + {}^-3 = 2,$$

$$5 - {}^-3 = 5 + {}^-({}^-3) = 5 + 3 = 8,$$

$$3 - 5 = 3 + {}^-5 = {}^-2, 3 - {}^-5 = 3 + {}^-({}^-5) = 3 + 5 = 8,$$

$$0 - {}^-5 = 0 + {}^-({}^-5) = 0 + 5 = 5,$$

$${}^-3 - {}^-5 = {}^-3 + {}^-({}^-5) = {}^-3 + 5 = 2,$$

and

$$3 - 3 = 3 + {}^-3 = 0.$$

Although we do not state definitions of addition and multiplication of integers, we remark that the definitions are phrased so that the various laws stated previously for $(C_0, +, \times)$ will govern $(I, +, \times)$. Moreover, $(I, +, \times)$ will obey some laws which $(C_0, +, \times)$ does not. For example $(C_0, +, \times)$ does not obey the *additive inverse law*, but $(I, +, \times)$ does.

Inverse Law for Addition. *If a is any integer, then there exists a unique integer ${}^-a$* [*called* **the additive inverse of a**] *such that $a + {}^-a = 0$.*

We may compute the *product* of any two integers as in the following examples:

$$5 \times 0 = 0, \qquad 5 \times 3 = 15,$$

$${}^-5 \times 0 = 0, \qquad 0 \times {}^-5 = 0,$$

$$5 \times {}^-3 = {}^-(5 \times 3) = {}^-15,$$

$${}^-5 \times 3 = 3 \times {}^-5 = {}^-(3 \times 5) = {}^-15,$$

$${}^-5 \times {}^-3 = 5 \times 3 = 15.$$

Although we can solve every equation of the form $a + x = b$ in $(I, +, \times)$, we cannot solve every equation of the form $ax = b$. For example, the equations

$5x = 2$ and $^-5x = 8$ are not solvable in $(I, +, \times)$. In order to make such equations solvable, we invent new numbers which we call *rational numbers*. We denote any rational number by the symbol "a/b," in which a is an integer and b is a nonzero integer, and we denote the set of rational numbers by the symbol "R_a." That is,

$$R_a = \left\{ \frac{a}{b} : a \in I \text{ and } b \in I \setminus \{0\} \right\}.$$

Since it is provable that

$$\{ \ldots, \ ^-3, \ ^-2, \ ^-1, \ 0, \ 1, \ 2, \ 3, \ldots \}$$

is abstractly identical with

$$\left\{ \ldots, \ \frac{^-3}{1}, \ \frac{^-2}{1}, \ \frac{^-1}{1}, \ \frac{0}{1}, \ \frac{1}{1}, \ \frac{2}{1}, \ \frac{3}{1}, \ldots \right\},$$

we agree that every integer is a rational number. However, since $\frac{5}{8}$ is a rational number but is not an integer, we see that I is a *proper subset of* R_a.

The equation $5x = 2$ is solvable in $(R_a, +, \times)$; the solution is $\frac{2}{5}$, as the following computation indicates:*

$$5x = 2,$$

$$\tfrac{1}{5}(5x) = \tfrac{1}{5}(2),$$

$$(\tfrac{1}{5} \cdot 5)x = \tfrac{1}{5}(2),$$

$$1x = \tfrac{2}{5},$$

$$x = \tfrac{2}{5}.$$

Although $(I, +, \times)$ does not obey the *multiplicative inverse law*, $(R_a, +, \times)$ does.

> **Inverse Law for Multiplication.** *If a/b is any nonzero rational number, then there exists a unique rational number b/a [called* **the multiplicative inverse of a/b**] *such that*
>
> $$\frac{a}{b} \cdot \frac{b}{a} = 1.$$

We denote the set of fractions [i.e., the set of rational numbers which are not integers] by the symbol "F_r." Thus $R_a = I \cup F_r$.

All simple equations of the form $a + bx = c$ [in which a, b, and c are integers] are solvable in the system of rational numbers; the solution is a rational number, which may be an integer or a fraction. We may compute the sum and the

---

* We assume that the reader is familiar with multiplication of fractions. We are interested in the reasons for development of the rational numbers.

product of any two rational numbers as follows:

$$\frac{a}{b} + \frac{c}{d} = \frac{ad + bc}{bd}; \qquad \frac{a}{b} \times \frac{c}{d} = \frac{ac}{bd}.$$

For example,

$$\frac{2}{3} + \frac{5}{8} = \frac{2 \times 8 + 3 \times 5}{3 \times 8} = \frac{16 + 15}{24} = \frac{31}{24}$$

and

$$\frac{2}{3} \times \frac{8}{9} = \frac{2 \times 8}{3 \times 9} = \frac{16}{27}.$$

Although we can solve every equation of the form $a + bx = c$ in $(R_a, +, \times)$, we cannot solve every equation of the form $x^2 = a$ in $(R_a, +, \times)$. For example, the equation $x^2 = 2$ is not solvable in $(R_a, +, \times)$. In order to make such an equation solvable, we invent new numbers which we call *irrational numbers*. For example, the two *roots* [or *solutions*] of $x^2 = 2$ are both irrational numbers which we denote by "$\sqrt{2}$" and "$^-\sqrt{2}$." Thus $(\sqrt{2})^2 = 2$ and $(^-\sqrt{2})^2 = 2$.* We denote the set of irrational numbers by "I_r." Thus I_r consists of such numbers as

$$\sqrt{2}, \ \sqrt{3}, \ \sqrt{5}, \ \sqrt[3]{17}, \ \pi, \ e, \ \frac{\pi}{2}, \quad \text{and} \quad \sqrt{\pi}.$$

The union of R_a and I_r is called the set of *real numbers* and is denoted by "R." That is, $R = R_a \cup I_r$. We extend the definitions of *addition* and *multiplication* so that it is possible to compute sums and products of any two (or more) real numbers. The set of positive real numbers is denoted by "R^+" and the set of negative real numbers is denoted by "R^-." Similar notations are used for R_a and I_r. We extend the definition of the order relation *is less than* to the set of real numbers. Thus *the real number r is less than the real number s if and only if there exists a positive real number t such that $r + t = s$.* The real number system $(R, +, \times)$ obeys all the laws which $(R_a, +, \times)$ obeys. In addition, R obeys some laws which R_a does not. For example, although the set of rational numbers does not obey the *Dedekind law*,† the set of real numbers does. The Dedekind law, which is not an algebraic law, is known as a *completeness law* and guarantees *continuity* of the set of real numbers.

Dedekind Law. If $A \neq \varnothing$, $B \neq \varnothing$, $A \cap B = \varnothing$, $A \cup B = R$, and each element of A is less than each element of B, then either A contains a greatest element or B contains a least element.

---

*   Any number whose square is equal to b is called *a square root of b*. The positive square root of b is called *the principal square root of b* [or *the square root of b*]. Thus the square root of 2 is $\sqrt{2}$; $^-\sqrt{2}$ is also a square root of 2.

†   The Dedekind law is named for J.W. Richard Dedekind (1831–1916).

For example, if

$$A = \{r: r \in R \text{ and } r \le 2\} \quad \text{and} \quad B = \{s: s \in R \text{ and } s > 2\},$$

then A contains a greatest element; however, if

$$A = \{r: r \in R \text{ and } r < 2\} \quad \text{and} \quad B = \{s: s \in R \text{ and } s \ge 2\},$$

then B contains a least element. Since $A \cap B = \varnothing$, it follows that the exclusive *or* is implied in the Dedekind law.

We summarize the basic laws which the real number system obeys. The reader may assume those laws as axioms of the real number system and may prove other laws from them.

Closure Laws

If a and b are any elements of R, then the sum of a and b [denoted by "$a + b$"] is defined and is a unique element of R.   [*Closure law for addition*]

If a and b are any elements of R, then the product of a and b [denoted by "ab"] is defined and is a unique element of R.   [*Closure law for multiplication*]

Associative Laws

If a, b, and c are any elements of R, then

$$(a + b) + c = a + (b + c). \qquad [\textit{Associative law for addition}]$$

If a, b, and c are any elements of R, then

$$(ab)c = a(bc). \qquad [\textit{Associative law for multiplication}]$$

Identity Laws

There exists a unique element [denoted by "0" and called the *additive identity*] in R such that

$$a + 0 = a \quad \text{for any real number } a. \qquad [\textit{Identity law for addition}]$$

There exists a unique element [denoted by "1" and called the *multiplicative identity*] in R such that

$$a \times 1 = a \quad \text{for any real number } a.$$

Moreover,

$$1 \ne 0.$$

[*Identity law for multiplication*]

Inverse Laws

If a is any element of R, then there exists a unique element [denoted by "^-a" and called the *additive inverse* of a] in R such that

$$a + {}^-a = 0. \qquad [\textit{Inverse law for addition}]$$

If a is any element of R except 0, then there exists a unique element [denoted by "$1/a$" and called *the multiplicative inverse of a*] in R such that

$$a \times 1/a = 1. \qquad [\textit{Inverse law for multiplication}]$$

Commutative Laws

If a and b are any elements of R, then

$a + b = b + a.$ [*Commutative law for addition*]

If a and b are any elements in R, then

$a \times b = b \times a.$ [*Commutative law for multiplication*]

Distributive Law

If a, b, and c are any elements in R, then

$a \times (b + c) = a \times b + a \times c.$ [*Distributive law*]

Dedekind Law

If $A \neq \varnothing$, $B \neq \varnothing$, $A \cap B = \varnothing$, $A \cup B = R$, and each element of A is less than each element of B, then either A contains a greatest element or B contains a least element.

Archimedian Law

If a and b are any two elements of R, and if $a \neq 0$, then there exists an element k in R such that $b < ak$.

The rational number system obeys all of the above listed laws except the Dedekind law. The Dedekind law makes it possible to distinguish between rational numbers and real numbers.

EXERCISE SET 5.1

   I. Solve each of the following equations in the real number system.

1. $x + 3 = 8$ 2. $x + 5 = 8$

3. $2x + 3 = 13$ 4. $2x + 5 = 13$

5. $2x + 13 = 3$ 6. $2x + 13 = 5$

7. $2x + 7 = 10$ 8. $3x + 7 = 9$

9. $2x^2 = 6$ 10. $3x^2 = 12$

  II.

1. Which of the equations in Exercise I are solvable in the rational number system?

2. Which of the equations in Exercise I are solvable in the system of integers?

3. Which of the equations in Exercise I are solvable in the counting number system?

4. Which of the equations in Exercise I are solvable in the system of positive integers?

  III. By counterexample, disprove each of the following.

1. The product of any two negative integers is negative.

2. The product of any two irrational numbers is irrational.

3. The sum of any negative integer and any positive integer is positive.

4. The sum of any negative integer and any positive integer is negative.
5. The square root of every positive integer is irrational.
6. Every counting number has two distinct square roots.
7. The product of any fraction and any integer is a fraction.
8. The product of any fraction and any integer is an integer.
9. The sum of any two fractions is a fraction.
10. The product of any two fractions is a fraction.

5.2 THE FIELD OF REAL NUMBERS

In the preceding section we sketched the development of the real numbers from the counting numbers and listed some laws governing the real number system. The actual development of the real number system from the counting number system is much more subtle and detailed than we have indicated; it involves appropriate definitions, axioms, and theorems, which we have neglected in the interest of saving time for the study of other topics. Since the real number system is fundamental to mathematical analysis, we define the real number system as a *complete simply ordered field*. That is, the real number system is any system which is (1) a field, (2) simply ordered, and (3) complete. The meanings of *field*, *simple order*, and *completeness* are given in Definitions 1, 2, and 4.

The 11 laws in Definition 1 completely characterize the *algebraic structure* of the real number system. That is, all the familiar algebraic properties are provable from the laws in Definition 1. Moreover, *subtraction* is implied by F4, and *division* is implied by F9. We define the *difference* [denoted by "$a - b$"] and the *quotient* [denoted by "$a \div b$" or "a/b" or "$\dfrac{a}{b}$"], in which a and b are elements of R, as follows:

$$a - b = a + {}^{-}b; \qquad a \div b = a \times \frac{1}{b}, \quad \text{provided } b \neq 0.$$

Since the sum and product are unique [by F1 and F6, respectively], it follows that the difference and quotient are unique.

In the following list of the more familiar properties which follow from Definition 1, a, b, and c are elements of R.

1. ${}^{-}(a + b) = {}^{-}a + {}^{-}b$.
2. $a + b = a + c$ if and only if $b = c$ [*cancellation law for addition*].
3. ${}^{-}a \times {}^{-}b = a \times b$.   4. ${}^{-}a \times b = {}^{-}(a \times b)$.
5. $a \times {}^{-}b = {}^{-}(a \times b)$.   6. ${}^{-}({}^{-}a) = a$.
7. $a \times b = 0$ if and only if $a = 0$ or $b = 0$.
8. If $a \times b = a \times c$ and $a \neq 0$, then $b = c$ [*cancellation law for multiplication*].
9. If $a = b$, then $a \times c = b \times c$.
10. $\dfrac{a}{b} \times \dfrac{c}{d} = \dfrac{a \times c}{b \times d}$, provided $b \neq 0$ and $d \neq 0$.

11. $\dfrac{a}{b} + \dfrac{c}{d} = \dfrac{ad + bc}{b \times d}$, provided $b \neq 0$ and $d \neq 0$.

12. $\dfrac{a}{b} = \dfrac{c}{d}$ if and only if $ad = bc$, provided $b \neq 0$ and $d \neq 0$.

13. $\dfrac{a}{b} \div \dfrac{c}{d} = \dfrac{a}{b} \times \dfrac{d}{c}$, provided $b \neq 0$, $c \neq 0$, and $d \neq 0$.

Definition 1. *A mathematical system* $(R, +, \times)$*, consisting of a set R and two binary operators* $+$ *and* $\times$ *[addition and multiplication], which obeys the laws F1 through F11 is called a* **field.**

F1. If a and b are any elements of R, then the sum of a and b [denoted by "$a + b$"] is defined and is a unique element of R.

[*Closure law for addition*]

F2. If a, b, and c are any elements of R, then

$$(a + b) + c = a + (b + c).$$

[*Associative law for addition*]

F3. There exists a unique element [denoted by "0" and called the *additive identity*] in R such that

$$a + 0 = a \quad \text{for any } a \text{ in } R.$$

[*Identity law for addition*]

F4. If a is any element of R, then there exists a unique element [denoted by "^-a" and called *the additive inverse of a*] in R such that

$$a + {}^-a = 0.$$

[*Inverse law for addition*]

F5. If a and b are any elements of R, then

$$a + b = b + a.$$

[*Commutative law for addition*]

F6. If a and b are any elements of R, then the product of a and b [denoted by "$a \times b$" or "$a \cdot b$" or "ab" or "$a(b)$" or "$(a)(b)$"] is defined and is a unique element of R.

[*Closure law for multiplication*]

F7. If a, b, and c are any elements of R, then

$$(a \times b) \times c = a \times (b \times c).$$

[*Associative law for multiplication*]

F8. There exists a unique element [denoted by "1" and called the *multiplicative identity*] in R such that

$$a \times 1 = a \quad \text{for any } a \text{ in } R.$$

Moreover, $1 \neq 0$.

[*Identity law for multiplication*]

F9. If a is any element of R except 0, then there exists a unique element [denoted by "$1/a$" and called *the multiplicative inverse of a*] in R such that $a \times 1/a = 1$.

[*Inverse law for multiplication*]

F10. If a and b are any elements of R, then $a \times b = b \times a$.

[*Commutative law for multiplication*]

F11. If a, b, and c are any elements of R, then

$$a \times (b + c) = a \times b + a \times c. \quad [\textit{Distributive law}]$$

Definition 2. *A field* $(R, +, \times)$ *which contains a subsystem* $(P, +, \times)$ *obeying the laws* O1 *through* O4 *is called a* **simply ordered field** *or a* **field with simple order** *[denoted by* "$(R, +, \times, <)$"*], and the subset P of R is called* **the set of positive elements of R.**

O1. If a and b are any elements of P, then $a + b$ is a unique element of P.

O2. If a and b are any elements of P, then $a \times b$ is a unique element of P.

O3. The additive identity 0 is not an element of P.

O4. If $c \notin P$, then $c = 0$ or $\bar{}c \in P$.

We may convert the laws O1 through O4 to the familiar order properties by defining the familiar *simple order relation* $<$ on R.

Definition 3. *The element a of R* **is less than** *the element b of R [denoted by* "$a < b$" *or* "$b > a$"*] if and only if* $b - a \in P$ *and P is the set of positive elements in R.*

We may employ Definitions 2 and 3 to prove the following familiar order properties, in which a, b, and c are elements of R.

1. $a > 0$ if and only if $a \in P$.

2. If $a < b$ and $b < c$, then $a < c$.

3. $a < b$ if and only if $a + c < b + c$.

4. If $a < b$ and $c > 0$, then $ac < bc$.

5. If $a < b$ and $c < 0$, then $ac > bc$.

6. If $a \neq b$, then $a < b$ or $a > b$.

7. $\dfrac{a}{b} < \dfrac{c}{d}$ if and only if $ad < bc$ and $bd > 0$.

The idea of *completeness* of an order relation may be formulated in various ways. We introduce completeness by means of the *Dedekind law.*[*]

Definition 4. *A simply ordered field* $(R, +, \times, <)$ *which obeys the Dedekind law is called a* **complete simply ordered field.**

Dedekind Law. *If* $A \neq \varnothing$, $B \neq \varnothing$. $A \cap B = \varnothing$, $A \cup B = R$, *and each element of A is less than each element of B, then either A contains a greatest element or B contains a least element.*

Since the Dedekind law requires that $A \cap B$ be empty, it follows that the exclusive *or* is implied in the Dedekind law.

The reader may wonder whether there is more than one complete simply ordered field. Since it is provable that all complete simply ordered fields are abstractly identical, we can assume that there is only one complete simply ordered field. In Definition 5, we name that system.

---

[*]   The Dedekind law is named for J.W. Richard Dedekind (1831–1916).

Definition 5. *A complete simply ordered field is called **the real number system** [denoted by "$(R, +, \times, <)$"].*

The real number system is characterized by the 11 *field laws* (in Definition 1), the four *simple order laws* (in Definition 2), and the *Dedekind law*. All algebraic properties of the real number system follow from Definition 1; all order properties follow from Definition 2 and the Dedekind law. Geometrically we may represent R as a line $\mathscr{L}$ (called the *real line*) in such a manner that there is a one-to-one correspondence between R and $\mathscr{L}$. The Dedekind law guarantees that there exists a real number corresponding to each point on $\mathscr{L}$ and hence that there are no holes in $\mathscr{L}$; i.e., the Dedekind law guarantees that the real line is *complete*.* We frequently denote the real line $\mathscr{L}$ by "R" for emphasis; that is, we speak of the real line $\mathscr{L}$ as if it were the set R of real numbers. Abstractly, the two sets are identical, and a single notation for both sets should cause no confusion.

The set of real numbers has several important proper subsets which we indicate in Fig. 5.1. Each indicated set is a proper subset of the set indicated immediately above it, and each set is the union of the two sets indicated immediately below it.

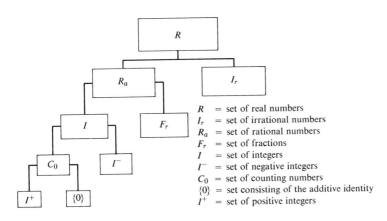

R = set of real numbers
I_r = set of irrational numbers
R_a = set of rational numbers
F_r = set of fractions
I = set of integers
I^- = set of negative integers
C_0 = set of counting numbers
$\{0\}$ = set consisting of the additive identity
I^+ = set of positive integers

Fig. 5.1

Each proper subset of R in Fig. 5.1 is defined as follows:

$$I^+ = \{1, 2, 3, \ldots\}$$
$$= \{^+1, \,^+2, \,^+3, \ldots\};$$

$$C_0 = \{0, 1, 2, 3, \ldots\};$$

$$I^- = \{^-1, \,^-2, \,^-3, \ldots\}$$
$$= \{\ldots, \,^-3, \,^-2, \,^-1\};$$

---

*   In his *Elements*, Euclid of Alexandria (*circa* 300 B.C.) neglected to state a completeness axiom but tacitly assumed one when he proved the theorems.

$$I = \{\ldots, {}^-3, {}^-2, {}^-1, 0, 1, 2, 3, \ldots\};$$

$$F_r = \left\{ \frac{a}{b} : a \in I, b \in I \setminus \{0\}, \text{ and } b \not\mid a \right\};$$

$$R_a = \left\{ \frac{a}{b} : a \in I \text{ and } b \in I \setminus \{0\} \right\};$$

$$I_r = R \setminus R_a$$
$$= \{r : r \in R \text{ and } r \notin R_a\}.$$

The real line is illustrated in Fig. 5.2, in which some real numbers are indicated by dots on the line.*

Fig. 5.2

We refer to the point corresponding to the real number r as *the point r* [or simply r]. For example, we refer to the point corresponding to the real number 0 as the point 0. Observing that $\sqrt{2}$ and ${}^-\sqrt{2}$ are equidistant from 0, and e and ${}^-e$ are equidistant from 0, and every real number r and its additive inverse ${}^-r$ are equidistant from 0, we define the *absolute value* of any real number as its distance from 0. For example, the absolute value of ${}^-2$ is 2, and the absolute value of 2 is 2. However, the absolute value of 0 is 0.

Definition 6. *The absolute value of the real number r [denoted by "$|r|$"] is equal to*

a) ${}^-r$ *if $r < 0$,*

b) 0 *if $r = 0$,*

c) r *if $r > 0$.*

We have mentioned that the Dedekind law makes it possible to distinguish between the real number system and the rational number system. The rational number system obeys the 11 field laws and the four simple order laws, but not the Dedekind law. It is the Dedekind law which asserts the existence of such numbers as $\sqrt{2}$ and π, both of which are irrational. The rational number system is a simply ordered field but is not complete; the real number system is a complete simply ordered field.

---

* The irrational numbers $\sqrt{2}$, e, and π are approximately equal to 1.414, 2.718, and 3.142, respectively.

Rational numbers and irrational numbers are distinguishable by their decimal expansions. For example,

$$\tfrac{1}{3} = 0.333\ldots = 0.\bar{3},*$$

$$\tfrac{3}{4} = 0.75 = 0.75000\ldots = 0.75\bar{0},$$

$$\tfrac{5}{11} = 0.454545\ldots = 0.\overline{45},$$

and

$$\tfrac{1}{7} = 0.142857142857142857\ldots = 0.\overline{142857}.$$

However, there is no way to express $\sqrt{2}$, π, and e as repeating or terminating decimals.

The following theorem, which we state without proof, guarantees that every rational number can be expressed as a terminating decimal or as a repeating decimal. The usual definitions of *numerator* and *denominator* are understood.

Theorem 1

a) *If a/b is any rational number, then a/b can be expressed as a terminating decimal or as a repeating decimal.*

b) *If a/b is any rational number whose denominator has no prime factors other than 2 or 5, then a/b can be expressed as a terminating decimal.*

c) *If a/b is any rational number whose denominator has a prime factor other than 2 or 5 and if a and b are relatively prime, then a/b cannot be expressed as a terminating decimal.*

Converting a rational number from a/b-form to decimal form is simply a matter of division. However, converting a rational number from decimal form to a/b-form requires multiplication and subtraction, as well as expressed division. The following examples illustrate the procedure, which is general.

Example 1. To convert $0.\overline{213}$ to a/b-form, we multiply $0.\overline{213}$ by 10^3 and by 1, and then subtract as follows:

$$r = 0.\overline{213},$$

$$1000r = 213.\overline{213},$$

$$r = 0.\overline{213},$$

$$999r = 213,$$

$$r = \tfrac{213}{999},$$

$$r = \tfrac{71}{333}.$$

---

*   The bar over a digit [or sequence of digits] indicates that the digit [or sequence of digits] repeats indefinitely.

Example 2. To convert $0.2\overline{13}$ to a/b-form, we multiply $0.2\overline{13}$ by 10^3 and by 10, and then subtract as follows:

$$r = 0.2\overline{13},$$

$$1000r = 213.\overline{13},$$

$$10r = 2.\overline{13},$$

$$990r = 211,$$

$$r = \tfrac{211}{990}.$$

The above examples indicate the method of proof of the following theorem, which we state without proof.

Theorem 2. *Every repeating decimal is a rational number.*

It follows immediately from Theorems 1 and 2 that *the set of rational numbers is abstractly identical to the set of repeating decimals* (provided we consider a terminating decimal to be a repeating decimal which repeats 0). Moreover, *the set of irrational numbers is abstractly identical to the set of nonrepeating decimals.*

EXERCISE SET 5.2

I.

1. Express R as the union of two disjoint sets.
2. Express R as the union of three disjoint sets.
3. Express R as the union of four disjoint sets.
4. Express R as the union of five disjoint sets.
5. Express R_a as the union of two disjoint sets.
6. Express R_a as the union of three disjoint sets.
7. Express R_a as the union of four disjoint sets.
8. Express I as the union of two disjoint sets.
9. Express I as the union of three disjoint sets.
10. Express C_0 as the union of two disjoint sets.

II. Recall that $I_r = R \setminus R_a$. Similarly, $R_a = R \setminus I_r$.

1. Express I as a relative complement.
2. Express F_r as a relative complement.
3. Express C_0 as a relative complement.
4. Express I^- as a relative complement.
5. Express I^+ as a relative complement.

III. Prove each of the following.

1. $\dfrac{2}{^-3} = \dfrac{^-2}{3}$
2. $\dfrac{5}{7} < \dfrac{9}{10}$
3. $\dfrac{^-9}{10} < \dfrac{^-5}{7}$

4. $\dfrac{^-9}{10} < \dfrac{5}{^-7}$ 　　　　 5. $\dfrac{9}{^-10} < \dfrac{5}{^-7}$ 　　　　 6. $\dfrac{6}{9} = \dfrac{2}{3}$

7. $\dfrac{^-8}{^-10} = \dfrac{4}{5}$ 　　　　 8. $^-5 \times {}^-7 \times {}^-3 = {}^-105$ 　　　 9. $^-2 \times 5 \times {}^-3 = 30$

10. $^-(a + 5) = {}^-a - 5$

IV. By means of a statement of the form "$a \in A$," state each set [in Fig. 5.1] of which each of the following real numbers is an element. [For example, $5 \in I^+$, $5 \in C_0$, $5 \in I$, $5 \in R_a$, $5 \in R$.]

1. 2 　　　　　　 2. 3 　　　　　　 3. $^-7$ 　　　　　 4. 7

5. $^-7 + 7$ 　　　 6. $4 + {}^-4$ 　　　 7. $\sqrt{3}$ 　　　　 8. $\sqrt{5}$

9. $\sqrt{16}$ 　　　 10. $\sqrt{25}$ 　　　 11. $\frac{2}{3}$ 　　　　 12. $\frac{5}{7}$

13. 1.5 　　　　 14. 2.9 　　　　 15. $1.\overline{23}$ 　　　 16. $1.2\overline{3}$

17. π 　　　　　 18. e 　　　　　 19. $\frac{51}{17}$ 　　　 20. $\frac{91}{13}$

V. Compute the *absolute value* of each of the following.

1. $5 + {}^-7$ 　　　　　　 2. $^-5 + 7$ 　　　　　　 3. $^-(5 + {}^-3)$

4. $^-({}^-5 + 3)$ 　　　　 5. $\dfrac{4}{5} \times \dfrac{^-2}{3}$ 　　　　 6. $\dfrac{^-4}{3} \times \dfrac{2}{5}$

7. $\dfrac{^-4 \times 3}{5 \times {}^-7}$ 　　　　 8. $\dfrac{4 \times {}^-7}{^-5 \times 3}$ 　　　　 9. $^-2 + |5 - 8|$

10. $^-3 + |5 - 7|$

VI. Express each of the following rational numbers as a decimal.

1. $\frac{4}{5}$ 　　　　　　 2. $\frac{3}{10}$ 　　　　　 3. $\frac{2}{7}$ 　　　　　 4. $\frac{3}{7}$

5. $\frac{9}{8}$ 　　　　　　 6. $\frac{11}{8}$ 　　　　　 7. $\frac{16}{15}$ 　　　　 8. $\frac{14}{15}$

9. $\frac{20}{30}$ 　　　　　 10. $\frac{10}{30}$

VII. Express each of the following decimals in the a/b-form.

1. $0.\overline{123}$ 　　　　　　　　　　　 2. $0.2\overline{31}$

3. $0.1\overline{23}$ 　　　　　　　　　　　 4. $0.2\overline{31}$

5. $0.12\overline{3}$ 　　　　　　　　　　　 6. $0.23\overline{1}$

7. $5.\overline{42}$ 　　　　　　　　　　　 8. $5.2\overline{4}$

9. 5.42 　　　　　　　　　　　　 10. 5.24

VIII.

1. Let
$$A = \{a: a \in R \text{ and } a < 3\} \quad \text{and} \quad B = \{b: b \in R \text{ and } b \geq 3\}.$$

Verify that A and B satisfy the hypotheses of the Dedekind law, and compute the greatest element of A or the least element of B.

2. Let
$$A = \{a: a \in R \text{ and } a \leq \sqrt{2}\} \quad \text{and} \quad B = \{b: b \in R \text{ and } b > \sqrt{2}\}.$$

Verify that A and B satisfy the hypotheses of the Dedekind law, and compute the greatest element of A or the least element of B.

3. Let

$$A = \{a: a \in R \text{ and } a \leq 5\} \quad \text{and} \quad B = \{b: b \in R \text{ and } b \geq 5\}.$$

Explain why A and B do not obey the Dedekind law. Does A contain a greatest element? Does B contain a least element?

4. Let

$$A = \{a: a \in R \text{ and } a < {}^-5\} \quad \text{and} \quad B = \{b: b \in R \text{ and } b > {}^-5\}.$$

Explain why A and B do not obey the Dedekind law. Does A contain a greatest element? Does B contain a least element?

5. Let

$$A = \{a: a \in R_a \text{ and } a < \sqrt{2}\} \quad \text{and} \quad B = \{b: b \in R_a \text{ and } b \geq \sqrt{2}\}.$$

Explain why A and B do not obey the Dedekind law.

IX. The set of 11 field laws is *redundant* because F5 can be proved from the other 10 field laws. In order to prove F5, we would first prove that $0 + a = a$ and $^-a + a = 0$ for every a in R and then we would employ F10, F11, and the cancellation law for addition to prove that $a + b = b + a$ for every a in R and every b in R. Prove the commutative law for addition.

[*Hint*: Observe that $(a + b)(1 + 1) = (1 + 1)(a + b)$.]

X.

1. Which field laws does $(I^+, +, \times)$ obey?
2. Which field laws does $(I^-, +, \times)$ obey?
3. Which field laws does $(C_0, +, \times)$ obey?
4. Which field laws does $(I^0, +, \times)$ obey?
5. Which field laws does $(R_a, +, \times)$ obey?
6. Which field laws does $(F_r, +, \times)$ obey?
7. Which field laws does $(I_r, +, \times)$ obey?
8. Which field laws does $(\{0\}, +, \times)$ obey?

5.3 FINITE FIELDS

We have learned that the real number system is a field which is infinite, simply ordered, and complete; and the rational number system is a field which is infinite and simply ordered but not complete. Moreover, the system of integers is infinite, simply ordered, and complete, but it is not a field. Are there any fields which are not simply ordered? Are there any finite fields? Are there any fields which are not complete?

To answer the above questions, we consider a dial (such as a clock face) which has the numerals "0," "1," and "2" imprinted on it, as shown in Fig. 5.3.

Fig. 5.3

The numerals on the dial represent a set of *numbers*, which we denote by
"M_3." Thus $M_3 = \{0, 1, 2\}$. We agree to *add* as in Fig. 5.4. That is, the definition
of *addition* in M_3 is given in Fig. 5.4. The symbol "$\oplus$" for addition in M_3 should
not be confused with the symbol "$+$" for addition in R.

M_3 Addition Table

$\oplus$	0	1	2
0	0	1	2
1	1	2	0
2	2	0	1

Fig. 5.4

We observe from Fig. 5.4 the following addition facts:

$$0 \oplus 0 = 0, \quad 0 \oplus 1 = 1, \quad 0 \oplus 2 = 2,$$
$$1 \oplus 0 = 1, \quad 1 \oplus 1 = 2, \quad 1 \oplus 2 = 0,$$
$$2 \oplus 0 = 2, \quad 2 \oplus 1 = 0, \quad 2 \oplus 2 = 1.$$

The following definition is equivalent to that in Fig. 5.4.

Definition 7. *The* **sum** *[denoted by "$a \oplus b$"] of any two elements a and b in M_3
is as follows:*

a) $a \oplus b = a + b$ *if and only if* $a + b < 3$;

b) $a \oplus b = (a + b) - 3$ *if and only if* $a + b \geq 3$.

According to Fig. 5.4 (and Definition 7), the sum of any two elements of
M_3 is a unique element of M_3. That is, the *sum* is well defined. Hence $(M_3, \oplus)$
obeys the closure law (for addition). The reader may prove that $(M_3, \oplus)$ obeys
the associative, the identity, the inverse, and the commutative laws (for *addition*).

We agree to *multiply* as in Fig. 5.5. That is, the definition of *multiplication*
in M_3 is given in Fig. 5.5. The symbol "$\otimes$" for multiplication in M_3 should not
be confused with the symbol "$\cdot$" or "$\times$" for multiplication in R.

M_3 Multiplication Table

$\otimes$	0	1	2
0	0	0	0
1	0	1	2
2	0	2	1

Fig. 5.5

We observe from Fig. 5.5 the following multiplication facts:

$0 \otimes 0 = 0$, $0 \otimes 1 = 0$, $0 \otimes 2 = 0$,

$1 \otimes 0 = 0$, $1 \otimes 1 = 1$, $1 \otimes 2 = 2$,

$2 \otimes 0 = 0$, $2 \otimes 1 = 2$, $2 \otimes 2 = 1$.

The following definition is equivalent to that in Fig. 5.5.

Definition 8. *The **product** [denoted by "$a \otimes b$"] of any two elements a and b in M_3 is as follows:*

a) *$a \otimes b = a \times b$ if and only if $a \times b < 3$;*

b) *$a \otimes b = (a \times b) - 3$ if and only if $a \times b \geq 3$.*

According to Fig. 5.5 (and Definition 8), the product of any two elements of M_3 is a unique element of M_3. That is, the *product* is well defined. Hence $(M_3, \otimes)$ obeys the closure law (for multiplication). The reader may prove that $(M_3, \otimes)$ obeys the associative, the identity, the inverse, and the commutative laws (for multiplication). Moreover, $(M_3, \oplus, \otimes)$ obeys the distributive law. Hence $(M_3, \oplus, \otimes)$ is a field.

The additive identity is 0, and the multiplicative identity is 1. Since there are no negative numbers and no fractions in M_3, the reader may think that 2 does not have an additive or multiplicative inverse in M_3. However, since $2 \oplus 1 = 0$ and $2 \otimes 2 = 1$, we see that an additive inverse of 2 is 1 and a multiplicative inverse of 2 is 2. Moreover, 1 is the only additive inverse of 2, and 2 is the only multiplicative inverse of 2. Hence the additive inverse of 2 is unique, and the multiplicative inverse of 2 is unique. In Fig. 5.6, we exhibit the additive inverse of each element of M_3 and the multiplicative inverse of each element of M_3 except 0, which has no multiplicative inverse.

Element of M_3	0	1	2
Additive Inverse	0	2	1
Multiplicative Inverse	None	1	2

Fig. 5.6

Can we define a simple order relation $<$ in M_3 such that $(M_3, \oplus, \otimes, <)$ obeys the laws O1 through O4 listed in Section 5.2? If we can, then P (the set of positive elements) should be $\{1, 2\}$. However, since $1 \oplus 2 = 0$ and $0 \notin \{1, 2\}$, it follows that the system does not obey O1. Hence $P \neq \{1, 2\}$. Similarly, $P \neq \{2\}$ and $P \neq \{1\}$. If the system obeys O3, then $0 \notin P$. Hence there is no way to choose P so that the system obeys O1 through O4. Thus there is no simple order in M_3. Therefore $(M_3, \oplus, \otimes)$ is a field but is not a simply ordered field and is not complete.

Now we consider the number system $(M_5, \oplus, \otimes)$, in which

$$M_5 = \{0, 1, 2, 3, 4\}$$

and $\oplus$ and $\otimes$ are as defined in Fig. 5.7.

$\oplus$	0	1	2	3	4
0	0	1	2	3	4
1	1	2	3	4	0
2	2	3	4	0	1
3	3	4	0	1	2
4	4	0	1	2	3

a)

$\otimes$	0	1	2	3	4
0	0	0	0	0	0
1	0	1	2	3	4
2	0	2	4	1	3
3	0	3	1	4	2
4	0	4	3	2	1

b)   **Fig. 5.7**

The reader may prove that $(M_5, \oplus, \otimes)$ is a field which is neither simply ordered nor complete. In Fig. 5.8, we exhibit the additive inverse of each element of M_5 and the multiplicative inverse of each element of M_5 except 0, which has no multiplicative inverse.

Element of M_5	0	1	2	3	4
Additive Inverse	0	4	3	2	1
Multiplicative Inverse	None	1	3	2	4

Fig. 5.8

EXERCISE SET 5.3

I. Prove that $(M_3, \oplus, \otimes)$ is a field.

II. Prove that $(M_5, \oplus, \otimes)$ is a field.

[You may assume both associative laws and the distributive law.]

III.
1. Construct the addition table for M_7.
2. Construct the multiplication table for M_7.
3. State a definition of addition in M_7.
4. State a definition of multiplication in M_7.

IV.
1. Construct the addition table for M_6.
2. Construct the multiplication table for M_6.
3. Construct the addition table for M_8.

4. Construct the multiplication table for M_8.

5. Construct the addition table for M_9.

6. Construct the multiplication table for M_9.

7. Construct the addition table for M_2.

8. Construct the multiplication table for M_2.

9. Construct the addition table for M_4.

10. Construct the multiplication table for M_4.

V.

1. Is $(M_7, \oplus, \otimes)$ a field?

2. Is $(M_6, \oplus, \otimes)$ a field?

3. Is $(M_8, \oplus, \otimes)$ a field?

4. Is $(M_2, \oplus, \otimes)$ a field?

5. Is $(M_4, \oplus, \otimes)$ a field?

6. Is $(M_9, \oplus, \otimes)$ a field?

5.4 MODULAR NUMBER SYSTEMS

The number systems we studied in Section 5.3 are known as *modular number systems*. For example, $(M_5, \oplus, \otimes)$ is a modular number system [whose modulus is 5], also known as *the mod 5 number system* [or *the system of integers modulo 5*]. We learned that the mod 3 number system and the mod 5 number system are finite fields. In Exercise Set 5.3 we considered other modular number systems, whose moduli are 2, 4, 6, 7, 8, and 9. We learned that some are fields and the others are not. Is there a general criterion which enables us to decide whether $(M_m, \oplus, \otimes)$ [the mod m number system] is a field, for any positive integer m? Before we answer the above question, we consider the reason that the mod 6 number system is not a field. The addition and multiplication tables for the mod 6 number system are exhibited in Fig. 5.9.

Mod 6 Addition Table

$\oplus$	0	1	2	3	4	5
0	0	1	2	3	4	5
1	1	2	3	4	5	0
2	2	3	4	5	0	1
3	3	4	5	0	1	2
4	4	5	0	1	2	3
5	5	0	1	2	3	4

a)

Mod 6 Multiplication Table

$\otimes$	0	1	2	3	4	5
0	0	0	0	0	0	0
1	0	1	2	3	4	5
2	0	2	4	0	2	4
3	0	3	0	3	0	3
4	0	4	2	0	4	2
5	0	5	4	3	2	1

b) **Fig. 5.9**

The reader may verify from Fig. 5.9 that the mod 6 number system obeys all field laws except F9. According to F9, every nonzero element a must have a multiplicative inverse b such that $a \otimes b = 1$. However, we observe from Fig. 5.9(b) that 2 has no multiplicative inverse because $2 \otimes 0 = 0$, $2 \otimes 1 = 2$, $2 \otimes 2 = 4$, $2 \otimes 3 = 0$, $2 \otimes 4 = 2$, and $2 \otimes 5 = 4$. Hence there exists a nonzero element which does not have a multiplicative inverse. In a similar manner, the reader may prove that 3 and 4 do not have multiplicative inverses. Hence $(M_6, \oplus, \otimes)$ is not a field.

Similarly, the mod 4, and mod 8, and mod 9 number systems are not fields. However, the mod 2, mod 3, mod 5, and mod 7 number systems are fields. Since 4, 6, 8, and 9 are composite numbers and 2, 3, 5, and 7 are prime numbers, we conjecture that a modular number system is a field if and only if the modulus is prime. In fact, there is a theorem which guarantees that the conjecture is true. Before we state the theorem, we define *sum* and *product* in any modular number system.

Definition 9. *The **sum** [denoted by "$a \oplus b$"] and the **product** [denoted by "$a \otimes b$"] of any two elements a and b of M_m is as follows:*

a) *$a \oplus b$ is the remainder in the division of $a + b$ by m;*

b) *$a \otimes b$ is the remainder in the division of $a \times b$ by m.*

For example, in $(M_9, \oplus, \otimes)$, $7 \oplus 8 = 6$ because $7 + 8 = 15$ and 6 is the remainder in the division of 15 by 9. Moreover, $7 \otimes 8 = 2$ because $7 \times 8 = 56$ and 2 is the remainder in the division of 56 by 9.

Since every composite number c has factors j and k other than 1 and c such that

$$c = j \times k,$$

and since the remainder in the division of $j \times k$ by c is 0, it follows that $j \otimes k = 0$. Hence, if the modulus of a modular number system is composite, then that modular number system does not obey the multiplication law of zero [which guarantees that $j \times k = 0$ if and only if $j = 0$ or $k = 0$, and which every field obeys]. Consequently a *composite modular number system* [i.e., a modular number system with composite modulus] cannot be a field. Specifically, the inverse law for multiplication fails in every composite modular number system.

The above argument is an informal proof of the following theorem. We omit the formal proof.

Theorem 3. *If m is any composite number, then $(M_m, \oplus, \otimes)$ is not a field.*

Can we be certain that every prime modular number system is a field? The following theorem, whose proof is omitted because it is beyond the scope of the text, guarantees that every prime modular number system is a field.

Theorem 4. *If p is any prime number, then $(M_p, \oplus, \otimes)$ is a field.*

It follows from Definition 1 that every field contains at least two elements [the additive identity and the multiplicative identity, usually denoted by "0" and "1," respectively]. Hence $(M_1, \oplus, \otimes)$ is not a field. Therefore Theorems 3 and 4 can be combined into one theorem.

Theorem 5. *A modular number system is a field if and only if the modulus is prime.*

As we mentioned previously, every field obeys the multiplication law of zero, which is closely related to the inverse law for multiplication. Another law closely related to the inverse law for multiplication is the cancellation law for multiplication. In any field, the cancellation law for multiplication is equivalent to the multiplication law of zero. In any composite modular number system there is no cancellation law for multiplication. For example, in $(M_6, \oplus, \otimes)$,

$$2 \otimes 3 = 4 \otimes 3, \quad \text{but} \quad 2 \neq 4.$$

The following theorem, whose proof we omit, summarizes the above discussion.

Theorem 6

a) *Every prime modular number system obeys the cancellation law for multiplication and the multiplication law of zero.*

b) *Every composite modular number system obeys neither the cancellation law for multiplication nor the multiplication law for zero.*

Because of Theorems 3 through 6, we make the following observations:

1. In $(M_m, \oplus, \otimes)$, in which m is any integer greater than 1, every equation $a \oplus x = b$ has a solution x_0 [which is an element of M_m];

2. In $(M_c, \oplus, \otimes)$, in which c is a composite number, not every equation $a \otimes x = b$ has a solution x_0 [e.g., the equation $2 \otimes x = 5$ has no solution in $(M_6, \oplus, \otimes)$];

3. In $(M_p, \oplus, \otimes)$, in which p is a prime number and $a \neq 0$, every equation $a \otimes x = b$ has a solution x_0 [which is an element of M_p].

From the above observations, we conclude that $(M_c, \oplus, \otimes)$, in which c is a composite number, is very similar to $(I, +, \times)$; and $(M_p, \oplus, \otimes)$, in which p is a prime number, is very similar to $(R_a, +, \times)$.

EXERCISE SET 5.4

I. Decide which of the following modular number systems do not obey the inverse property for multiplication [and hence are not fields]. Identify each nonzero element of each system which does not have a multiplicative inverse, and compute the GCD of each nonzero element and the modulus. [For example, $(M_6, \oplus, \otimes)$ does not obey F9; 2, 3, and 4 do not have multiplicative inverses; the GCD of 1 and 6 is 1, the GCD of 2 and 6 is 2, the GCD of 3 and 6 is 3, the GCD of 4 and 6 is 2, and the GCD of 5 and 6 is 1.]

1. $(M_{10}, \oplus, \otimes)$ 2. $(M_9, \oplus, \otimes)$

3. $(M_{12}, \oplus, \otimes)$ 4. $(M_{14}, \oplus, \otimes)$

5. $(M_{15}, \oplus, \otimes)$ 6. $(M_{16}, \oplus, \otimes)$

7. $(M_{13}, \oplus, \otimes)$ 8. $(M_{17}, \oplus, \otimes)$

9. $(M_{19}, \oplus, \otimes)$ 10. $(M_{23}, \oplus, \otimes)$

II. Solve each of the following equations in the indicated modular number system.

1. $3 \otimes x = 1 \pmod 5$ 2. $4 \otimes x = 1 \pmod 5$

3. $3 \otimes x = 1 \pmod 7$ 4. $4 \otimes x = 1 \pmod 7$

5. $5 \otimes x = 1 \pmod 7$ 6. $6 \otimes x = 1 \pmod 7$

7. $5 \otimes x = 2 \pmod 7$ 8. $6 \otimes x = 2 \pmod 7$

9. $9 \otimes x = 8 \pmod{11}$ 10. $8 \otimes x = 9 \pmod{11}$

III. By *trial*, prove that each of the following equations has *no* solution in the mod 6 number system. [*Hint:* Refer to Fig. 5.9.]

1. $2 \otimes x = 1$ 2. $3 \otimes x = 2$

3. $2 \otimes x = 3$ 4. $3 \otimes x = 4$

5. $2 \otimes x = 5$ 6. $3 \otimes x = 1$

7. $3 \otimes x = 5$ 8. $4 \otimes x = 1$

9. $4 \otimes x = 3$ 10. $4 \otimes x = 5$

IV. By *trial*, prove that each of the following equations has *no* solution in the indicated modular number system.

1. $2 \otimes x = 1 \pmod 8$ 2. $2 \otimes x = 3 \pmod 8$

3. $2 \otimes x = 5 \pmod 8$ 4. $2 \otimes x = 7 \pmod 8$

5. $3 \otimes x = 5 \pmod{15}$ 6. $3 \otimes x = 4 \pmod{15}$

7. $3 \otimes x = 7 \pmod{15}$ 8. $3 \otimes x = 8 \pmod{15}$

9. $7 \otimes x = 1 \pmod{21}$ 10. $7 \otimes x = 6 \pmod{21}$

V.

1. Let x be any element of the mod m number system which has a multiplicative inverse. What is the GCD of x and m?

2. Let y be any element of the mod m number system which does not have a multiplicative inverse. What is the GCD of y and m?

PUZZLE PROBLEMS

1. A farmboy kept track of his cows and hens by counting the legs and the heads. He counted 78 legs and 34 heads. How many cows did he have? How many chickens did he have?

2. There are 64 squares on a standard checkerboard. A puzzle enthusiast notices that a domino covers exactly two squares of the board and hence that 32 dominoes will cover the entire board. Since he has only 31 dominoes, he wishes to cover all but the two black squares at diagonally opposite corners of the board. Explain how he can do so, or explain why he cannot do so.

The life of Evariste Galois, like that of Niels Henrik Abel, is one of the shameful tragedies in mathematical history. Abel was a victim of poverty, and Galois was a victim of stupidity.

Evariste Galois was born in the Greater Paris village of Bourg-la-Reine on October 25, 1811. His father was a cultivated intellectual and an ardent lover of liberty. His mother came from a long line of distinguished jurists and had a thorough classical and religious education. Until he was 12 years old, Galois had no teacher except his mother. There is no history of mathematical talent on either side of Galois's family and no record of his possession of such talent as a small child. His own mathematical genius seemed to appear quite suddenly and unexpectedly during his early years of adolescence.

When he was 12 years old, Galois entered his first school, the Lycée Louis-le-Grand in Paris—probably the worst school that could have been chosen. France was still feeling the effects of the Revolution; and the school was a dismal, barred, and grilled building dominated by a supervisor who was more of a jailer than a teacher.

Galois displayed only a docile interest in literature and the classics, but then the geometry of Legendre came his way. While the normal schoolboy required two to three years to master Legendre's works, Galois read the geometry as easily as the other boys read novels. One reading was enough to reveal the whole structure of elementary geometry to the fascinated boy. Galois ignored the regular textbook in algebra; he considered it to be a mere schoolbook, and nothing more. Instead, he went directly for his algebra to Lagrange, the greatest algebraist of his era. He absorbed masterpieces of algebraic analysis written for mature mathematicians— memoirs on the numerical solutions of equations, the theory of analytical functions, and the calculus of functions.

Galois had the amazing gift of being able to carry on the most difficult mathematical investigations without use of writing implements or the printed page. The insistence by his teachers, who were his mental inferiors, upon details which to him were obvious or trivial exasperated him so much that he frequently lost his temper.

At the age of 16, without preparatory study, he insisted on taking the entrance examination to the École Polytechnique, a great school which was founded during the French Revolution and considered to be the mother of French mathematicians. Galois failed the examination, probably because of a stupid injustice, and he was quite bitter over the experience.

At the age of 17, Galois was making such significant discoveries in the theory of equations that their consequences are not yet exhausted. He had saved the fundamental discoveries he had made before he was 17 so that Cauchy, the leading French mathematician of his era, could present them to the Academy of Sciences. Cauchy not only forgot to present them, but he also lost Galois's abstracts of them. The above episode is one of many in a series of disasters which served to further embitter young Galois, to increase his contempt for academicians, and to abet his hatred for the entire

GALOIS
(1811–1832)

society—which he considered stupid and from which he tried to isolate himself.

When he was 18, he tried again to pass the entrance examination to the École Polytechnique. Again, men he considered his inferiors refused to admit him.

At the age of 19, he wrote three papers on the theory of algebraic equations which were far superior to, and more advanced than, any which had been written previously. He submitted them to the Academy of Sciences in competition for the grand prize in mathematics. Experts agree that Galois's memoir was more than worthy of the prize. However, as fate would have it, the Academy of Sciences lost the papers before the judging; and Galois never heard any more of his papers.

To Galois, this experience was the last straw. So he turned to revolutionary politics and devoted practically all of his time to it. Early in the morning of May 31, 1832, before he reached his twenty-first birthday, Galois was killed in a senseless political duel.

Chapter 6

Algebraic Structure

6.1 GROUPS

We have studied some systems which are fields and some systems which are not fields. For example, the real number system, the rational number system, and the mod p number system (in which p is a prime) are fields; however, the system of integers and the mod c number system (in which c is a composite number) are not fields because they do not obey the inverse law for multiplication. Do the latter two systems belong to a more general class of systems?

The above question is of the type which compels the mathematician to search for a single general theory which unifies several branches of mathematics. The development of such a theory increases the power and beauty of mathematics because it simplifies the structure and facilitates learning, teaching, and application. In addition, the development of a subtle, master structure in mathematics affords the mathematician a personal, esthetic satisfaction and joy similar to that which an artist experiences when he creates a masterpiece. The artist is not the only person who enjoys and appreciates the masterpiece; others enjoy it long after the artist has died. Similarly, the mathematician should not be the only one to appreciate the beauty and significance of his creation and development. Others after him—mathematicians, scientists, engineers, and mankind in general— benefit from the mathematician's development of a general, unifying theory.

One of the systems more general than the *field* is the *group*, which consists of a nonempty set and a binary operation and which obeys laws G1 through G4.

Definition 1. Any system $(G, \#)$, *consisting of a set* G *and a binary operator* $\#$ [*which may represent addition, multiplication, or some other operation*], *which obeys the laws G1 through G4 is called a* **group**.

G1. If a and b are any elements of G, then $a \# b$ is a unique element of G.
  [*Closure law*]

G2. If a, b, and c are any elements of G, then

$$(a \# b) \# c = a \# (b \# c). \qquad [\textit{Associative law}]$$

G3. There exists a unique element i [called *the identity*] in G such that

$$a \,\#\, i = i \,\#\, a = a \quad \text{for any } a \text{ in } G. \qquad [\textit{Identity law}]^*$$

G4. If a is any element of G, then there exists a unique element $\bar{a}$ [called *the inverse of a*] in G such that

$$a \,\#\, \bar{a} = \bar{a} \,\#\, a = i. \qquad\qquad\qquad [\textit{Inverse law}]^*$$

According to Definition 1, G contains at least one element [the identity i]. Hence $G \,\#\, \varnothing$.

Since $(R, +, \times)$ is a field, it follows that $(R, +)$ is a group. However, $(R, \times)$ is not a group because 0 has no multiplicative inverse. Similarly, $(R_a, +)$ is a group but $(R_a, \times)$ is not.

To answer the question posed earlier, we observe that $(I, +)$ is a group and $(M_m, \oplus)$ is a group. In fact, $(I, +)$ and $(M_m, \oplus)$ obey a fifth law—the commutative law for addition. Any group which obeys the commutative law is called a *commutative group* (or an *abelian group*).†

*Definition 2. Any group $(G, \#)$ which obeys law G5 is called a **commutative group**.*

G5. If a and b are any elements of G, then $a \,\#\, b = b \,\#\, a$.

It follows from Definition 2 that $(I, +)$ and $(M_m, \oplus)$ are commutative groups. Is $(C_0, +)$ a commutative group? Since $(C_0, +)$ is not a group (it does not obey the inverse law), we conclude that it is not a commutative group.

The reader should observe that if $(A, +, \times)$ is a field, then $(A, +)$ is a commutative group. Thus *every field $(A, +, \times)$ generates a commutative additive group $(A, +)$.* However, not every group generates a field. Hence the set of all fields can be considered to be a proper subset of the set of all groups; i.e., a group is a more general, more inclusive system than a field.

In Exercise IX of Exercise Set 5.2 we learned that the commutative law for addition can be proved from the other 10 laws. In view of the foregoing definition and discussion of *group*, we can restate the definition of *field* as in Definition 3 on the following page.

The reader will observe that Law 1 is equivalent to F1 through F4, Laws 2 and 3 are equivalent to F6 through F10, and Law 4 is equivalent to F11. Since F5 follows from the other 10 field laws, we see that Definition 3 is equivalent to Definition 1 of Chapter 5.

---

*   The following laws (which are weaker than G3 and G4) can be used in Definition 1 in lieu of G3 and G4, and G3 and G4 can be derived from them. In a more advanced course, that procedure would probably be followed.

G3. There exists an element i in G such that $a \,\#\, i = a$ for any a in G.
G4. If a is any element of G, then there exists an element $\bar{a}$ in G such that $a \,\#\, \bar{a} = i$.

†   Because Niels H. Abel (1802–1829) made a detailed study of certain equations and rearrangements of roots, which led Evariste Galois (1811–1832) to investigate commutative groups, the word *abelian* is sometimes used in lieu of the word *commutative*. The word *group* is attributed to Galois.

Definition 3. *Any system $(F, +, \times)$, consisting of a set F and two binary operators $+$ and $\times$, which obeys the following laws is called a **field**.*

Law 1. $(F, +)$ is a group, whose identity is 0.

Law 2. $a \times 0 = 0 \times a = 0$ for every a in F.

Law 3. $(F \setminus \{0\}, \times)$ is a commutative group, whose identity is 1.

Law 4. $a \times (b + c) = a \times b + a \times c$ for every a, b, and c in F.

EXERCISE SET 6.1

I. Let S be the set of all square roots of 1. That is, let $S = \{-1, 1\}$.

1. Prove that $(S, +)$ is not a group.
2. Prove that $(S, \times)$ is a commutative group.
3. Prove that $(S, +, \times)$ is not a field.

II. Recall that the mod 4 number system $(M_4, \oplus, \otimes)$ is not a field.

1. Prove that $(M_4, \oplus)$ is a commutative group.
2. Prove that $(M_4, \otimes)$ is not a group.
3. Prove that $(M_4 \setminus \{0, 2\}, \otimes)$ is a commutative group.
   [*Hint:* $M_4 \setminus \{0, 2\} = \{1, 3\}$.]
4. Prove that $(M_4 \setminus \{1, 3\}, \oplus)$ is a commutative group.
5. Prove that $(M_4 \setminus \{1, 2\}, \oplus)$ is not a group.

III. A system $(S, \#)$, in which $S = \{i, a, b, c\}$ and $\#$ is a binary operator, is defined by the accompanying table. Assume the associative law, and prove that $(S, \#)$ is a commutative group.

$\#$	i	a	b	c
i	i	a	b	c
a	a	b	c	i
b	b	c	i	a
c	c	i	a	b

IV. Prove that the system $(S, \#)$ defined by the accompanying table is not a group. Does the system resemble $(M_4, \times)$? Explain.

$\#$	i	a	b	c
i	i	i	i	i
a	i	a	b	c
b	i	b	i	b
c	i	c	b	a

V. Prove each of the following theorems.

1. If a, b, and c are any elements of a group, then $a \# b = a \# c$ if and only if $b = c$.

2. If a and b are any elements of a group, then the equation

$$a \# x = b$$

has the unique solution $\bar{a} \# b$.

VI. Let $(G, \#)$ be a group. State a generalized associative law.

VII. Let $(G, \#)$ be a commutative group. State a generalized commutative and associative law.

VIII.

1. Explain why Law 2 of Definition 3 is necessary.

2. Explain why $(I, +)$ is a commutative group.

3. Explain why $(I, \times)$ is not a group.

6.2 PERMUTATION GROUPS

Since every group we have considered is a commutative group, the reader may wonder whether there are any noncommutative groups. If all groups were commutative, then there would be no reason for Definition 1; it would suffice to define the *commutative group*. However, there are groups which are noncommutative, but the group operator of a noncommutative group is not that of ordinary addition or multiplication. In order to prove that noncommutative groups exist, we develop the concept of *permutation* and define the *product* of two permutations, and then we prove that the system of permutations on n symbols is a group.

Let us assume that a young mother has just returned home from the maternity ward of a hospital with three baby boys (identical triplets) who will sleep in three identical cribs. Each boy has on his left arm a blue identification tag, which contains his first name and the symbol "1," "2," or "3." Each crib is labeled with the name and identifying number of the baby who is to sleep there. For example, the cribs are labeled as in Fig. 6.1, and the identification tags are labeled similarly.

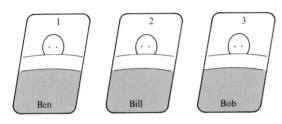

Fig. 6.1

Baby No. 1 (i.e., Baby Ben) is to sleep in Crib No. 1, Baby No. 2 (i.e., Baby Bill) is to sleep in Crib No. 2, and Baby No. 3 (i.e., Baby Bob) is to sleep in Crib

No. 3. We indicate the arrangement by means of the symbol

$$\begin{pmatrix} 1 & 2 & 3 \\ 1 & 2 & 3 \end{pmatrix},$$

which informs us that Crib 1 is occupied by Baby 1, Crib 2 is occupied by Baby 2, and Crib 3 is occupied by Baby 3.

One evening after the father has returned from work, he helps the mother to feed and bathe the babies. However, after he has replaced the babies in their cribs, the mother discovers that he has rearranged them so that Crib 2 is occupied by Baby 3 and Crib 3 is occupied by Baby 2. We indicate the rearrangement (i.e., the new arrangement) by the symbol

$$\begin{pmatrix} 1 & 2 & 3 \\ 1 & 3 & 2 \end{pmatrix}.$$

When the mother informs the father that he has interchanged Baby 2 and Baby 3, he begins to wonder how many arrangements there are. Then he and his wife sit down and write on a sheet of paper the symbols

$$\begin{pmatrix} 1 & 2 & 3 \\ 1 & 2 & 3 \end{pmatrix}, \quad \begin{pmatrix} 1 & 2 & 3 \\ 1 & 3 & 2 \end{pmatrix}, \quad \begin{pmatrix} 1 & 2 & 3 \\ 3 & 2 & 1 \end{pmatrix},$$

$$\begin{pmatrix} 1 & 2 & 3 \\ 2 & 1 & 3 \end{pmatrix}, \quad \begin{pmatrix} 1 & 2 & 3 \\ 3 & 1 & 2 \end{pmatrix}, \quad \text{and} \quad \begin{pmatrix} 1 & 2 & 3 \\ 2 & 3 & 1 \end{pmatrix}$$

for the *six* possible arrangements, and conclude that there are no other arrangements.

Of course, the conclusion of the young parents is correct. There are exactly six arrangements of the babies in the cribs. In mathematics each arrangement is called a *permutation*; to *permute* is to rearrange. For example, when the father interchanged the babies, he *permuted* the symbols. Interchanging two cribs without interchanging the babies is not considered a rearrangement. For example,

$$\begin{pmatrix} 1 & 2 & 3 \\ 1 & 2 & 3 \end{pmatrix} = \begin{pmatrix} 2 & 3 & 1 \\ 2 & 3 & 1 \end{pmatrix} = \begin{pmatrix} 3 & 1 & 2 \\ 3 & 1 & 2 \end{pmatrix}$$

because each baby is in his own crib.

Each permutation is an element of the set of six permutations on the three symbols. We denote the set of permutations on three symbols by "P_3," and we denote the permutations by letters as follows:

$$i = \begin{pmatrix} 1 & 2 & 3 \\ 1 & 2 & 3 \end{pmatrix}, \quad a = \begin{pmatrix} 1 & 2 & 3 \\ 1 & 3 & 2 \end{pmatrix}, \quad b = \begin{pmatrix} 1 & 2 & 3 \\ 3 & 2 & 1 \end{pmatrix},$$

$$c = \begin{pmatrix} 1 & 2 & 3 \\ 2 & 1 & 3 \end{pmatrix}, \quad x = \begin{pmatrix} 1 & 2 & 3 \\ 3 & 1 & 2 \end{pmatrix}, \quad y = \begin{pmatrix} 1 & 2 & 3 \\ 2 & 3 & 1 \end{pmatrix}.$$

Thus $P_3 = \{i, a, b, c, x, y\}$.

We define the operation *followed by* [denoted by "#"] as in Fig. 6.2.

#	i	a	b	c	x	y
i	i	a	b	c	x	y
a	a	i	x	y	b	c
b	b	y	i	x	c	a
c	c	x	y	i	a	b
x	x	c	a	b	y	i
y	y	b	c	a	i	x

Fig. 6.2

For example, *a followed by b* is *x*. That is, if we begin with permutation (arrangement) *a* and follow it by permutation (arrangement) *b*, we obtain permutation (arrangement) *x* as the result; $a \# b = x$. We may verify the computation as follows:

$$a = \begin{pmatrix} 1 & 2 & 3 \\ 1 & 3 & 2 \end{pmatrix} \quad \text{[Interchange Baby 2 and Baby 3]};$$

$$b = \begin{pmatrix} 1 & 2 & 3 \\ 3 & 2 & 1 \end{pmatrix} \quad \begin{bmatrix} \text{Interchange Baby 1 and Baby 3 } (in \\ arrangement \; a \; \text{because } b \text{ follows } a) \end{bmatrix};$$

$$a \# b = \begin{pmatrix} 1 & 2 & 3 \\ 1 & 3 & 2 \end{pmatrix} \# \begin{pmatrix} 1 & 2 & 3 \\ 3 & 2 & 1 \end{pmatrix}$$

$$= \begin{pmatrix} 1 & 2 & 3 \\ 1 & 3 & 2 \end{pmatrix} \# \begin{pmatrix} 1 & 3 & 2 \\ 3 & 1 & 2 \end{pmatrix} = \begin{pmatrix} 1 & 2 & 3 \\ 3 & 1 & 2 \end{pmatrix} = x.$$

Abstractly, we may consider *a followed by b* to mean

1 corresponds to 1 (in *a*), and 1 corresponds to 3 (in *b*), and hence 1 corresponds to 3 (in $a \# b$);

2 corresponds to 3 (in *a*), and 3 corresponds to 1 (in *b*), and hence 2 corresponds to 1 (in $a \# b$);

3 corresponds to 2 (in *a*), and 2 corresponds to 2 (in *b*), and hence 3 corresponds to 2 (in $a \# b$).

Although $a \# b = x$, we see from Fig. 6.2 that $b \# a = y$. Hence $a \# b \neq b \# a$; that is, the binary operator # is not commutative. Is $(P_3, \#)$ a group? It follows immediately from Fig. 6.2 that $(P_3, \#)$ obeys the closure law. Although the proof that $(P_3, \#)$ obeys the associative law is too tedious and lengthy for inclusion in the text, the reader may verify several cases. For example, he may prove that

$$(a \# b) \# x = a \# (b \# x).$$

The identity is *i*, and it is unique. The inverse of *i* is *i*, the inverse of *a* is *a*, the inverse of *b* is *b*, the inverse of *c* is *c*, the inverse of *x* is *y*, and the inverse of *y* is *x*. Hence $(P_3, \#)$ is a group, which is called *the symmetric group on three symbols*. It is not a commutative group, its elements are permutations, and the operation is neither ordinary addition nor ordinary multiplication. Frequently, we speak of $a \# b$ as the *product of a and b*, and we use the familiar terminology *multiplication* and *a times b*. However, permutation multiplication is *not* the multiplication (of numbers) with which the reader is familiar.

Now we define the *order* of a group.

Definition 4

a) *The* **order** *of a finite group* $(G, \#)$ *is equal to* $\mathbf{n}(G)$;

b) *The* **order** *of an infinite group is zero.*

What is the order of the symmetric group on 4 symbols? Since $1 \times 2 \times 3 = 6$ and there are 6 permutations on 3 symbols, we conjecture that there are $1 \times 2 \times 3 \times 4$ permutations on 4 symbols, $1 \times 2 \times 3 \times 4 \times 5$ permutations on 5 symbols, etc. It is easy to verify the conjecture and, in fact, to prove that there are $1 \times 2 \times 3 \times \cdots \times k$ permutations on k symbols.

Four of the 24 permutations on 4 symbols, namely,

$$\begin{pmatrix} 1 & 2 & 3 & 4 \\ 1 & 2 & 3 & 4 \end{pmatrix}, \quad \begin{pmatrix} 1 & 2 & 3 & 4 \\ 2 & 3 & 4 & 1 \end{pmatrix}, \quad \begin{pmatrix} 1 & 2 & 3 & 4 \\ 3 & 4 & 1 & 2 \end{pmatrix},$$

and

$$\begin{pmatrix} 1 & 2 & 3 & 4 \\ 4 & 1 & 2 & 3 \end{pmatrix},$$

are especially interesting because of their relation to the set of rotations of a square, which we will discuss in the following section. We denote the above set by "S_4" and the elements by "i," "u," "v," and "w," respectively. Thus

$$S_4 = \{i, u, v, w\}$$

$$= \begin{pmatrix} 1 & 2 & 3 & 4 \\ 1 & 2 & 3 & 4 \end{pmatrix}, \quad \begin{pmatrix} 1 & 2 & 3 & 4 \\ 2 & 3 & 4 & 1 \end{pmatrix}, \quad \begin{pmatrix} 1 & 2 & 3 & 4 \\ 3 & 4 & 1 & 2 \end{pmatrix}, \quad \begin{pmatrix} 1 & 2 & 3 & 4 \\ 4 & 1 & 2 & 3 \end{pmatrix}.$$

We define $\#$ for any elements of S_4 in a manner similar to that in P_3. The *multiplication* table is exhibited in Fig. 6.3.

Multiplication Table for S_4

$\#$	i	u	v	w
i	i	u	v	w
u	u	v	w	i
v	v	w	i	u
w	w	i	u	v

Fig. 6.3

From Fig. 6.3, we observe that $(S_4, \#)$ obeys the closure law. The proof that $(S_4, \#)$ obeys the associative law is tedious; however, the reader may verify several cases. The unique identity is i. The inverse of i is i, the inverse of u is w, the inverse of v is v, and the inverse of w is u. Hence $(S_4, \#)$ is a group. Moreover, it follows readily from the table that $(S_4, \#)$ obeys the commutative law. Hence it is a commutative group. The reader may prove that $(P_4, \#)$ [the symmetric group on 4 symbols] is a group but is not a commutative group. Since P_4 contains 24 elements, it is tedious to prove that $(P_4, \#)$ obeys the associative law.

EXERCISE SET 6.2

I. Employ Fig. 6.2 to prove each of the following.

1. $(a \# b) \# c = a \# (b \# c)$ 2. $(a \# x) \# y = a \# (x \# y)$
3. $(a \# y) \# x = a \# (y \# x)$ 4. $(a \# c) \# x = a \# (c \# x)$
5. $(b \# x) \# y = b \# (x \# y)$ 6. $(b \# c) \# x = b \# (c \# x)$

II. Employ Fig. 6.2 to prove each of the following.

1. $a \# x \neq x \# a$ 2. $a \# c \neq c \# a$
3. $y \# b \neq b \# y$ 4. $c \# b \neq b \# c$
5. $i \# a = a \# i$ 6. $i \# y = y \# i$
7. $x \# y = y \# x$ 8. $i \# (x \# y) = (y \# x) \# i$

III. Employ Fig. 6.3 to prove each of the following.

1. $(u \# v) \# w = u \# (v \# w)$ 2. $(v \# u) \# w = v \# (u \# w)$
3. $(w \# u) \# v = w \# (u \# v)$ 4. $(v \# w) \# u = v \# (w \# u)$
5. $(w \# v) \# u = w \# (v \# u)$ 6. $(u \# w) \# v = u \# (w \# v)$

IV. Compute each of the following.

1. $\begin{pmatrix} 1 & 2 & 3 & 4 & 5 \\ 2 & 3 & 4 & 5 & 1 \end{pmatrix} \# \begin{pmatrix} 1 & 2 & 3 & 4 & 5 \\ 3 & 4 & 5 & 1 & 2 \end{pmatrix}$

2. $\begin{pmatrix} 1 & 2 & 3 & 4 & 5 \\ 3 & 4 & 5 & 1 & 2 \end{pmatrix} \# \begin{pmatrix} 1 & 2 & 3 & 4 & 5 \\ 4 & 5 & 1 & 2 & 3 \end{pmatrix}$

3. $\begin{pmatrix} 1 & 2 & 3 & 4 & 5 \\ 5 & 4 & 3 & 2 & 1 \end{pmatrix} \# \begin{pmatrix} 1 & 2 & 3 & 4 & 5 \\ 1 & 3 & 5 & 2 & 4 \end{pmatrix}$

4. $\begin{pmatrix} 1 & 2 & 3 & 4 & 5 \\ 1 & 3 & 5 & 2 & 4 \end{pmatrix} \# \begin{pmatrix} 1 & 2 & 3 & 4 & 5 \\ 5 & 4 & 3 & 2 & 1 \end{pmatrix}$

V.

1. Let

$$I = \left\{ \begin{pmatrix} 1 & 2 & 3 & 4 \\ 1 & 2 & 3 & 4 \end{pmatrix} \right\}.$$

Prove that $(I, \#)$ is a commutative group, or else prove that it is not a group.

2. Let

$$A = \left\{ \begin{pmatrix} 1 & 2 & 3 & 4 \\ 1 & 2 & 3 & 4 \end{pmatrix}, \begin{pmatrix} 1 & 2 & 3 & 4 \\ 1 & 2 & 4 & 3 \end{pmatrix} \right\}.$$

Prove that $(A, \#)$ is a commutative group, or else prove that it is not a group.

3. Let

$$B = \left\{ \begin{pmatrix} 1 & 2 & 3 & 4 \\ 1 & 2 & 3 & 4 \end{pmatrix}, \begin{pmatrix} 1 & 2 & 3 & 4 \\ 1 & 2 & 4 & 3 \end{pmatrix}, \begin{pmatrix} 1 & 2 & 3 & 4 \\ 2 & 1 & 3 & 4 \end{pmatrix} \right\}.$$

Prove that $(B, \#)$ is a commutative group, or else prove that it is not a group.

4. Let

$$C = \left\{ \begin{pmatrix} 1 & 2 & 3 & 4 \\ 1 & 2 & 3 & 4 \end{pmatrix}, \begin{pmatrix} 1 & 2 & 3 & 4 \\ 1 & 3 & 2 & 4 \end{pmatrix}, \begin{pmatrix} 1 & 2 & 3 & 4 \\ 4 & 2 & 3 & 1 \end{pmatrix} \right\}.$$

Prove that $(C, \#)$ is a commutative group, or else prove that it is not a group.

VI. List the 24 elements of P_4.

6.3 SUBGROUPS

In the preceding section we learned that $(P_3, \#)$ is a group and that $(P_4, \#)$ is a group. We learned also that $(S_4, \#)$ is a commutative group and S_4 is a subset of P_4. Since S_4 is a subset of P_4 and both $(S_4, \#)$ and $(P_4, \#)$ are groups, we say that $(S_4, \#)$ is a *subgroup* of $(P_4, \#)$. In general, we define *subgroup* in Definition 5.

Definition 5. *The system $(S, \#)$ is a* **subgroup** *of $(G, \#)$ if and only if $(S, \#)$ is a group, $(G, \#)$ is a group, and S is a subset of G.*

The reader should observe that the binary operator of a subgroup of a group is the same binary operator as that of the group. Moreover, every group is a subgroup of itself; and if i is the identity of a group $(G, \#)$, then $(i, \#)$ is a subgroup of $(G, \#)$. Hence every group contains (at least) two subgroups. The subgroups $(\{i\}, \#)$ and $(G, \#)$ of the group $(G, \#)$ are sometimes called the *trivial subgroups* of $(G, \#)$.

Now we consider the *group of rotations of the square*. First we number the four corners of a square, counterclockwise, as in Fig. 6.4.

Fig. 6.4

Next we consider the clockwise rotations of the square about its center to be the elements of a set R as follows:

r_0 is a clockwise rotation of $0°$,

r_1 is a clockwise rotation of $90°$ (1 right angle),

r_2 is a clockwise rotation of $180°$ (2 right angles),

and

r_3 is a clockwise rotation of 270° (3 right angles).

Thus $R_4 = \{r_0, r_1, r_2, r_3\}$. Finally, we define the operation *followed by* [denoted by $\oplus$] so that r_i followed by r_j is that single rotation which produces the same position as the two rotations. For example,

$$r_1 \oplus r_2 = r_3 \quad \text{and} \quad r_2 \oplus r_3 = r_1.$$

The *addition* table is exhibited in Fig. 6.5.

$\oplus$	r_0	r_1	r_2	r_3
r_0	r_0	r_1	r_2	r_3
r_1	r_1	r_2	r_3	r_0
r_2	r_2	r_3	r_0	r_1
r_3	r_3	r_0	r_1	r_2

Fig. 6.5

It is easy to prove that $(R_4, \oplus)$ is a commutative group, whose identity is r_0. The inverse of r_0 is r_0, the inverse of r_1 is r_3, the inverse of r_2 is r_2, and the inverse of r_3 is r_1.

Is the group of rotations of the square a new group? Or is it abstractly the same group we have already studied under another name and with different notation? To answer these questions, we compare Fig. 6.3 with Fig. 6.5. For convenience of comparison, we reproduce them in Fig. 6.6(a) and 6.6(b), respectively.

#	i	u	v	w
i	i	u	v	w
u	u	v	w	i
v	v	w	i	u
w	w	i	u	v

a)

$\oplus$	r_0	r_1	r_2	r_3
r_0	r_0	r_1	r_2	r_3
r_1	r_1	r_2	r_3	r_0
r_2	r_2	r_3	r_0	r_1
r_3	r_3	r_0	r_1	r_2

b)   **Fig. 6.6**

We observe that (*except for notation*) Fig. 6.6(a) is identical to Fig. 6.6(b). In other words, if we replace

    #   by $\oplus$,

    i by r_0,

    u by r_1,

    v by r_2,

and

    w by r_3,

then we convert Fig. 6.6(a) to Fig. 6.6(b).

Two apparently different groups which are identical except for notation are said to be *isomorphic* (or *abstractly identical*) to each other. Thus $(S_4, \#)$ is isomorphic to $(R_4, \oplus)$.

Since $(S_4, \#)$ is isomorphic to $(R_4, \oplus)$, there is a one-to-one correspondence between S_4 and R_4; that is, $S_4 \approx R_4$. Because of the isomorphism, we can interpret each element of S_4 as if it were an element of R_4. For example, we can interpret

$$\begin{pmatrix} 1 & 2 & 3 & 4 \\ 2 & 3 & 4 & 1 \end{pmatrix} \qquad [u \text{ in } S_4]$$

as

$$\boxed{\begin{array}{cc} 3 & 2 \\ 4 & 1 \end{array}} \qquad [r_1 \text{ in } R_4],$$

and we observe that the rotation r_1 is really a permutation of the corners of the square.

The reader may wonder whether the isomorphism between the group of 4 rotations of the square and the subgroup $(S_4, \#)$ of $(P_4, \#)$ is coincidental. The following theorem (known as *Cayley's theorem**) guarantees that the isomorphism is not a coincidence. We omit the proof.

> **Theorem 1 (Cayley's theorem).** *Every finite group of order k is isomorphic to some subgroup of $(P_k, \#)$.*

The importance of Cayley's theorem is due to the fact that the theory of permutation groups is well known to mathematicians. Since every finite group is isomorphic to some group of permutations (known as a *regular permutation group*), we can apply the theory of permutation groups to finite groups, and avoid the necessity of developing a separate theory.

The reader may wonder whether there is any relationship between the order of a group and the order of any of its subgroups. The following theorem (known as *Lagrange's theorem†*) guarantees that the order of each subgroup of any finite group divides the order of the group. We omit the proof.

> **Theorem 2 (Lagrange's theorem).** *If $(S, \#)$ is a subgroup of the finite group $(G, \#)$, then the order of $(S, \#)$ divides the order of $(G, \#)$.*

Because of Lagrange's theorem, we are certain that the only subgroups of $(M_3, \oplus)$ are the two trivial ones $[(\{0\}, \oplus) \text{ and } (M_3, \oplus)]$.

---

* Cayley's theorem was named for the English mathematician Arthur Cayley (1821–1895).

† Lagrange's theorem was named for the French-Italian mathematician Joseph Louis Lagrange (1736–1813).

EXERCISE SET 6.3

I.

1. Explain why the only subgroups of a group of order 3 are the trivial subgroups.
2. Explain why the only subgroups of a group of order 5 are the trivial subgroups.
3. What are the only possible orders of the subgroups of a group of order 6?
4. What are the only possible orders of the subgroups of a group of order 24?

II.

1. List the elements of R_4.
2. List the elements of S_4.
3. List the elements of M_4.
4. Compare $(M_4, \oplus)$ with $(S_4, \#)$.

III.

1. Exhibit all subgroups of $(M_{12}, \oplus)$.
2. Exhibit all subgroups of $(S, \times)$. [See Exercise I of Exercise Set 6.1.]
3. Exhibit all subgroups of $(M_7, \oplus)$.
4. Exhibit all subgroups of $(M_6, \oplus)$.

IV. A mathematical system $(R, +, \times)$, consisting of a set R and two binary operators $+$ and $\times$, which obeys field laws F1 through F7 of Definition 1 of Chapter 5 and the two distributive laws, $a(b + c) = ab + ac$ and $(b + c)a = ba + ca$ for every a, b, and c in R, is called a *ring*. Prove each of the following.

1. If $(R, +, \times)$ is a ring, then $(R, +)$ is a commutative group.
2. If $(R, +, \times)$ is a field, then $(R, +, \times)$ is a ring.
3. $(I, +, \times)$ is a ring.
4. $(R, +, \times)$ is a ring.
5. $(R_a, +, \times)$ is a ring.
6. $(I^+, +, \times)$ is not a ring.
7. $(C_0, +, \times)$ is not a ring.
8. $(M, \oplus, \otimes)$ is a ring.
9. $(M_5, \oplus, \otimes)$ is a ring.
10. Every ring has at least one element.

René Descartes was born in La Haye, France, on March 31, 1596, into a noble family of comfortable means. Descartes's mother died a few days after his birth. To make up for the loss of the mother, the father employed an excellent nurse and kept a vigilant and intelligent watch on his young son. Although Descartes was not a precocious child, he always was very intelligent and was not satisfied with mere facts; he wanted reasons.

Because of poor health as a child, Descartes did not enter school until he was eight years old. He enrolled at the Jesuit college at La Flèche. The rector, Father Charlet, became attached to the frail little boy. As part of a program to improve Descartes's physical condition, Father Charlet encouraged him to remain in bed each morning until he felt well enough to attend classes. In later life Descartes claimed that the source of his mathematics and philosophy was those long mornings of silent meditation while he lay in bed.

He did very well in school and became especially fond of mathematics. However, by the age of 14 he suspected that the courses in the humanities on which he was spending so much time were comparatively lacking in human significance. By 18 years of age Descartes became bored with his studies and decided to leave school and learn something about life in the real world of flesh and blood instead of the vicarious world of paper and ink. So he eagerly began a life of pleasure, leisure, and adventure— in which he probably overcompensated for his previous quiet and sheltered existence.

However, he soon grew bored with a life of pleasure, and withdrew from it to begin a period of intensive reading and study of mathematics, during which time he began to formulate his concepts of analytical geometry (which later became known as *Cartesian geometry*).

Descartes required periods of quiet seclusion during which he studied mathematics and philosophy. Periodically he would tire of the secluded life and crave adventure. Eventually, he enlisted and reenlisted in the army several times and served with bravery and distinction. In fact, during one of his tours he was offered the rank of Lieutenant General but refused it.

In his early thirties, Descartes left France and moved to Holland. For the next twenty years he lived a relatively secluded life, studying mathematics and philosophy, corresponding with the great scholars, and delivering occasional lectures.

In his early fifties he was persuaded to go to Sweden to act as a personal tutor to Queen Christine, a very sturdy and stubborn young lady who insisted that her studies commence at 5:00 each morning. Poor Descartes, who was accustomed since the days of his youth to lying in bed until late morning, could do little but oblige the young monarch. The cold winter weather of Sweden, together with the lack of proper rest, caused Descartes to contract an inflammation of the lungs. On February 11, 1650, he died in Stockholm, where he was buried until Queen Christine permitted his remains to be returned to Paris and interred in the Panthéon.

DESCARTES
(1596–1650)

Chapter 7

Functions and Graphs

7.1 THE FUNCTION CONCEPT

The concept of *function* is one which is useful in all branches of mathematics and in the applications of mathematics to other fields. For example, the physicist and chemist say that the pressure of a gas in a closed nonexpandable container is a *function* of its temperature, and the business analyst says that the price of a commodity is a *function* of its supply and demand. Both uses convey the idea that a *function* is (or expresses) some relationship between two or more variables. In fact, many older algebra texts define *function* essentially in that manner. For example, one of the older texts contains the following statement, which uses the words *relate* and *correspond*.

> If a variable *y* is so related to a variable *x* that to each value of *x* there corresponds one or more values of *y*, then *y* is said to be a *function* of *x*.

On the other hand, newer texts define *function* essentially as a rule or correspondence between two sets, or as a certain set of ordered pairs. Since each definition has its advantages, both of them are in common use today. Consequently we state the two definitions as Definitions 1 and 2.

Definition 1. *Any rule of correspondence or transformation which pairs each element of a set A with a unique element of a set B is called a **function** from A to B [denoted by "f: A → B" and read "f is a function from A to B"].*

For example, the correspondence which pairs each of the first 25 letters of the English alphabet with its successor (i.e., the following letter) is a function from

$$\{a, b, c, \ldots, w, x, y\} \quad \text{to} \quad \{a, b, c, d, \ldots, x, y, z\}.$$

We may represent the function as in Fig. 7.1. For some purposes it may be preferable to represent the function as in Fig. 7.2.

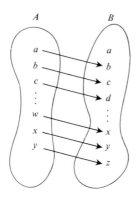

Fig. 7.1

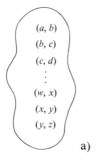

a)

$\{(a, b), (b, c), (c, d), \ldots, (w, x), (x, y), (y, z)\}$ b)   **Fig. 7.2**

Figure 7.1 portrays the function as a *correspondence, mapping,* or *transformation.* That is, each element of *A corresponds* to a unique element of *B*; each element of *A* is *mapped* into a unique element of *B*; or each element of *A* is *transformed* into a unique element of *B*. For example, *y* is transformed into *z*.

On the other hand, Fig. 7.2 portrays the function as a set of ordered pairs, in which the second coordinate of any ordered pair is the successor of the first coordinate of the ordered pair. For example, (y, z) is one of the ordered pairs of the function, and *z* is the successor of *y*. Because the concept of function from *A* to *B* as a set of ordered pairs is widely accepted, we state that definition.

Definition 2. *Any subset of $A \times B$ in which each element a of A is the first coordinate of exactly one element (a, b) is called a **function from A to B** [denoted by "$f: A \to B$" and read "f is a function from A to B"].*

When there is no danger of confusion, we frequently do not indicate the sets *A* and *B*, and denote the function by the symbol "*f*." Since *f* is a subset of $A \times B$, we see that *f* is a set of ordered pairs. The reader should observe that each element *a* of *A* must be a first coordinate of one element (a, b) of *f*; furthermore, no element of A can be the first coordinate of two different ordered pairs in f. That is, if $(a, b_1) \in f$ and $(a, b_2) \in f$, then $b_1 = b_2$.

It is traditional to refer to the set A in Definitions 1 and 2 as the *domain* of f and to that subset of B consisting of all second coordinates of the ordered pairs of f as the *range* of f.

Definition 3. *The set A of the function $f: A \to B$ is called the **domain** of f and is denoted by "$\mathscr{D}(f)$." The element b of B which is paired with any element a of A is called the **image** of a (under f) [or the **value** of f (at a)] and is denoted by "$f(a)$." The set of all images is called the **range** of f and is denoted by "$\mathscr{R}(f)$." Any element a of A whose image is b of B is called a **preimage** of b.*

We observe from Definitions 2 and 3 that $\mathscr{D}(f)$ is the set of all first coordinates, $\mathscr{R}(f)$ is the set of all second coordinates, and $f(a)$ is the second coordinate b of the ordered pair (a, b). For example, in Fig. 7.1 (or Fig. 7.2),

$$\mathscr{D}(f) = A = \{a, b, c, \ldots, y\},$$
$$\mathscr{R}(f) = \{b, c, d, \ldots, z\} \subset B,$$

and

$$f(a) = b, \qquad f(b) = c, \qquad f(c) = d, \qquad \ldots, \qquad f(y) = z.$$

According to Definition 1, a function performs or acts upon the elements of one set (the domain) and transforms them into elements of a second set (the range). In that sense, a function performs an action. However, according to Definition 2, a function does not perform any action; it is a set of ordered pairs. Since it is intuitively obvious that either concept of function follows from the other, the apparent difference should cause no difficulty. In other words, a rule of correspondence between two sets (given by a formula or table or otherwise) generates a set of ordered pairs, and a set of ordered pairs generates a rule of correspondence between two sets. For example, the rule of correspondence between the sets A and B in Fig. 7.3(a) generates the set of ordered pairs in Fig. 7.3(b). Conversely, the set of ordered pairs in Fig. 7.3(b) generates the rule of correspondence in Fig. 7.3(a).

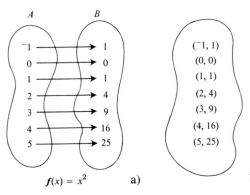

$$f(x) = x^2 \qquad \text{a)} \qquad\qquad \text{b)} \qquad \textbf{Fig. 7.3}$$

Usually, the rule of correspondence defining a function is given by a formula [such as $f(x) = x^2$], the domain A is specified, and a table is constructed as in Fig. 7.4.

x	$f(x)$
$^-1$	1
0	0
1	1
2	4
3	9
4	16
5	25

$A = \{^-1, 0, 1, 2, 3, 4, 5\}$
$f(x) = x^2$

Fig. 7.4

The reader will observe that the table in Fig. 7.4 is merely another scheme for expressing the set $\{(^-1, 1), (0, 0), (1, 1), (2, 4), (3, 9), (4, 16), (5, 25)\}$. That is, the rule generates the table and the table generates the set of ordered pairs.

Sometimes it is necessary to specify a given function by a table. For example, a meteorologist may record temperature readings at various times during the day in a table, as in Fig. 7.5.

Time: x	Temperature: $f(x)$
1:00 PM	$^-5°$
2:00 PM	$^-3°$
3:00 PM	$0°$
4:00 PM	$4°$
5:00 PM	$10°$
6:00 PM	$5°$
7:00 PM	$0°$

Fig. 7.5

The table may be interpreted either as a rule of correspondence [the temperature corresponds to the time] or a set of ordered pairs [the time is the first coordinate and the temperature is the second coordinate].

EXERCISE SET 7.1

I. Let f be a function from A to B. Employ Definitions 1, 2, and 3 to answer each of the following.

1. Explain why $\mathscr{D}(f) = A$.   2. Explain why $\mathscr{R}(f) \subset B$.

3. Explain why $y = y'$ if (x, y) and (x, y') are both elements of f.

4. Explain why (x, y) and (x', y) may both be elements of f even if $x \neq x'$.

5. Explain why no element of A may have two different images in B.

6. Explain why two different elements of *A* may have the same image in *B*.

7. Explain why each element of *A* must have an image in *B*.

8. Explain why there may be an element in *B* which is not the image of any element in *A*.

II. Which of the following rules of correspondence are functions from *A* to *B*?

1.

2.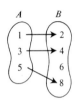

3.

4.

5.

6.

7.

8.

9.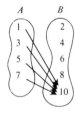

10.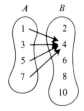

III. Let *A* = {0, 1, 2, 3} and *B* = {1, 3, 5, 7, 9}. Which of the following sets of ordered pairs are functions from *A* to *B*?

1. {(0, 1), (1, 3), (2, 3), (3, 9)}   2. {(0, 3), (1, 7), (2, 9), (3, 9)}

3. $\{(0, 3), (2, 3), (3, 3)\}$
4. $\{(0, 5), (1, 5), (3, 5)\}$
5. $\{(0, 5), (1, 5), (2, 5), (3, 5)\}$
6. $\{(0, 3), (1, 3), (2, 3) (3, 3)\}$
7. $\{(0, 1), (0, 3), (1, 5), (2, 7), (3, 9)\}$
8. $\{(0, 1), (1, 3), (1, 5), (2, 7), (3, 9)\}$
9. $\{(0, 1), (1, 2), (2, 5), (3, 7)\}$
10. $\{(0, 1), (1, 3), (2, 4), (3, 7)\}$

IV. Let $A = \{1, 2, 3\}$ and $B = \{2, 4, 6, 8\}$. Which of the following tables define functions from A to B?

1.

x	y
1	2
2	4
3	6

2.

x	y
1	6
2	4
3	2

3.

x	y
1	2
2	4
3	4

4.

x	y
1	2
2	6
3	6

5.

x	y
1	2
2	4
3	5

6.

x	y
1	4
2	6
3	7

7.

x	y
1	2
2	4
2	6
3	8

8.

x	y
1	2
2	4
3	6
3	8

9.

x	y
1	8
2	8
3	8

10.

x	y
1	6
2	6
3	6

7.2 REAL FUNCTIONS

The functions of most interest to the mathematician and to the user of mathematics are those functions whose domains are subsets of the set of real numbers. The ranges may be subsets of the set of reals or may be subsets of a more inclusive set. For example, the domain of a function may be a subset of the set of reals, and the range may be a subset of the set of complex numbers (which we have not introduced). In the following examples we consider functions whose domains and ranges are both subsets of R. In each case the rule of correspondence is a specific formula, and the domain is a specific set; the range is determined by the rule and the domain.

Example 1. If the rule of correspondence is the formula $f(x) = x + 2$, the domain A is $\{^-4, \,^-3, \,^-2, \,^-1, 0, 1, 2\}$, and B is $\{^-2, \,^-1, 0, 1, 2, 3, 4\}$, then the rule pairs each element of A with a unique element of B as follows:

$$f(^-4) = \,^-4 + 2 = \,^-2,$$
$$f(^-3) = \,^-3 + 2 = \,^-1,$$
$$f(^-2) = \,^-2 + 2 = 0,$$
$$f(^-1) = \,^-1 + 2 = 1,$$
$$f(0) = 0 + 2 = 2,$$
$$f(1) = 1 + 2 = 3,$$
$$f(2) = 2 + 2 = 4.$$

Thus

$$\mathscr{D}(f) = A = \{^-4, \,^-3, \,^-2, \,^-1, 0, 1, 2\},$$
$$\mathscr{R}(f) = B = \{^-2, \,^-1, 0, 1, 2, 3, 4\},$$

and f is a function from A to B [denoted by "$f\colon A \to B$"]. The function may be considered also as the set of ordered pairs

$$\{(^-4, \,^-2), (^-3, \,^-1), (^-2, 0), (^-1, 1), (0, 2), (1, 3), (2, 4)\},$$

in which the *image* of each first coordinate is the corresponding second coordinate. Each real number x of the domain [the first coordinate of any ordered pair] is transformed into the corresponding real number $x + 2$ of the range [the second coordinate of the ordered pair (x, y)]. Hence we frequently express the rule by the formula $y = x + 2$. Since $\mathscr{R}(f) = B$, the function meets the requirements of Definitions 1 and 2 that $\mathscr{R}(f)$ be a subset of B. The correspondence and table are exhibited in the accompanying figure.

x	y
$^-4$	$^-2$
$^-3$	$^-1$
$^-2$	0
$^-1$	1
0	2
1	3
2	4

Example 2. If $f(x) = x^2$ is the rule of correspondence, $A = \{^-3, \, ^-2, \, ^-1, 0, 1, 2, 3\}$ [the domain], and $B = \{1, 2, 3, 4, 5, 6, 7, 8, 9\}$, then $f(x) = x^2$ pairs each element of A with a unique element of B as follows:

$$f(^-3) = (^-3)^2 = 9,$$
$$f(^-2) = (^-2)^2 = 4,$$
$$f(^-1) = (^-1)^2 = 1,$$
$$f(0) \ = 0^2 = 0,$$
$$f(1) \ = 1^2 = 1,$$
$$f(2) \ = 2^2 = 4,$$
$$f(3) \ = 3^2 = 9.$$

Thus

$$\mathscr{D}(f) = A = \{^-3, \, ^-2, \, ^-1, 0, 1, 2, 3\},$$
$$\mathscr{R}(f) = \{0, 1, 4, 9\} \subset B,$$

and f is a function from A to B. The function may be considered also as the set of ordered pairs

$$\{(^-3, 9), (^-2, 4), (^-1, 1), (0, 0), (1, 1), (2, 4), (3, 9)\},$$

in which the image of each first coordinate is the corresponding second coordinate. Each real number x of the domain is transformed into the real number x^2 of the range. We may express the rule by the formula $y = x^2$. Although $(^-3, 9)$ and $(3, 9)$ are different ordered pairs which have the same *second* coordinate, no two different ordered pairs have the same *first* coordinate. Thus f meets the requirements of Definition 2. The correspondence and table are exhibited in the accompanying figure.

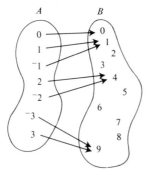

x	y
$^-3$	9
$^-2$	4
$^-1$	1
0	0
1	1
2	4
3	9

Example 3. If $f(x) = 5$ is the rule of correspondence, $A = \{^-2, \, ^-1, 0, 1, 2\}$, and $B = \{1, 3, 5, 7, 9\}$, then $f(x) = 5$ pairs each element of A [the domain] with

a unique element of B as follows:

$f(^-2) = 5,$

$f(^-1) = 5,$

$f(0) = 5,$

$f(1) = 5,$

$f(2) = 5.$

Thus

$\mathscr{D}(f) = A = \{^-2, ^-1, 0, 1, 2\},$

$\mathscr{R}(f) = \{5\} \subset B,$

and f is a function from A to B. The function may be considered also as the set of ordered pairs

$\{(^-2, 5), (^-1, 5), (0, 5), (1, 5), (2, 5)\},$

in which the image of each first coordinate is the corresponding second coordinate. Each real number x of the domain is transformed into the real number 5. We may express the rule by the formula $y = 5$. All ordered pairs have the same second coordinate, but no two different ordered pairs have the same first coordinate. The function is called a *constant function*. The correspondence and table are exhibited in the accompanying figure.

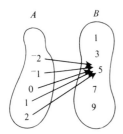

x	y
$^-2$	5
$^-1$	5
0	5
1	5
2	5

The functions in the above examples are real functions of a real variable.

Definition 4. *The function* $f: A \to B$ *is called a **function of a real variable** if and only if A is a subset of R; $f: A \to B$ is called a **real-valued function** [or a **real function**] if and only if its range is a subset of R; $f: A \to B$ is called a **real function of a real variable** if and only if A and the range of f are subsets of R.*

In a function defined by a formula [such as $f(x) = x^2$ or $y = x$] and its domain [such as $A = \{^-3, ^-2, ^-1, 0, 1, 2, 3\}$], we may choose any element of the domain and compute [from the formula] the corresponding element of the range. Similarly, in a function defined by a set of ordered pairs, we may choose any element of the domain [the first coordinate of any ordered pair] and observe that the corresponding element of the range is the second coordinate of the ordered pair. In either case, the element of the domain is chosen *independently*, and the element of the range *depends* on the element of the domain. It has been traditional in mathematics to employ the words *independent variable* and *dependent variable* as in Definition 5.

Definition 5. *The variable x which represents any element of the domain of a function is called the **independent variable**, and the variable y which represents the image of x is called the **dependent variable**.*

The reader should realize from the foregoing discussion and examples that a *formula* [such as $f(x) = x^2$ or $y = x^2$] does not define a function; the *domain* is a necessary part of the definition. That is, *both the formula and the domain are necessary to define a function as a correspondence.* However, in the study of real functions of a real variable, we usually choose the domain to be the set of reals [excluding those real numbers for which the formula is meaningless]. *The formula and the domain determine the range.* For example, if $f(x) = 1/x^2$, the domain is understood to be $R \setminus \{0\}$ because "$1/0^2$" is a meaningless expression and $1/x^2$ is defined for every nonzero real number. To determine the range of f, we observe that $1/x^2$ decreases toward 0 as $|x|$ increases. For example,

$$f(10) = \frac{1}{100},$$

$$f(^-10) = \frac{1}{(^-10)^2} = \frac{1}{100},$$

$$f(1000) = \frac{1}{(1000)^2} = 0.000001,$$

and

$$f(^-1000) = \frac{1}{(^-1000)^2} = 0.000001.$$

Thus $f(x)$ may be very near 0 but may never equal 0. Moreover, $1/x^2$ increases and becomes larger than any real number as $|x|$ decreases toward 0. For example,

$$f(0.01) = \frac{1}{(0.01)^2} = \frac{1}{0.0001} = 10,000$$

and

$$f(^-0.001) = \frac{1}{(^-0.001)^2} = \frac{1}{0.000001} = 1,000,000.$$

Hence $f(x)$ can be any positive real number but cannot be 0 or negative. Therefore the range of f is R^+. Henceforth, *if we do not specify the domain, we agree that the domain is the set R of real numbers* [or that subset of R for which the formula is meaningful]. For example, we may speak of

the function $f(x) = x^2$ [or $y = x^2$]

when we mean

the function $f: R \to R$ whose rule of correspondence is $f(x) = x^2$.

Similarly, when we say or write

    the function $y = \sqrt{x}$

we mean

    the function $f: R^+ \cup \{0\} \to R^+ \cup \{0\}$
    whose rule of correspondence is $f(x) = \sqrt{x}$.

In classical terminology, the expression

    y is a function of x   [or $y = f(x)$]

means that f is a function from R to R [or appropriate subsets of R], x is the independent variable, and y is the dependent variable. The classical terminology is used extensively in applications of mathematics to the physical, biological, and behavorial sciences.

    The reader should realize that the choice of letters is arbitrary. For example, we may express the function

    $y = x^2 + 5$ (domain $= R$)

as

    $v = u^2 + 5$ (domain $= R$)

or as

    $\triangle = \square^2 + 5$ (domain $= R$).

All of the above formulas generate the same set of ordered pairs and thus define the same function. We may express the function in any of the following ways:

    $\{(x, y): x \in R,\ y \in R,\ and\ y = x^2 + 5\}$,

    $\{(x, y): y = x^2 + 5\}$,

    $\{(x, x^2 + 5): x \in R\}$,

or simply

    $\{(x, x^2 + 5)\}$.

EXERCISE SET 7.2

I. Employ the agreement concerning the domain of a function to determine the domain and range of each of the following functions.

1. $f(x) = 3x$ 2. $f(x) = {}^-3x$

3. $f(x) = {}^-2x^2$ 4. $f(x) = 2x^2$

5. $f(r) = r^2 + 5$ 6. $f(r) = r^2 - 5$

7. $f(t) = {}^-3\sqrt{5t}$ 8. $f(t) = 2\sqrt{5t}$

9. $f(s) = 2/s^2$ 10. $f(s) = 3/s^2$

II. Compute $f(5)$ for each function in Exercise I.

III. Compute $f(\frac{4}{5})$ for each function in Exercise I.

IV. Let $\{(0, {}^-1), (1, 0), (2, 3), (3, 8), (4, 15), (5, 24), (6, 35)\}$ be a function from A to B.
1. List the elements of A [the domain].
2. List the elements of the range.
3. State the formula for the rule of correspondence, and identify the independent variable and the dependent variable.
4. Exhibit the correspondence as in each example.
5. Exhibit the table as in each example.

V. Use the rule of correspondence derived in Exercise IV to define a function whose domain is R.
1. Compute $f({}^-1)$.
2. Compute $f(0)$.
3. Compute $f(1)$.
4. Compute $f({}^-3)$.
5. Identify the range of f.
6. Compute $f(1) - f({}^-3)$.
7. Compute $f({}^-3) + f(1)$.
8. Compute $f(1) \div f({}^-3)$.
9. Compute $f(x + 3)$.
10. Compute $f(t + 3)$.

7.3 THE GRAPH OF A FUNCTION

The reader is probably familiar with the *Cartesian coordinate plane*. We may visualize the Cartesian plane as any plane whose points are coordinatized in such a manner that there is a one-to-one correspondence between $R \times R$ [the set of all ordered pairs of real numbers] and the set of points in the plane, according to the following convention: We choose two perpendicular lines—one horizontal and one vertical. We denote the horizontal line by "X" and call it the *X-axis*; we denote the vertical line by "Y" and call it the *Y-axis*; and we denote their point of intersection by "0" and call it the *origin*. Since the X-axis and the Y-axis are both models of the real line, we label each axis to indicate the one-to-one correspondence between the set of points on each axis and the set of real numbers. The set of points on the X-axis to the *left* of the origin corresponds to the set of *negative* reals, and the set of points to the *right* of the origin corresponds to the set of *positive* reals. Similarly, the set of points on the Y-axis *below* the origin corresponds to the set of *negative* reals, and the set of points *above* the origin corresponds to the set of *positive* reals. The *origin* corresponds to the real number *zero*. The Cartesian plane is shown in Fig. 7.6. The arrowheads on each axis indicate that the axis does not terminate but extends indefinitely in both directions.

The X-axis and Y-axis separate the Cartesian plane into four quarter-planes called *quadrants*. According to convention, the quadrants are numbered counterclockwise I, II, III, and IV, as indicated in Fig. 7.6, and are called the *first, second, third,* and *fourth quadrants,* respectively.

In order to illustrate the method of establishing the one-to-one correspondence between the Cartesian plane and $R \times R$, we *sketch* (or plot) the graph of

$\{(4, 3), ({}^-4, 3), ({}^-5, {}^-2), (3, {}^-5), (0, 0), (5, 0)\}.$

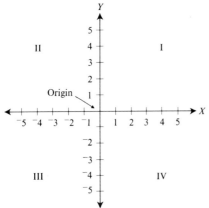

Fig. 7.6

The *ordered pair* (4, 3) corresponds to that *point* in the Cartesian plane which is
4 units to the *right* of the origin and 3 units *above* the origin. For convenience, we
indicate the point by a dot and the label "(4, 3)." The *ordered pair* (⁻4, 3) corresponds to that *point* in the Cartesian plane which is 4 units to the *left* of the origin
and 3 units *above* the origin. The *ordered pair* (⁻5, ⁻2) corresponds to that *point*
in the Cartesian plane which is 5 units to the *left* of the origin and 2 units *below*
the origin. The *ordered pair* (3, ⁻5) corresponds to that *point* in the Cartesian
plane which is 3 units to the *right* of the origin and 5 units *below* the origin. The
ordered pair (0, 0) corresponds to the *origin*. The *ordered pair* (5, 0) corresponds
to that *point* in the Cartesian plane which is 5 units to the *right* of the origin and
0 units *above* (or *below*) the origin.* The *graph* of the set of ordered pairs, which
is a function from {4, ⁻4, ⁻5, 3, 0, 5} to {3, ⁻2, ⁻5, 0}, is the set of points
indicated in Fig. 7.7.

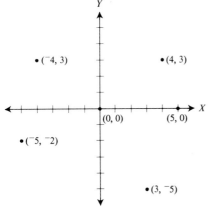

Fig. 7.7

---

*   The reader should observe the dual representation of any point on either axis. For
example, the point in the Cartesian plane corresponding to the ordered pair (5, 0) is the
same as the point on the *X*-axis corresponding to the real number 5.

Every point in the Cartesian plane corresponds to a unique ordered pair of real numbers, and every ordered pair of real numbers corresponds to a unique point of the Cartesian plane. Hence *there is a one-to-one correspondence between the set of points in the Cartesian plane and the Cartesian product R × R.* Thus we may denote any point of the Cartesian plane by the ordered pair which corresponds to it, and we refer to the ordered pair as the point. For example, we denote the *point* which corresponds to the ordered pair (4, 3) by "(4, 3)" and we actually say and write

the point (4, 3).

It is clear that a graph is a set of points. In particular, the graph of a set of ordered pairs of real numbers is that set of points of the Cartesian plane which corresponds to the set of ordered pairs. The following definition of the graph of a function is a generalization of the graph in Fig. 7.7.

Definition 6. *The **graph** of $f: A \to B$, in which A and B are subsets of R, is the set of all points of the Cartesian plane which correspond to*

$$\{(x, y): x \in A \text{ and } y = f(x)\}.$$

The *graph* is a mathematical idealized concept; a *sketch of the graph* is a physical representation of the graph. The accuracy of the sketch depends on the care we exercise in *plotting* several representative points and joining those points by smooth curves. The sketch is primarily a visual aid to memory, and it helps us to better understand the function, even if the sketch is not very accurate. The sketch calls attention to the set of points we wish to isolate from the other points of the plane so that we can concentrate better on the heart of the problem. It is an intuitively illuminating representation of the function which quickly yields important properties of the function. If the graph of a function is unbounded [i.e., if it extends indefinitely in one or more directions], then we make a partial sketch of the graph. We may indicate that the sketch is incomplete by the use of arrowheads at the ends of the partial sketch.

The graph in Fig. 7.7 is that of a *discrete** function. To sketch the graph of a *continuous** function we sketch several representative points and then join those points by means of smooth curves. [A curve may be a line segment.] For example, to sketch the graph of the function $f(x) = x + 2$ [domain = R], we may construct the table in Fig. 7.8(a) and plot the graph of the tabulated set of ordered pairs, as in Fig. 7.8(b).

Then we connect the points as in Fig. 7.9. The graph is a *straight line.*

To sketch the graph of $f(x) = x^2$ [domain = R], we construct the table in Fig. 7.10(a), plot the graph of the tabulated set of ordered pairs, and connect the points by a smooth curve. The graph of the tabulated set of ordered pairs and the

---

*   The intuitive meanings of the words *discrete* and *continuous* are probably clear to the reader. We do not state precise definitions of them.

x	y	(x, y)
⁻4	⁻2	(⁻4, ⁻2)
⁻3	⁻1	(⁻3, ⁻1)
⁻2	0	(⁻2, 0)
⁻1	1	(⁻1, 1)
0	2	(0, 2)
1	3	(1, 3)
2	4	(2, 4)

a)

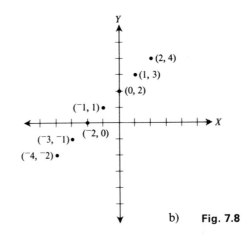

b)   Fig. 7.8

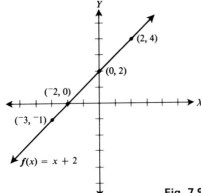

Fig. 7.9

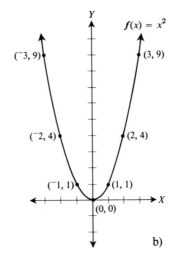

x	y	(x, y)
⁻3	9	(⁻3, 9)
⁻2	4	(⁻2, 4)
⁻1	1	(⁻1, 1)
0	0	(0, 0)
1	1	(1, 1)
2	4	(2, 4)
3	9	(3, 9)

a)

b)   Fig. 7.10

graph of the function are shown in Fig. 7.10(b). The graph of the function is a *parabola* whose vertex is the origin.*

To sketch the graph of $f(x) = 5$ [domain $= R$], we construct the table in Fig. 7.11(a), plot the graph of the tabulated set of ordered pairs, and connect the points by a smooth curve. The graph of the tabulated set of ordered pairs and the graph of the function are exhibited in Fig. 7.11(b). The graph of the function is a *horizontal line* 5 units above the X-axis [the line intersects the Y-axis at $(0, 5)$].

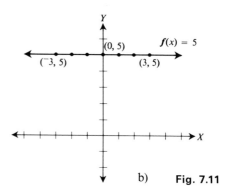

x	y	(x, y)
$^-3$	5	$(^-3, 5)$
$^-2$	5	$(^-2, 5)$
$^-1$	5	$(^-1, 5)$
0	5	$(0, 5)$
1	5	$(1, 5)$
2	5	$(2, 5)$
3	5	$(3, 5)$

a)   b)   **Fig. 7.11**

In general, to sketch the graph of $\{(x, y): y = f(x)\}$, we construct a table (if necessary) and plot the graph of the tabulated set of ordered pairs. If the function is *continuous* [intuitively, the graph of the function is a connected set], we connect the points by a smooth curve. The smooth curve is the graph of the function. If the function is *discrete* [intuitively, the graph of the function is a set of disconnected points], we do not draw a curve to connect the points. We recall that Fig. 7.7 exhibits the graph of a discrete function.

EXERCISE SET 7.3

I. Sketch the graph of each of the following functions. The domain is R [the set of reals] unless otherwise indicated.

1. $f(x) = x + 3$ 2. $f(x) = x - 1$

3. $f(x) = 3x$ 4. $f(x) = 4x$

5. $f(x) = x^2 + 3$ 6. $f(x) = x^2 + 2$

7. $f(x) = 2x^2$ 8. $f(x) = 3x^2$

9. $f(x) = {}^-3$ 10. $f(x) = {}^-2$

11. $f(x) = 2/x$ [$\mathscr{D}(f) = \{x: x \in R \text{ and } x > 0\}$]

12. $f(x) = 2/x$ [$\mathscr{D}(f) = \{x: x \in R \text{ and } x < 0\}$]

---

*   In Section 7.4 we will learn that the graph of every quadratic function is a parabola. The function $f(x) = x^2$ is a special quadratic function.

13. $\{(x, y): x \in R^+ \text{ and } y = x^2\}$ 14. $\{(x, y): x \in R^- \text{ and } y = x^2\}$
15. $\{(x, y): x \in I^- \text{ and } y = x\}$ 16. $\{(x, y): x \in I^+ \text{ and } y = x\}$
17. $\{(x, y): x \in R^+ \cup \{0\} \text{ and } y = \sqrt{x}\}$
18. $\{(x, y): x \in R^+ \cup \{0\} \text{ and } y = -\sqrt{x}\}$
19. $\{(x, y): x \in R \text{ and } y = x^3\}$ 20. $\{(x, y): x \in R \text{ and } y = x^3 + 2\}$

II. Explain why each of the following is *not* a function. If necessary, sketch its graph.

1. $\{(2, 3), (3, 2), (5, 2), (7, 2), (2, 7)\}$ 2. $\{(1, 1), (2, 2), (3, 5), (5, 3), (3, 3)\}$
3. $\{(x, y): x \in I^+ \text{ and } y^2 = 9\}$ 4. $\{(x, y): x \in I^+ \text{ and } y^2 = 4\}$
5. $\{(x, y): x \in R \text{ and } x^2 + y^2 = 4\}$ 6. $\{(x, y): x \in R \text{ and } x^2 + y^2 = 9\}$
7. $\{(x, y): x \in I^+ \text{ and } y^2 = 4x\}$ 8. $\{(x, y): x \in I^+ \text{ and } y^2 = 9x\}$
9. $\{(x, y): x \in R \text{ and } x < y\}$ 10. $\{(x, y): x \in R \text{ and } y < x\}$

7.4 POLYNOMIAL FUNCTIONS

Polynomial functions and their graphs are important in mathematics and the applications of mathematics to the sciences. In order to study them, we first define a *polynomial*.

Definition 7. *Any expression of the form*

$$a_0 + a_1 x + a_2 x^2 + \cdots + a_m x^m,$$

in which each a_i is a real number, $a_m \neq 0$, x is a real variable, and m is a positive integer, is called an **mth-degree polynomial in x over the field of real numbers** *[or an* **mth-degree polynominal with real coefficients**]. *Any expression of the form a_0, in which $a_0 \neq 0$, is called a* **polynomial of degree 0** *[or a* **constant**], *and the constant 0 is called a* **polynomial of no degree.***

For example, $3 + 4x - 3x^2 + 5x^3$ is a *third*-degree polynomial in x; $\pi + 3x^2 + x^3 - 3x^4$ is a *fourth*-degree polynomial in x; and $\sqrt{2} + u$ is a *first*-degree polynomial in u. All of the above polynomials are over the field of real numbers because the coefficients are real numbers. Whenever there is no danger of confusion, we may refer to the polynomial of Definition 7 as simply *an mth-degree polynomial* or *a polynomial of degree m*. The following polynomials are especially simple and useful:

1. $a_0 + a_1 x$ (*first-degree* or *linear* polynomial),
2. $a_0 + a_1 x + a_2 x^2$ (*second-degree* or *quadratic* polynomial),
3. $a_0 + a_1 x + a_2 x^2 + a_3 x^3$ (*third-degree* or *cubic* polynomial).

In the first-degree polynomial, $a_1 \neq 0$; in the second-degree polynomial, $a_2 \neq 0$; and in the third-degree polynomial, $a_3 \neq 0$.

---

*   Each real number a_i is called a *coefficient* (or a *numerical coefficient*).

Any function defined by a formula such as

$f(x) = $ *a polynomial in x*

is called a *polynomial function.* For example, the function defined by the formula $f(x) = 3 - 2x + 4x^3$ is a polynomial (cubic) function, in which $a_0 = 3, a_1 = {}^-2, a_2 = 0$, and $a_3 = 4$.

Definition 8. *Any function of the form*

$$\{(x, y): y = a_0 + a_1x + a_2x^2 + \cdots + a_mx^m\},$$

in which $a_0 + a_1 + a_1x + a_2x^2 + \cdots + a_mx^m$ *is a polynomial of degree m, is called an* **mth-degree polynomial function.**

For example, $f(x) = 3 + x - x^2 + x^3 + 3x^4$ is a *fourth*-degree polynomial function; $f(x) = 3 + 2x^2 - x^3 + 7x^8$ is an *eighth*-degree polynomial function; $f(x) = 3 + 2x$ is a *first*-degree polynomial function; $f(x) = 3 + x - 5x^2$ is a *second*-degree polynomial function; and $f(x) = 2 - x + x^2 - 5x^3$ is a *third*-degree polynomial function. The first-degree polynomial function is usually called a *linear function,** the second-degree polynomial function is usually called a *quadratic function,* and the third-degree polynomial function is usually called a *cubic function.*

In Section 7.3 we sketched the graph of a linear function and the graph of a quadratic function. Since the graph of any linear function is a straight line, we may sketch its graph by plotting any two distinct points of the graph and joining them by use of a straightedge. Frequently the formula defining a linear function is stated in the form

$ax + by = c,$

in which $b \neq 0$. For example, the equation $3x - 6y = 5$ defines the linear function

$$\{(x, y): y = \tfrac{1}{2}x - \tfrac{5}{6}\},$$

as the following analysis shows:

$3x - 6y = 5,$

$3x - 5 = 6y,$

$6y = 3x - 5,$

$y = \dfrac{3x - 5}{6},$

$y = \tfrac{3}{6}x - \tfrac{5}{6},$

$y = \tfrac{1}{2}x - \tfrac{5}{6}.$

---

* Also, the constant polynomial function [such as $f(x) = 5$ and $f(x) = 0$] is called a *linear function.* The graph is a horizontal line.

Since each step in the above analysis is reversible, we see that

$$\{(x, y): 3x - 6y = 5\} = \{(x, y): y = \tfrac{1}{2}x - \tfrac{5}{6}\}.$$

The reader may prove that

$$\{(x, y): ax + by = c \text{ and } b \neq 0\} = \left\{(x, y): y = \frac{-a}{b}x + \frac{c}{b} \text{ and } b \neq 0\right\}.$$

Since we may sketch the graph of the linear function $ax + by = c$ by plotting any two of its points, we may plot the two special points $(c/a, 0)$ and $(0, c/b)$ provided neither a nor b is zero. For example, to sketch the graph of

$$3x - 6y = 5 \qquad [a = 3, b = {}^-6, c = 5],$$

we plot the two points

$$(5/3, 0) \qquad \text{and} \qquad (0, {}^-5/6)$$

and join them by a straight line as in Fig. 7.12.

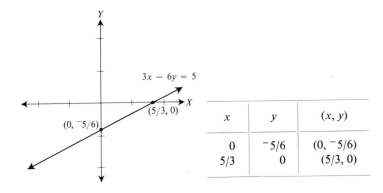

x	y	(x, y)
0	$^-5/6$	$(0, {}^-5/6)$
5/3	0	$(5/3, 0)$

Fig. 7.12

The x-coordinate [i.e., the first coordinate] of $(5/3, 0)$ is called the x-*intercept* of the linear function $3x - 6y = 5$, and the y-coordinate [i.e., the second coordinate] of $(0, {}^-5/6)$ is called the y-*intercept* of the linear function $3x - 6y = 5$. To compute the x-intercept, we let the y-coordinate be zero and compute the corresponding x-coordinate. To compute the y-intercept, we let the x-coordinate be zero and compute the corresponding y-coordinate.

Definition 9. *The x-coordinate of $(c/a, 0)$ of the linear function $\{(x, y): ax + by = c$, $a \neq 0$, and $b \neq 0\}$ is called the **x-intercept**, and the y-coordinate of $(0, c/b)$ is called the **y-intercept**.*

Another simple method of sketching the graph of a linear function is based on the *slope* and the y-intercept. Intuitively, the *slope* of a line is the rise divided by the run [the same as the pitch of a roof]. For example, the slope of the line in Fig. 7.13 is $\tfrac{3}{2}$.

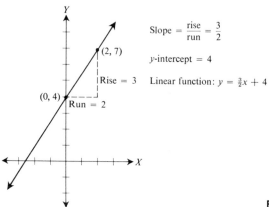

Slope $= \dfrac{\text{rise}}{\text{run}} = \dfrac{3}{2}$

y-intercept $= 4$

Linear function: $y = \frac{3}{2}x + 4$

Fig. 7.13

If we know the y-intercept of a linear function and the slope of its graph, we can plot the graph quite easily. For example, if the y-intercept is 4, we plot the point $(0, 4)$; if the slope is $\frac{3}{2}$, we plot a second point 3 units above $(0, 4)$ and 2 units to the right of $(0, 4)$. The second point is $(2, 7)$, as shown in Fig. 7.13. For convenience, we consider the slope of a linear function to be the same as the slope of its graph. Similarly, we consider the y-intercept of a linear function to be the same as the y-intercept of its graph. We now define the *slope* of the linear function $y = ax + b$.*

Definition 10. *The **slope** of the linear function $\{(x, y): y = ax + b\}$ is the real number a. The **slope** of the graph of any linear function $\{(x, y): y = ax + b\}$ is the real number a.*

For example, the slope of $\{(x, y): y = 5x + 3\}$ is 5, and the slope of $\{(x, y): y = {}^{-}3x + 5\}$ is ${}^{-}3$.

It follows from Definition 9 that the y-intercept of $\{(x, y): y = 5x + 3\}$ is 3 and the y-intercept of $\{(x, y): y = {}^{-}3x + 5\}$ is 5. The graphs are shown in Fig. 7.14.

In Section 7.3 we sketched the graph of the *quadratic function* $\{(x, y): y = x^2\}$ and observed that the graph is a *parabola*. The graph of *any* quadratic function $\{(x, y): y = ax^2 + bx + c$ and $a \neq 0\}$† is a *parabola*. The orientation of the parabola depends on the coefficients a, b, and c. If a is *positive*, the parabola opens *upward*; if a is *negative*, the parabola opens *downward*. The turning point of the parabola [the lowest point if a is positive, the highest point if a is negative] is called the *vertex* of the parabola. For example, the parabola in Fig. 7.10 opens upward and its vertex is $(0, 0)$; $a = 1$, $b = 0$, $c = 0$. If $b = 0$, the vertex is the point $(0, c)$ on the Y-axis. If $b = 0$ and $c = 0$, the vertex is the origin. If $b \neq 0$,

---

*   The coefficients [a and b] are the real numbers a_1 and a_0, respectively, of Definition 8.

†   The coefficients [a, b, and c] are the real numbers a_2, a_1, and a_0, respectively, of Definition 8.

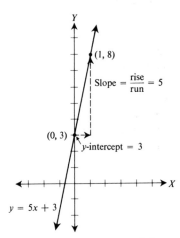

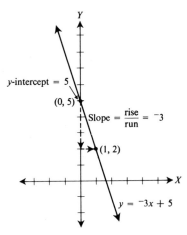

Since y-intercept $= 3$, we plot $(0, 3)$.
Since slope $= 5$, we plot a second point
5 units *above* $(0, 3)$ and 1 unit to the
right of $(0, 3)$. That point is $(1, 8)$.

a)

Since y-intercept $= 5$, we plot $(0, 5)$.
Since slope $= -3$, we plot a second point
3 units *below* $(0, 5)$ and 1 unit to the
right of $(0, 5)$. That point is $(1, 2)$.

b)

Fig. 7.14

the vertex is *not* on the Y-axis. The vertical line through the vertex is called the
axis of the parabola. The real number c is called the *y-intercept*.

To illustrate the above observations and terminology, we sketch the graph
of the quadratic function $y = -2x^2 + 3$. The table of sample points and the
graph are exhibited in Fig. 7.15. The vertex is $(0, 3)$, the y-intercept is 3, and the
parabola opens downward.

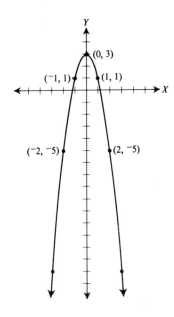

$y = -2x^2 + 3$
$a = -2, \quad b = 0, \quad c = 3$

Vertex $= (0, 3)$
y-intercept $= 3$

x	y	(x, y)
-3	-15	$(-3, -15)$
-2	-5	$(-2, -5)$
-1	1	$(-1, 1)$
0	3	$(0, 3)$
1	1	$(1, 1)$
2	-5	$(2, -5)$
3	-15	$(3, -15)$

Fig. 7.15

In Fig. 7.16, we sketch the graph of the quadratic function

$$y = {}^-2x^2 + 4x + 3.$$

The table of sample values and the graph are exhibited in Fig. 7.16. The vertex is (1, 5), the y-intercept is 3, and the parabola opens downward.

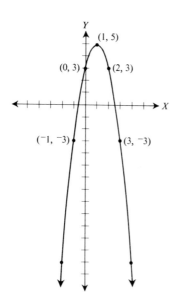

$y = {}^-2x^2 + 4x + 3$
$a = {}^-2, \quad b = 4, \quad c = 3$

Vertex $= (1, 5)$
y-intercept $= 3$

x	y	(x, y)
$^-2$	$^-13$	$(^-2, {}^-13)$
$^-1$	$^-3$	$(^-1, {}^-3)$
0	3	$(0, 3)$
1	5	$(1, 5)$
2	3	$(2, 3)$
3	$^-3$	$(3, {}^-3)$
4	$^-13$	$(4, {}^-13)$

Fig. 7.16

The reader will observe that the parabola in Fig. 7.16 is congruent to the parabola in Fig. 7.15, but its vertex is 2 units above and 1 unit to the right of the vertex of the parabola in Fig. 7.15. The reason for the congruence is that $a = {}^-2$ and $c = 3$ in both cases. The reason for the shift in the vertex is that $b = 0$ for the parabola in Fig. 7.15 and $b = 4$ for the parabola in Fig. 7.16.

The graph of the cubic function

$$\{(x, y): y = ax^3 + bx^2 + cx + d\}$$

is called a *cubical parabola*. Since the cube of every negative number is negative and the cube of every positive number is positive, the graph of a cubic function extends downward on one side and upward on the other side. In Fig. 7.17 we sketch the graph of

$$\{(x, y): y = x^3 - 2\}.$$

We chose the scale on the X-axis different from that on the Y-axis in order to facilitate plotting the points and to produce a more attractive sketch. We could accomplish the same objective by sketching the graph on a sheet of rubber and stretching the rubber sheet uniformly in a horizontal direction. Of course, we would have to be careful not to tear the rubber.

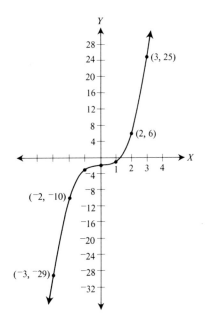

$$y = x^3 - 2$$
$$a = 1, \quad b = 0, \quad c = 0, \quad d = {}^-2$$

Vertex = $(0, {}^-2)$
y-intercept = $^-2$

x	y	(x, y)
$^-3$	$^-29$	$(^-3, {}^-29)$
$^-2$	$^-10$	$(^-2, {}^-10)$
$^-1$	$^-3$	$(^-1, {}^-3)$
0	$^-2$	$(0, {}^-2)$
1	$^-1$	$(1, {}^-1)$
2	6	$(2, 6)$
3	25	$(3, 25)$

Fig. 7.17

The graph of any cubic function can be plotted as in Fig. 7.17. The coefficients will determine the location of the vertex and the specific shape. The general shape will be the same as in Fig. 7.17.

In Fig. 7.18, we sketch the graphs of the functions (1) $y = x$, (2) $y = x^2$, (3) $y = x^3$, and (4) $y = x^4$ for comparison. The reader should observe that the

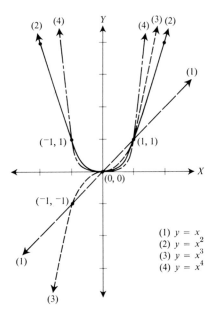

(1) $y = x$
(2) $y = x^2$
(3) $y = x^3$
(4) $y = x^4$

Fig. 7.18

even functions extend upward on both sides and the *odd* functions extend upward on the right side and downward on the left side.*

EXERCISE SET 7.4

I. Compute the slope, the x-intercept, and the y-intercept, and sketch the graph of each of the following linear functions.

1. $y = {}^-3x + 2$

2. $y = {}^-2x + 3$

3. $y = \frac{2}{3}x + 4$

4. $y = \frac{2}{3}x + 5$

5. $y = \frac{6}{11}x - 2$

6. $y = \frac{11}{6}x - 3$

7. $2x + 3y = 6$

8. $3x + 2y = 6$

9. $3x - 5y = {}^-15$

10. $5x - 3y = {}^-15$

II. Sketch the graph of each of the following quadratic functions. Estimate and label the vertex.

1. $y = x^2 + 4x + 4$

2. $y = x^2 - 4x + 4$

3. $y = x^2 - 2x$

4. $y = x^2 + 2x$

5. $y = {}^-2x^2 + 3$

6. $y = {}^-3x^2 + 2$

7. $y = x^2 - x + 1$

8. $y = x^2 + x + 1$

9. $y = {}^-2x^2 - x + 2$

10. $y = {}^-2x^2 + x - 2$

III. Sketch the graph of each of the following cubic functions.

1. $y = x^3 + 2$

2. $y = x^3 + 1$

3. $y = {}^-2x^3$

4. $y = {}^-3x^3$

5. $y = x^3 + x$

6. $y = x^3 - x$

7. $y = 2x - x^3$

8. $y = x - x^3$

9. $y = x^3 - x^2$

10. $y = x^2 - x^3$

IV. Identify each of the following functions as *linear*, *quadratic*, or *cubic*, and sketch its graph.

1. $y = {}^-3$

2. $y = 3$

3. $y = 3x$

4. $y = {}^-3x$

5. $y = 3 - x^3$

6. $y = 2 - x^3$

7. $y = x^2 + x^3$

8. $y = x + x^3$

9. $y = 1 - 2x + x^2$

10. $y = 1 + 2x + x^2$

V. Prove each of the following:

1. $\{(x, y): ax + by = c \text{ and } b \neq 0\} = \left\{(x, y): y = \frac{-a}{b}x + \frac{c}{b} \text{ and } b \neq 0\right\}.$

2. The x-intercept of $\dfrac{x}{x_0} + \dfrac{y}{y_0} = 1$ is x_0, and the y-intercept is y_0.

---

*   The statement refers to the functions in Fig. 7.18. The graphs of the functions (1) $y = {}^-x$, (2) $y = {}^-x^2$, (3) $y = {}^-x^3$, and (4) $y = {}^-x^4$ are reflections about the X-axis of the graphs in Fig. 7.18.

3. The slope of $\{(x, y): y = 6\}$ is 0, and the y-intercept is 6.

4. The slope of $\{(x, y): y = x\}$ is 1, and the y-intercept is 0.

VI. Employ the accompanying figure to verify that the slope a of the linear function

$$\{(x, y): y = ax + b\}$$

is equal to the rise over the run.

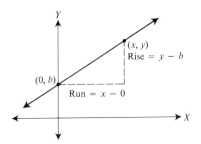

7.5   LINEAR INEQUALITIES AND RELATIONS

In Section 7.1 we defined a *function* from a set A to a set B. In Section 2.3 we accepted *relation* as one of the undefined concepts. Then in Section 2.7 we stated that it is possible to define *relation* in terms of the Cartesian product. Now we define *relation* and conclude that a function is a special kind of relation.

Definition 11. *Any subset of the Cartesian product $A \times B$ of the sets A and B is called a **relation from A to B**. The **domain** is the set of all first coordinates of the elements of the relation. The **range** is the set of all second coordinates of the elements of the relation.*

For example, if $A = \{1, 2\}$ and $B = \{0, 3\}$, then

$$A \times B = \{(1, 0), (1, 3), (2, 0), (2, 3)\},$$

and every one of the 16 subsets of $A \times B$ is a relation from A to B.* However, only certain relations from A to B are functions from A to B. Although

$$\{(1, 0), (1, 3), (2, 0)\}$$

is a relation from A to B, it is *not* a function from A to B because 1 is the first coordinate of both (1, 0) and (1, 3). On the other hand, the relation $\{(1, 3), (2, 3)\}$ is a function from A to B. We observe that *a function from A to B is any relation from A to B* which satisfies the following conditions:

1. Every element of A is the first coordinate of some ordered pair of the relation.

2. No two different ordered pairs of the relation have the same first coordinate.

---

*   The empty set is a trivial and uninteresting relation from A to B.

Thus every function from A to B is a relation from A to B, but some relations from A to B are not functions from A to B.

Now we define *linear inequality* in two real variables x and y.

Definition 12. *The relations* $\{(x, y): ax + by < c,$ *and* $a \neq 0$ *or* $b \neq 0\}$ *and* $\{(x, y): ax + by \leq c,$ *and* $a \neq 0$ *or* $b \neq 0\}$ *are called* **linear inequalities** *in the two real variables* x *and* y.

Sometimes, for emphasis, the former relation is called a *strong linear inequality*, and the latter is called a *weak linear inequality*. To sketch the graph of *either* linear inequality [which is a half-plane], we first sketch the graph of the corresponding relation $\{(x, y): ax + by = c,$ and $a \neq 0$ or $b \neq 0\}$, and then we decide which of the two half-planes determined by the line is the graph of the linear inequality. To determine the correct half-plane, we may determine whether any point (x_0, y_0) *not on the line* [the graph of $ax + by = c$] *satisfies* the relation in the sense that the sentence

$$ax_0 + by_0 < c$$

is true. If (x_0, y_0) satisfies the relation [i.e., if $ax_0 + by_0 < c$], then (x_0, y_0) is a point of the graph of the relation. However, if (x_0, y_0) does not satisfy the relation [i.e., if $ax_0 + by_0 > c$], then (x_0, y_0) is not a point of the graph of the relation. The following examples illustrate the method of graphing inequalities in two real variables.

Example 1. To sketch the graph of $\{(x, y): x < y\}$ we first sketch the graph of $\{(x, y): y = x\}$, and then we choose any point *not* on the line so that we can decide which half-plane is the graph of the linear inequality. The graph of $\{(x, y): x < y\}$ is the shaded region in the accompanying figure, in which we have dashed the line to indicate that it is *not* part of the graph of the linear inequality.

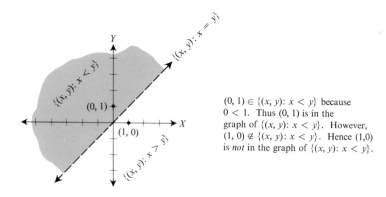

$(0, 1) \in \{(x, y): x < y\}$ because $0 < 1$. Thus $(0, 1)$ is in the graph of $\{(x, y): x < y\}$. However, $(1, 0) \notin \{(x, y): x < y\}$. Hence $(1,0)$ is *not* in the graph of $\{(x, y): x < y\}$.

Example 2. To sketch the graph of $\{(x, y): 2x + 3y < 6\}$, we first sketch the graph of $\{(x, y): 2x + 3y = 6\}$, and then we choose any point not on the line so that we can decide which half-plane is the graph of $\{(x, y): 2x + 3y < 6\}$. The graph is the shaded region in the accompanying figure. The dashed line is *not* part of the graph.

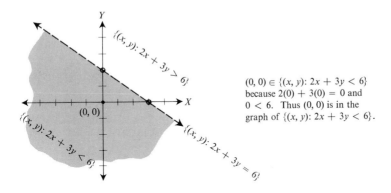

$(0, 0) \in \{(x, y): 2x + 3y < 6\}$ because $2(0) + 3(0) = 0$ and $0 < 6$. Thus $(0, 0)$ is in the graph of $\{(x, y): 2x + 3y < 6\}$.

Example 3. To sketch the graph of $\{(x, y): 2x - 3y \leq 6\}$, we first sketch the graph of $\{(x, y): 2x - 3y = 6\}$, and then we choose any point not on the line so that we can decide which half-plane is the graph of $\{(x, y): 2x - 3y < 6\}$. The graph of $\{(x, y): 2x - 3y \leq 6\}$ is the union of the graphs of

$$\{(x, y): 2x - 3y < 6\} \quad \text{and} \quad \{(x, y): 2x - 3y = 6\}.$$

That is, the graph is the union of the shaded region and the line in the accompanying figure.

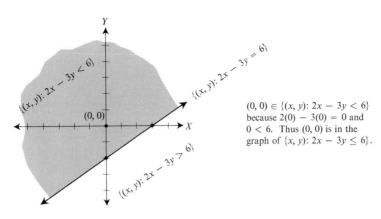

$(0, 0) \in \{(x, y): 2x - 3y < 6\}$ because $2(0) - 3(0) = 0$ and $0 < 6$. Thus $(0, 0)$ is in the graph of $\{x, y): 2x - 3y \leq 6\}$.

Example 4. To sketch the graph of $\{(x, y): y \leq 2\}$, we sketch the graph of $\{(x, y): y = 2\}$, and then we shade the graph of $\{(x, y): y < 2\}$ as in the accompanying figure. The graph of $\{(x, y): y \leq 2\}$ is the union of the line and the shaded region.

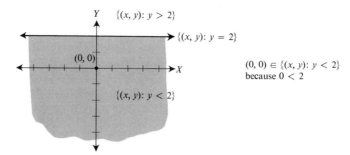

$(0, 0) \in \{(x, y): y < 2\}$
because $0 < 2$

Example 5. To sketch the graph of $\{(x, y): x < y \text{ and } y \leq 2\}$, we sketch the graph of $\{(x, y): x < y\}$ as in Example 1, and then we sketch the graph of $\{(x, y): y \leq 2\}$ as in Example 4. The graph of $\{x, y): x < y \text{ and } y \leq 2\}$ is the *intersection* of the two graphs of Examples 1 and 4. The graph is the *heavily shaded* region in the accompanying figure. The dashed line is *not* part of the graph.

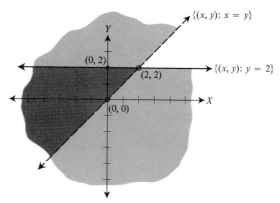

Example 6. To sketch the graph of $\{(x, y): x < y \text{ or } y \leq 2\}$, we proceed as in Example 5. However, the graph is the *union* of the graphs of Examples 1 and 4. That is, the graph is the shaded region in the accompanying figure. Some of the dashed line is part of the graph, and some is *not*.

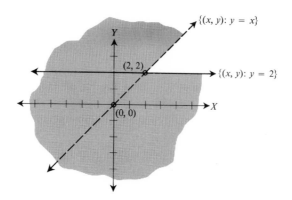

Example 7. To sketch the graph of $\{(x, y): x < 2 \text{ and } x \geq {}^-3\}$, we sketch the graph of $\{(x, y): x < 2\}$ and the graph of $\{(x, y): x \geq {}^-3\}$. The graph of

$$\{(x, y): x < 2 \text{ and } x \geq {}^-3\}$$

is the intersection of the two graphs. That is, the graph is the heavily shaded region in the accompanying figure. The dashed line is *not* part of the graph. We observe that

neither $\{(x, y): x = 2\}$ *nor* $\{(x, y): x = {}^-3\}$

is a function because all ordered pairs in each set have the same first coordinate. The first coordinate of every ordered pair in the former is 2 and the first coordinate of every ordered pair in the latter is $^-3$.

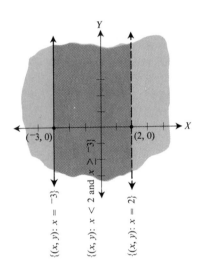

The relations in Examples 1 through 7 are not functions. In fact, no inequality is a function, but many equations define functions. For example, every linear equation $ax + by = c$ [in which $b \neq 0$] defines a function. However, if $b = 0$, the equation reduces to $x = c/a$, which does *not* define a function. Although in Definition 9 we defined *x-intercept* and *y-intercept* only for a linear *function*, we can extend the definition to linear relations which are not functions. For example, the x-intercept of $\{(x, y): x = 2\}$ is 2. Of course, there is no y-intercept. Similarly, the y-intercept of the linear function $\{(x, y): y = 3\}$ is 3, and there is no x-intercept.

Any strong inequality is a *simple inequality*. However, any weak inequality is a *compound inequality*. Moreover, any inequality involving a connective [*or*, *and*, *not*, *if...then*, *if and only if*] is a *compound inequality*. For example, the inequalities in Examples 1 and 2 are simple linear inequalities, whereas those in Examples 3 through 7 are compound inequalities.

EXERCISE SET 7.5

I. Sketch the graph of each of the following relations. In each case the domain is the set of reals.

1. $\{(x, y): x + y < 5\}$

2. $\{(x, y): x + y < 4\}$

3. $\{(x, y): x - y \leq 4\}$

4. $\{(x, y): x - y \leq 5\}$

5. $\{(x, y): {}^-2x + y \leq 4\}$

6. $\{(x, y): {}^-2x + y \leq 2\}$

7. $\{(x, y): x + y \leq 5 \text{ and } y < 3\}$

8. $\{(x, y): x + y \leq 3 \text{ and } y < 5\}$

9. $\{(x, y): x + y < 5 \text{ or } y \leq 3\}$

10. $\{(x, y): x + y < 3 \text{ or } y \leq 5\}$

11. $\{(x, y): y < 2 \text{ or } y \geq 4\}$

12. $\{(x, y): y \leq 2 \text{ or } y > 4\}$

13. $\{(x, y): y \leq 4 \text{ and } y \geq {}^-2\}$

14. $\{(x, y): y \leq 2 \text{ and } y \geq {}^-4\}$

15. $\{(x, y): y < 2 \text{ and } x > 3\}$

16. $\{(x, y): y > 2 \text{ and } x < 3\}$

17. $\{(x, y): y > 2 \text{ or } x < 3\}$

18. $\{(x, y): y < 2 \text{ or } x > 3\}$

19. $\{(x, y): {}^-3 < x \text{ and } x < 2\}$

20. $\{(x, y): {}^-2 < x \text{ and } x < 3\}$

II.

1. Explain why $\{(x, y): y = 3\}$ is a function, whereas $\{(x, y): x = 3\}$ is not a function.

2. Explain why $\{(x, y): y \leq 3\}$ is not a function.

3. In how many points can a *vertical* line intersect the graph of a function?

4. Can a *horizontal* line intersect the graph of a function in more than one point? Why?

5. Is a circle the graph of a function? Explain.

6. Under what conditions is a semicircle the graph of a function?

7. The graph of $\{(x, y): y = x^2\}$ is a parabola whose axis is the Y-axis. Is $\{(x, y): y = x^2\}$ a function? Why?

8. The graph of $\{(x, y): x = y^2\}$ is a parabola whose axis is the X-axis. Is $\{(x, y): x = y^2\}$ a function? Why?

9. Is the X-axis the graph of a function? Why?

10. Is the Y-axis the graph of a function? Why?

Intuitive Calculus

Sir Isaac Newton was born in Woolsthorpe, England, on December 25, 1642, after his father's death. Isaac was such a frail baby that he was not expected to live; in fact, throughout his childhood he remained in very poor health. When he was three years old, his mother remarried and sent young Isaac to live with his grandmother. There is no evidence that he exhibited any unusual degree of talent in mathematics as a young boy. At first, chemistry seemed to be his chief interest, and he retained a strong interest in it throughout his life.

At the age of 19 he enrolled at Trinity College, and during his first year he became absorbed in the reading and study of mathematics. By the end of his third year at Trinity, Newton seems to have reached the frontiers of the mathematical knowledge of his time and was ready to make contributions of his own. He had discovered how to express functions in terms of infinite series, a method which aided him greatly in four of his chief discoveries: (1) the binomial theorem, (2) the calculus, (3) the law of gravitation, and (4) the nature of colors.

Since the binomial coefficients for integral powers had been known for at least 500 years before the time of Newton, it seems almost unbelievable today that the binomial theorem had not been formulated before Newton's time. However, the earlier mathematicians had not had the advantage of the exponential notation of Descartes; moreover, fractional exponents had not yet come into common use. In the process of formulating the binomial theorem as part of his infinite series development, Newton made a discovery far more important than the binomial theorem. He discovered that many of the laws governing finite series also governed infinite series.

Newton never published his binomial theorem, but he did publish several accounts of his infinite analysis (including the calculus). He began to develop the calculus in 1665, and by 1669 he had composed his first account of his infinite analysis.

Newton's book, *Philosophiae Naturalis Principia Mathematica*, which was published in 1687, contained the first account of his calculus. It is probably the most admired scientific treatise of all time. Newton was neither the first mathematician to integrate and differentiate, nor the first to perceive the relationship between the two operations of integration and differentiation. However, he consolidated both into a general algorithm applicable to both algebraic and transcendental functions.

While Newton was developing the calculus, the German mathematician Gottfried Wilhelm Leibniz was developing it independently. Since Leibniz published his development of calculus in 1684, before Newton published his, the followers of Leibniz claimed that he was the sole discoverer of calculus. The two sets of followers of the two great mathematicians engaged in a dispute which lasted many years. Documents reveal that Newton's discovery occurred about ten years before that of Leibniz.

Newton is considered by many to have been the greatest intellect that the world has produced. In fact, Leibniz said of Newton, "Taking mathematics from the beginning of the world to the time of Newton, what he has done is much the better half." Isaac Newton, however,

NEWTON
(1642–1727)

was basically a modest man, and he proclaimed in a letter to a friend, "If I have seen farther than Descartes, it is because I have stood on the shoulders of giants."

During his long lifetime Newton received all the honors he deserved and had about as fortunate a life as any great man ever had. In fact, Queen Anne knighted him in 1705. He had excellent health until the last two years of his life. On March 20, 1727, at the age of 85, he died in his sleep. Sir Isaac Newton is buried in Westminster Abbey along with other great Englishmen.

Chapter 8

Intuitive Calculus

8.1 THE LIMIT CONCEPT

The reader now has a general idea of the nature of a mathematician's work and the methods a mathematician uses to study and solve problems. An important concept in mathematics is that of *limit* of a function, and it is upon this concept that the study of *calculus* depends. So much of modern physical, biological, and managerial science depends on calculus that some brief introduction to calculus is practically essential to a twentieth-century college graduate, regardless of his profession. We warn the reader, however, that the development is intuitive and informal rather than rigorous and formal.

The British mathematician Sir Isaac Newton (1642–1727) and the German mathematician Gottfried Wilhelm von Leibniz (1646–1716) developed calculus practically independently and simultaneously. However, they did not solve the basic difficulties involving the limit concept upon which calculus depends. Many mathematicians of the nineteenth and twentieth centuries have devoted some of their efforts toward formalizing the limit concept and laying a logical foundation for its study. Nevertheless, the reader can understand most of an intuitive introduction to calculus even if he does not understand the limit concept as thoroughly as the mathematician does.

In order to gain an intuitive understanding of the limit of a function, we consider the average speed of an object (e.g., a falling body or a moving automobile) traveling according to the formula

$$s = 16t^2,$$

in which t is the number of units of time the object has been moving and s is the number of units of distance the body moves in t units of time. For example, after 2 seconds the body has moved 64 feet. The average speed during the 2 sec is 32 ft/sec because

$$\text{average speed} = \frac{\text{change in distance}}{\text{change in time}} = \frac{64}{2} = 32.$$

Similarly, the average speed from 2 sec to 4 sec is 96 ft/sec because

$$\text{average speed} = \frac{\text{change in distance}}{\text{change in time}} = \frac{16(4^2) - 16(2^2)}{4 - 2}$$

$$= \frac{256 - 64}{4 - 2} = \frac{192}{2} = 96.$$

Although the average speed over the former 2-sec period (from 0 sec to 2 sec) is 32 ft/sec, the average speed over the latter 2-sec period (from 2 sec to 4 sec) is 96 ft/sec. Neither *average* speed is an indication of the *instantaneous* speed at the end of 2 sec nor at the end of 4 sec. The instantaneous speed could be *measured* by a *speedometer* on the object. An accurate speedometer would indicate 64 ft/sec at 2 sec and 128 ft/sec at 4 sec. One problem in calculus is the calculation of such an instantaneous speed (or rate of change) without the use of a speedometer. For the present, we can verify that 64 ft/sec is a reasonable estimate of the *instantaneous* speed of the object at 2 sec by calculating the *average* speed of the object during a very small period of time in a small neighborhood* of 2 sec. The average speed during 0.1 sec from 2.0 sec to 2.1 sec is 65.6 ft/sec because

$$\text{average speed} = \frac{\text{change in distance}}{\text{change in time}} = \frac{16(2.1)^2 - 16(2.0)^2}{2.1 - 2.0}$$

$$= \frac{16(4.41) - 16(4.00)}{0.1} = \frac{16(0.41)}{0.1} = \frac{6.56}{0.1} = 65.6.$$

If we reduce the increment of time to 0.01 sec and calculate the average speed from 2.00 sec to 2.01 sec, we see that the average speed is closer to the estimate of the instantaneous speed. The average speed is 64.16 ft/sec because

$$\text{average speed} = \frac{\text{change in distance}}{\text{change in time}} = \frac{16(2.01)^2 - 16(2.00)^2}{2.01 - 2.00}$$

$$= \frac{0.6416}{0.01} = 64.16.$$

Further reduction in the increment of time yields an average speed even closer to 64 ft/sec. For example, the average speed between 2.000 sec and 2.001 sec is 64.016 ft/sec.

If the increment of time is h sec [for example, $h = 0.1$ or $h = 0.01$ or $h = 0.001$], then the average speed from 2 sec to $2 + h$ sec is $64 + 16h$ ft/sec

---

* Intuitively, a neighborhood of a real number r is a subset of R which includes r. Usually, some numbers in the neighborhood are less than r and some are greater than r, and $|x - r|$ is very small for every real number x in the neighborhood of r.

because

$$\text{average speed} = \frac{\text{change in distance}}{\text{change in time}} = \frac{16(2 + h)^2 - 16(2)^2}{(2 + h) - 2}$$

$$= \frac{16(4 + 4h + h^2) - 64}{h} = \frac{64h + 16h^2}{h}$$

$$= \frac{(64 + 16h)h}{h} = 64 + 16h,$$

provided, of course, $h \neq 0$.

Now, as h *approaches* 0 [intuitively, as h gets closer and closer to 0], it is intuitively obvious that $64 + 16h$ *approaches* 64 [intuitively, $64 + 16h$ gets closer and closer to 64]. That is, the *average* speed in a neighborhood of 2 sec *approaches* the *instantaneous* speed at 2 sec as the neighborhood gets smaller [i.e., as the time approaches 2 sec]. In exact mathematical terminology we say that *the limit, as h approaches 0, of the average speed $64 + 16h$ is the instantaneous speed 64*, and we write

$$\lim_{h \to 0} (64 + 16h) = 64,$$

which we may read more briefly as *the limit, as h approaches 0, of $(64 + 16h)$ is 64*.

More generally, if the object is moving according to the formula

$$s = f(t),$$

then the *average* speed from a to $(a + h)$ sec is

$$\frac{f(a + h) - f(a)}{h} \text{ ft/sec}$$

because

$$\text{average speed} = \frac{\text{change in distance}}{\text{change in time}} = \frac{f(a + h) - f(a)}{(a + h) - a}$$

$$= \frac{f(a + h) - f(a)}{h},$$

and the *instantaneous* speed at a sec is

$$\lim_{h \to 0} \frac{f(a + h) - f(a)}{h} \text{ ft/sec.}$$

Of course, we have not given a formal definition of the limit of a function, but we have given an intuitive description which should be sufficient to enable the reader to calculate certain limits of interest in elementary calculus. The following examples illustrate the standard methods of computing simple limits.

Example 1. If $f(x) = x^2 - x + 1$, then

$$\lim_{x \to 0} f(x) = \lim_{x \to 0} (x^2 - x + 1) = 1$$

because $x^2 - x + 1$ gets closer to 1 as x gets closer to 0. Moreover,

$$\lim_{x \to 1} f(x) = 1$$

because $x^2 - x + 1$ gets closer to 1 as x gets closer to 1.

Example 2. If $f(x) = (x^2 + 5)/x^2$, then

$$\lim_{x \to 0} f(x)$$

does not exist because $x^2 + 5$ approaches 5 as x approaches 0; i.e., the numerator approaches 5 and the denominator approaches 0. Hence $(x^2 + 5)/x^2$ grows larger as x approaches 0. We may indicate that the limit does not exist by writing

$$\lim_{x \to 0} \frac{x^2 + 5}{x^2} = \infty.$$

The reader is cautioned that the above notation is merely a shorthand method of indicating that the limit does not exist because $f(x)$ [i.e., the image of x] grows larger and larger without bound as x approaches 0.* It does *not* mean that the limit exists and is equal to ∞. However,

$$\lim_{x \to 1} f(x) = 6$$

because $f(x)$ approaches $(1^2 + 5)/1^2$ as x approaches 1.

Example 3. If $f(x) = x^2/x$, then

$$\lim_{x \to 1} f(x) = \frac{1^2}{1} = 1.$$

Moreover,

$$\lim_{x \to 2} f(x) = \frac{2^2}{2} = 2, \quad \text{and} \quad \lim_{x \to 5} f(x) = \frac{5^2}{5} = 5.$$

It seems that

$$\lim_{x \to a} f(x) = \frac{a^2}{a} = a$$

for any real number a. However, can we replace "x" in "x^2/x" by "a" and evaluate, for every a in R? If $a = 0$, then $a^2/a = 0^2/0 = 0/0$, which is meaningless. At first glance we are tempted to write

$$\lim_{x \to 0} f(x) = \infty,$$

as in Example 2. However, the basic difference between the two examples is that *both* numerator and denominator of x^2/x approach 0, whereas only the denominator of $(x^2 + 5)/x^2$ approaches 0 as x approaches 0. Thus the limit of x^2/x *may*

---

*   It is possible that $\lim_{x \to a} f(x)$ fails to exist even if $f(x)$ does not grow larger without bound as x approaches a. Discussion of *left-hand* and *right-hand* limits (which are beyond the scope of this chapter) is necessary for an understanding of such functions.

exist as x approaches 0. The accompanying table displays certain images of x^2/x corresponding to preimages near (but not equal to) 0.

x	0.1	0.01	0.001	0.0001
$f(x)$	0.1	0.01	0.001	0.0001

It appears from the table that

$$\lim_{x \to 0} f(x) = 0.$$

Since $f(x) = x^2/x = x$ if $x \neq 0$, we see that $f(x)$ approaches the real number a as x approaches a. Thus $f(x)$ approaches 0 (but is never equal to 0) as x approaches 0 (but is never equal to 0). That is,

$$\lim_{x \to 0} f(x) = 0.$$

In Example 3, we observed that

$$\lim_{x \to 0} \frac{x^2}{x}$$

exists even though x^2/x is not defined for $x = 0$. The fact that *both* numerator and denominator approach 0 as x approaches 0 made us suspect that the limit *might* exist and that further investigation was necessary. Further investigation involved dividing numerator and denominator of x^2/x by x to obtain x. Since

$$\lim_{x \to 0} x = 0,$$

we conclude that

$$\lim_{x \to 0} \frac{x^2}{x} = 0.$$

The above examples *illustrate* the limit concept and methods of computing certain limits. For the benefit of the reader who would like to have a precise mathematical definition of the limit of a function, we state Definition 1.

Definition 1. *The **limit of** $f(x)$ **as** x **approaches the real number** a **is the real number** b* [*denoted by* "$\lim_{x \to a} f(x) = b$" *or* "$\lim_{x \to a} f(x) = b$"] *if and only if for each positive real number ε there exists a positive real number δ such that $|f(x) - b| < \varepsilon$ for all x in $\mathscr{D}(f)$ satisfying the inequality $0 < |x - a| < \delta$.*

Definition 1 is a precise mathematical statement of the intuitive definition of the limit. According to Definition 1,

$$\lim_{x \to a} f(x) = b$$

if and only if $f(x)$ approaches b as x approaches a. The numbers ε and δ in

Definition 1 give precise meaning to the terms *approach* and *get closer and closer to*. If ε is very small, the corresponding δ must be small also; that is, δ depends on ε.*

EXERCISE SET 8.1

I. A particle is traveling according to the formula

$$s = 16t^2 + 17t.$$

Compute the average speed during each of the following intervals of time.

1. 0 sec to 2 sec   2. 1 sec to 3 sec

3. 2 sec to 4 sec   4. 3 sec to 5 sec

5. 1 sec to 5 sec   6. 0 sec to 4 sec

7. 0 sec to 0.1 sec   8. 0 sec to 0.01 sec

9. 0 sec to 0.001 sec   10. 0 sec to 0.0001 sec

II. Calculate each of the following limits.

1. $\lim\limits_{x \to 0} \dfrac{x}{x + 1}$ 2. $\lim\limits_{x \to 0} \dfrac{x}{x - 1}$

3. $\lim\limits_{x \to 1} \dfrac{x - 1}{x + 1}$ 4. $\lim\limits_{x \to 1} \dfrac{x - 1}{x + 2}$

5. $\lim\limits_{x \to 1} \dfrac{x - 1}{x - 1}$ 6. $\lim\limits_{x \to 2} \dfrac{x - 2}{x - 2}$

7. $\lim\limits_{x \to 2} \dfrac{x^2 - 4}{x - 2}$ 8. $\lim\limits_{x \to 1} \dfrac{x^2 - 1}{x - 1}$

9. $\lim\limits_{x \to 5} 6$ 10. $\lim\limits_{x \to 6} 5$

III. In each of the following, calculate $\lim\limits_{h \to 0} \dfrac{f(a + h) - f(a)}{h}$.

1. $f(x) = 3x$ 2. $f(x) = 2x$

3. $f(x) = 2x^2$ 4. $f(x) = 3x^2$

5. $f(x) = 3x + 2$ 6. $f(x) = 2x + 3$

7. $f(x) = \dfrac{1}{x}$ 8. $f(x) = \dfrac{x}{x^2}$

IV. Sketch the graph of $\{(x, y): y = x^2\}$. Label the curve and axes to illustrate what we mean when we say that

$$\lim_{x \to 2} x^2 = 4.$$

[*Hint:* Choose an arbitrary ε and illustrate $\{(0, y): y \in R \text{ and } 4 - \varepsilon < y < 4 + \varepsilon\}$ and $\{(x, 0): x \in R \text{ and } 2 - \delta < x < 2 + \delta\}$].

---

*   Sometimes it is possible to select δ sufficiently small that it satisfies Definition 1 for any positive real number ε.

8.2 CONTINUITY

In Section 8.1 we learned a procedure for computing certain limits. In particular, we learned that the computation is quite simple in some instances. For example, if $f(x) = x^2 - 3x + 2$, then

$$\lim_{x \to 0} f(x) = 2;$$

moreover, $f(0) = 0^2 - 3(0) + 2 = 2$. Thus if $f(x) = x^2 - 3x + 2$, we can compute $\lim_{x \to 0} f(x)$ by actual substitution. That is,

$$\lim_{x \to 0} f(x) = \lim_{x \to 0} (x^2 - 3x + 2) = 0^2 - 3(0) + 2 = 2 = f(0).$$

However, if $g(x) = x^2/x$, then

$$\lim_{x \to 0} g(x) = 0,$$

but $g(0)$ is not defined because $0/0$ is meaningless. Hence we *cannot* compute $\lim_{x \to 0} g(x)$ by actual substitution. If we *could* compute the limit of every function by substitution, then we could give a much simpler definition of the limit; we would say that

$$\lim_{x \to a} f(x) = f(a).$$

However, as we have just observed, not all functions are so simple; $\lim_{x \to 0} g(x)$ exists, although $g(0)$ does not.

The class of functions whose limits can be computed by actual substitution is an especially simple and useful class. Each function of the class is called a *continuous function.* In particular, every polynomial function is continuous on R.

Definition 2. *The function* $f: A \to B$ *is* **continuous at the number** a *if and only if*

$$\lim_{x \to a} f(x) = f(a);$$

$f: A \to B$ *is* **continuous on** A *if and only if* f *is continuous at each* a *in* A.

The condition

$$\lim_{x \to a} f(x) = f(a)$$

really implies three conditions:

1. $\lim_{x \to a} f(x)$ exists;

2. $f(a)$ exists;*

3. $\lim_{x \to a} f(x)$ is the same number as $f(a)$.

---

*   If a is not in the domain of f, then $f(a)$ does not exist [that is, $f(a)$ is not defined], and hence f is not continuous at a.

A given function may be *continuous* at one or more numbers but *discontinuous* (i.e., not continuous) at some other number. For example, $f(x) = x^2/x$ is continuous at all real numbers *except* 0 but is discontinuous at 0. Hence it is *not* continuous on R, but it is continuous on $R \setminus \{0\}$. According to Definition 2, any function which is continuous *at* every number in its domain is continuous *on its domain*. Frequently, we refer to the *numbers* in the domain of a function as the *points* in the domain. For example, we may say that f is continuous at the *point* a if and only if $\lim_{x \to a} f(x) = f(a)$.

Intuitively, a real-valued function of a real variable is *continuous* (on its domain) if its graph is all in one piece (i.e., its graph is not broken or disconnected). The intuitive concept of continuity suffices for most elementary applications, but there are less elementary problems in which the intuitive concept is unreliable. However, in an introduction to intuitive calculus we are not concerned with the more sophisticated aspects of continuity.

Sometimes the domain of a function of a real variable is a proper subset of R. Frequently the domain is an *interval*.

Definition 3. $\{x: a < x < b,\ a \in R,\ and\ b \in R\}$ *is called* **the open interval from a to b**; $\{x: a \le x \le b,\ a \in R,\ and\ b \in R\}$ *is called* **the closed interval from a to b**; *a and b are called* **the endpoints of either interval.**

If there is no danger of confusion, we may denote the open interval from a to b by "(a, b)" and the closed interval from a to b by "$[a, b]$." For example, $(^-3, 2)$ is the set of all real numbers from $^-3$ to 2, exclusive; and $[^-3, 2]$ is the set of all real numbers from $^-3$ to 2, inclusive. We observe that an open interval contains *neither* of its endpoints but a closed interval contains *both* of its endpoints. We may employ the notations "$(a, b]$" and "$[a, b)$" in a similar manner. The various intervals are illustrated geometrically on the number lines in Fig. 8.1.

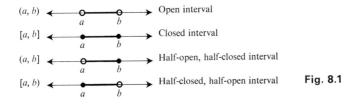

(a, b)		Open interval
$[a, b]$		Closed interval
$(a, b]$		Half-open, half-closed interval
$[a, b)$		Half-closed, half-open interval **Fig. 8.1**

If a is any negative real number, then

$$\left\{(x,\, g(x)): g(x) = \frac{x^2}{x} \text{ and } a < x < 0\right\}$$

is continuous. If b is any positive real number, then

$$\left\{(x,\, g(x)): g(x) = \frac{x^2}{x} \text{ and } 0 < x < b\right\}$$

is continuous. That is, g is continuous on the open intervals $(a, 0)$ and $(0, b)$.

The graph of

$$\left\{ (x,\ g(x)) \colon g(x) = \frac{x^2}{x} \right\}$$

for each of the above domains is shown in Fig. 8.2.

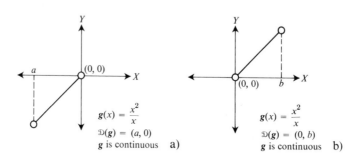

$g(x) = \dfrac{x^2}{x}$

$\mathcal{D}(g) = (a, 0)$

g is continuous   a)

$g(x) = \dfrac{x^2}{x}$

$\mathcal{D}(g) = (0, b)$

g is continuous   b)   **Fig. 8.2**

The graph of $\{(x, h(x)) \colon h(x) = x^2/x\}$ on the union of the above domains [i.e., on $(a, 0) \cup (0, b)$] is shown in Fig. 8.3(a). We observe that the graph is broken at $(0, 0)$ and hence the function h is discontinuous at 0. Since a is any negative real number and b is any positive real number, we see that h is continuous on $R \setminus \{0\}$. The graph is shown in Fig. 8.3(b).

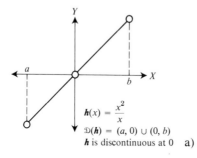

$h(x) = \dfrac{x^2}{x}$

$\mathcal{D}(h) = (a, 0) \cup (0, b)$

h is discontinuous at 0   a)

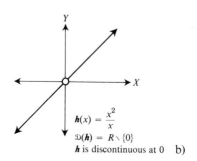

$h(x) = \dfrac{x^2}{x}$

$\mathcal{D}(h) = R \setminus \{0\}$

h is discontinuous at 0   b)

Fig. 8.3

EXERCISE SET 8.2

I. Prove that each of the following functions is continuous at the real number 5.

1. $f(x) = x^2 + 1$ 2. $f(x) = x^2 - 1$

3. $f(x) = x^2 + x$ 4. $f(x) = x^2 - x$

5. $f(x) = x^2 + x + 2$ 6. $f(x) = x^2 + 2x + 1$

7. $f(x) = (x + 2)/(x - 3)$ 8. $f(x) = (x - 3)/(x + 2)$

9. $f(x) = 1/[x(x - 1)]$ 10. $f(x) = 1/[x(x - 2)]$

II. Determine the points of discontinuity (if any) of each function in Exercise I.

III. Sketch the graph of $f(x) = x^3/x + 1$ on $R \setminus \{0\}$, and indicate the discontinuity at 0. [*Hint:* Be certain to let x assume both negative and positive values, including $^-3$, $^-2$, $^-1$, $^-0.5$, $^-0.1$, 0, 0.1, 0.5, 1, 2, and 3.]

IV. Sketch the graph of $f(x) = x^2/x + 1$ on $R \setminus \{0\}$, and indicate the discontinuity at 0.

V. According to the comment following Definition 2, a function f may be discontinuous at a given point a for any one (or more) of three reasons:

i) $\lim_{x \to a} f(x)$ fails to exist;

ii) $f(a)$ fails to exist; or

iii) $\lim_{x \to a} f(x)$ exists and $f(a)$ exists, but $\lim_{x \to a} f(x)$ is a different number from $f(a)$.

Decide why each of the following functions is discontinuous at 2.

1. $f(x) = \dfrac{2}{x - 2}$

2. $f(x) = \dfrac{x}{x - 2}$

3. $f(x) = \dfrac{x - 2}{x - 2}$

4. $f(x) = \begin{cases} \dfrac{x - 2}{x - 2} & \text{if} \quad x \neq 2 \\ 3 & \text{if} \quad x = 2 \end{cases}$

5. $f(x) = \begin{cases} \dfrac{x - 2}{x - 2} & \text{if} \quad x \neq 2 \\ 2 & \text{if} \quad x = 2 \end{cases}$

6. $f(x) = \dfrac{x - 2}{x^2 - 4}$

7. $f(x) = \dfrac{x^2 - 4}{x - 2}$

8. $f(x) = \dfrac{x + 2}{x - 2}$

9. $f(x) = 1 + \dfrac{1}{x - 2}$

10. $f(x) = \begin{cases} ^-1 & \text{if} \quad x < 2 \\ 0 & \text{if} \quad x = 2 \\ 1 & \text{if} \quad x > 2 \end{cases}$

8.3 THE DERIVATIVE

The tangent line to a circle at a given point (a, b) is a line which intersects the circle at the point (a, b) and only at the point (a, b). That is, the tangent line at (a, b) *touches* the circle but does not *cross* the circle. The intuitive idea of a tangent line to a circle is satisfactory for a simple curve. However, the tangent line to an arbitrary curve at a given point may cross the curve at that point or at some other point. Both cases are illustrated in Fig. 8.4.

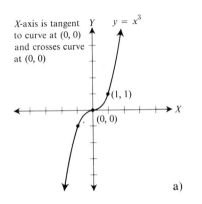

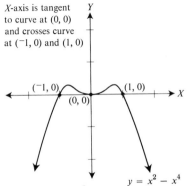

Fig. 8.4

Because the intuitive notion of tangency to a curve is unsatisfactory, we consider the graph of any function f and agree on a definition of the tangent line to the curve at any point P on the curve. To do so, we choose a second point Q close to P on the curve, and we compute the slope of the line [*the secant line*] through the two points.

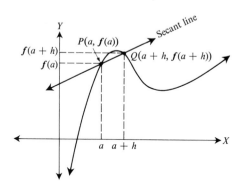

Fig. 8.5

Recalling that the slope of the secant line in Fig. 8.5 is equal to the rise divided by the run, we compute the slope of the secant line as follows:

$$\text{slope} = \frac{\text{rise}}{\text{run}} = \frac{y\text{-coordinate of } Q - y\text{-coordinate of } P}{x\text{-coordinate of } Q - x\text{-coordinate of } P}$$

$$= \frac{f(a + h) - f(a)}{(a + h) - a}$$

$$= \frac{f(a + h) - f(a)}{h}.$$

It seems reasonable to define the *tangent line* at P to be the limit of the *secant line* through P and Q as Q approaches P. Then the *slope* of the tangent line through P is

$$\lim_{h \to 0} \frac{f(a + h) - f(a)}{h}$$

because h approaches 0 as Q approaches P. For example, the slope of the tangent line to $\{(x, y): y = x^2\}$ at $(3, 9)$ is 6 because

$$\lim_{h \to 0} \frac{f(a + h) - f(a)}{h} = \lim_{h \to 0} \frac{(3 + h)^2 - 3^2}{h}$$

$$= \lim_{h \to 0} \frac{9 + 6h + h^2 - 9}{h} = \lim_{h \to 0} \frac{6h + h^2}{h}$$

$$= \lim_{h \to 0} (6 + h) = 6.$$

It is customary to speak of the slope of the tangent line to a curve at a given point A as *the slope of the curve at* A, or *the slope of the function at* A. For example, the slope of $\{(x, y): y = x^2\}$ at $(3, 9)$ is 6.

Definition 4. *The* **tangent line** *to the graph of a function* f *at a point* A, *whose coordinates are* a *and* $f(a)$, *is the limit of the secant line through* A *and* Q, *whose coordinates are* $a + h$ *and* $f(a + h)$, *as* Q *approaches* A *on the graph of* f. *The* **slope of the tangent line at** A *is*

$$\lim_{h \to 0} \frac{f(a + h) - f(a)}{h}.$$

The **slope of the graph at** A *is the slope of the tangent line at* A. *The* **slope of** f *at* A *is the slope of the tangent line at* A.

We have given a geometric meaning to

$$\lim_{h \to 0} \frac{f(a + h) - f(a)}{h};$$

it is the slope of the graph of f at $(a, f(a))$. In Section 8.1 we saw that

$$\lim_{h \to 0} \frac{f(a + h) - f(a)}{h}$$

was the instantaneous speed of an object. Because of its importance and its application to the sciences, we assign a special name to the above limit.

Definition 5. *The* **derivative of the function** f *is the function* [*denoted by* "f'" *and read* "f-prime"] *whose value at any point* a *in* $\mathscr{D}(f)$ *is*

$$\lim_{h \to 0} \frac{f(a + h) - f(a)}{h}$$

provided the limit exists. That is,

$$f'(a) = \lim_{h \to 0} \frac{f(a + h) - f(a)}{h},$$

provided the limit exists.*

The *derivative* of a function f is sometimes called the *derived function* of f, and $f'(a)$ is sometimes called the *derivative of* f (*with respect to* x) *at the point* (*or number*) a. Actually, since the derivative f' of f is a function, it may be thought of as a particular set of ordered pairs or as a rule, but *not* as a real number. The real number $f'(a)$ is one value of the derivative f'. If $x_0 \in \mathscr{D}(f)$, then $f'(x_0)$ is another value of f', provided $f'(x_0)$ exists, and $f'(x_0)$ is the slope of the tangent line at $(x_0, f(x_0))$.

The derivative may be denoted in many ways. The notations in Fig. 8.6, which appear in the literature, are all in common use. Some are relatively new;

---

*   The reader should observe that $\mathscr{D}(f') \subseteq \mathscr{D}(f)$.

others were used by Leibniz and Newton and their followers. The independent variable is x, and y is a function of x; that is, $y = f(x)$.

Various Notations for the Derivative of f at x:

$$f'(x) \qquad y' \qquad D_x f(x) \qquad D_x y \qquad \frac{df(x)}{dx} \qquad \frac{dy}{dx} \qquad \dot{y}$$

Fig. 8.6

The following examples illustrate the derivative and the various notations for it.

Example 1. If $f(x) = 3x^2$, then the derivative of f at $^-2$ is $^-12$ because

$$f'(^-2) = \lim_{h \to 0} \frac{f(^-2 + h) - f(^-2)}{h}$$

$$= \lim_{h \to 0} \frac{3(^-2 + h)^2 - 3(^-2)^2}{h}$$

$$= \lim_{h \to 0} \frac{3(4 - 4h + h^2) - 3(4)}{h}$$

$$= \lim_{h \to 0} \frac{^-12h + 3h^2}{h}$$

$$= \lim_{h \to 0} (^-12 + 3h)$$

$$= {}^-12.$$

Example 2. If $y = f(x) = x^2 + 3$, then $dy/dx = 2x$ because

$$\frac{dy}{dx} = \lim_{h \to 0} \frac{f(x + h) - f(x)}{h}$$

$$= \lim_{h \to 0} \frac{[(x + h)^2 + 3] - [x^2 + 3]}{h}$$

$$= \lim_{h \to 0} \frac{x^2 + 2hx + h^2 + 3 - x^2 - 3}{h}$$

$$= \lim_{h \to 0} \frac{2hx + h^2}{h}$$

$$= \lim_{h \to 0} (2x + h)$$

$$= 2x.$$

We may express the fact that the value of the derivative of

$$\{(x, y): y = x^2 + 3\}$$

at any point x in its domain is $2x$ by any of the following notations:

$$f'(x) = 2x, \qquad y' = 2x, \qquad D_x f(x) = 2x, \qquad D_x(y) = 2x,$$

$$\frac{df(x)}{dx} = 2x, \qquad \frac{dy}{dx} = 2x, \qquad \dot{y} = 2x.$$

The process of computing the derivative of a function is called *differentiation*; to *differentiate* a function f is to compute its derivative f'.

Example 3. If $f(x) = x^2 - 3x + 2$, then $f'(x_0) = 2x_0 - 3$ for any point x_0 in $\mathscr{D}(f)$ because

$$f'(x_0) = \lim_{h \to 0} \frac{f(x_0 + h) - f(x_0)}{h}$$

$$= \lim_{h \to 0} \frac{[(x_0 + h)^2 - 3(x_0 + h) + 2] - [x_0^2 - 3x_0 + 2]}{h}$$

$$= \lim_{h \to 0} \frac{x_0^2 + 2hx_0 + h^2 - 3x_0 - 3h + 2 - x_0^2 + 3x_0 - 2}{h}$$

$$= \lim_{h \to 0} \frac{2hx_0 + h^2 - 3h}{h}$$

$$= \lim_{h \to 0} (2x_0 + h - 3)$$

$$= 2x_0 - 3.$$

Example 4. If $f(x) = ax^2 + bx + c$, then $D_x f(x) = 2ax + b$ because

$$D_x f(x) = \lim_{h \to 0} \frac{f(x + h) - f(x)}{h}$$

$$= \lim_{h \to 0} \frac{[a(x + h)^2 + b(x + h) + c] - [ax^2 + bx + c]}{h}$$

$$= \lim_{h \to 0} \frac{ax^2 + 2ahx + ah^2 + bx + bh + c - ax^2 - bx - c}{h}$$

$$= \lim_{h \to 0} \frac{2ahx + ah^2 + bh}{h}$$

$$= \lim_{h \to 0} (2ax + ah + b)$$

$$= 2ax + b.$$

Example 5. The vertex of the parabola which is the graph of

$$\{(x, y): y = x^2 - 3x + 2\}$$

is $(3/2, {}^-1/4)$. The tangent line at the vertex of the parabola is horizontal, and thus the slope of the tangent line is 0. Since $f'(x_0) = 2x_0 - 3$ at any point in

$\mathcal{D}(f)$ [from Example 3], and since $f'(x_0)$ is the slope of the tangent line at $(x_0, f(x_0))$, it follows that $2x_0 - 3 = 0$ at the vertex. But if $2x_0 - 3 = 0$, then $x_0 = 3/2$; i.e., the x-coordinate of the vertex is $3/2$. The corresponding y-coordinate is $f(3/2)$. That is,

$$y_0 = f(3/2) = (3/2)^2 - 3(3/2) + 2 = {}^-1/4.$$

Hence the vertex is $(3/2, {}^-1/4)$.

If we know the coordinates of the vertex of a parabola, we may make a more accurate sketch of the parabola. In general, the vertex of

$$\{(x, y): y = ax^2 + bx + c, a \neq 0\}$$

is

$$\left(\frac{{}^-b}{2a}, \frac{{}^-b^2 + 4ac}{4a}\right).$$

EXERCISE SET 8.3

I. Compute the slope of the tangent line to each of the following at the indicated point.

1. $y = x^2 + x + 1$ at $(0, 1)$ 2. $y = x^2 + x + 1$ at $(1, 3)$

3. $y = x^2 - 1$ at $(1, 0)$ 4. $y = x^2 - 1$ at $(0, {}^-1)$

5. $f(x) = x^2 + 1$ at $({}^-1, 2)$ 6. $f(x) = x^2 + 1$ at $(1, 2)$

7. $f(x) = x^2 - 3x + 2$ at $(1, 0)$ 8. $f(x) = x^2 - 3x + 2$ at $(2, 0)$

9. $f(x) = x^2 + 4x + 4$ at $(0, 4)$ 10. $f(x) = x^2 + 4x + 4$ at $({}^-2, 0)$

II. Compute the coordinates of the vertex of each parabola in Exercise I, and sketch the graph.

III. Compute $f'(x)$ in each of the following.

1. $f(x) = 3x + 2$ 2. $f(x) = 2x + 3$

3. $f(x) = x^2 + 3$ 4. $f(x) = x^2 + 2$

5. $f(x) = x^3 + 2$ 6. $f(x) = x^3 + 3$

7. $f(x) = 3 - x^3$ 8. $f(x) = 2 - x^3$

9. $f(x) = (x^3 + 2)/3$ 10. $f(x) = (x^3 - 2)/3$

8.4 DIFFERENTIATION THEOREMS

To compute $f'(a)$ for a given function f by use of Definition 5, as in the examples of Section 8.3, can be very tedious. Hence we wish to state certain basic differentiation facts which we can use for rapid computation of the derivative of any polynomial function.

In Example 4 of Section 8.3 we learned that

$$D_x(ax^2 + bx + c) = 2ax + b$$

for any real numbers a, b, and c. In particular, if $a = 0$ and $b = 0$, then

$$D_x(ax^2 + bx + c) = 2ax + b = 2(0)x + 0 = 0 + 0 = 0.$$

That is, $D_xc = 0$. Frequently we say that the derivative of a constant is zero. We really mean that the derivative of the constant function $\{(x, y): y = c\}$ is 0. Since the graph of the constant function is a horizontal straight line, whose slope is 0, we should expect the derivative to be 0 at every point.

Similarly, if $a = 0$, then

$$D_x(ax^2 + bx + c) = 2ax + b = 2(0)x + b = b.$$

That is, $D_x(bx + c) = b$. Of course, we should expect the derivative to be equal to b at every point of $\{(x, y): y = bx + c\}$, since the slope of the line is b.

Before we state other differentiation facts, we state the following theorems involving limits. The proofs are omitted.

Theorem 1. *If f and g are any real functions of a real variable, if x is in both of their domains, and if $\lim_{x \to a} f(x)$ and $\lim_{x \to a} g(x)$ both exist, then*

$$\lim_{x \to a} [f(x) + g(x)] = \lim_{x \to a} f(x) + \lim_{x \to a} g(x),$$

$$\lim_{x \to a} [f(x) - g(x)] = \lim_{x \to a} f(x) - \lim_{x \to a} g(x),$$

and

$$\lim_{x \to a} [f(x)g(x)] = \lim_{x \to a} f(x) \lim_{x \to a} g(x).$$

Theorem 2. *If f and g are any real functions of a real variable, if x is in both of their domains, if $\lim_{x \to a} f(x)$ and $\lim_{x \to a} g(x)$ both exist, and if*

$$\lim_{x \to a} g(x) \neq 0,$$

then

$$\lim_{x \to a} \frac{f(x)}{g(x)} = \frac{\lim_{x \to a} f(x)}{\lim_{x \to a} g(x)}.$$

Theorem 3. *If k is any real number, if f is any real function of a real variable, if x is in the domain of f, and if $\lim_{x \to a} f(x)$ exists, then*

$$\lim_{x \to a} kf(x) = k \lim_{x \to a} f(x).$$

We can employ the above theorems to prove certain basic differentiation theorems. For convenience and reference, we restate the two previous differentiation facts as Theorems 4 and 5, which we have proved already. We omit the proofs of Theorems 6 through 10.

Theorem 4. *The derivative of the constant function $\{(x, y): y = k\}$ is equal to 0. That is,*

$$D_xk = 0.$$

Theorem 5. *The derivative of the linear function* $\{(x, y): y = ax + b\}$ *is equal to a. That is,*

$$D_x(ax + b) = a.$$

Theorem 6. *The derivative of the sum of any two functions is the sum of the derivatives of the two functions. That is,*

$$D_x[f(x) + g(x)] = D_x f(x) + D_x g(x) = f'(x) + g'(x)$$

for all numbers x in $\mathscr{D}(f') \cap \mathscr{D}(g')$.

Theorem 7. *The derivative of the product of any real number and any function is the product of the real number and the derivative of the function. That is,*

$$D_x k f(x) = k D_x f(x) = k f'(x)$$

for all numbers x in $\mathscr{D}(f')$.

Theorem 8. *If f and g are any real functions of a real variable x such that* $x \in \mathscr{D}(f') \cap \mathscr{D}(g')$, *then*

$$D_x[f(x)g(x)] = f(x)D_x g(x) + g(x)D_x f(x)$$
$$= f(x)g'(x) + g(x)f'(x).$$

Theorem 9. *If f and g are any real functions of a real variable x such that* $x \in \mathscr{D}(f') \cap \mathscr{D}(g')$ *and* $g(x) \neq 0$, *then*

$$D_x \frac{f(x)}{g(x)} = \frac{g(x)f'(x) - f(x)g'(x)}{[g(x)]^2}.$$

Theorem 10. *If n is any positive integer, then*

$$D_x x^n = n x^{n-1}.$$

The following examples illustrate the above theorems.

Example 1

$$D_x x = D_x x^1 = 1x^0 = 1 \qquad \text{[by Theorem 10].}$$

Example 2

$$D_x x^7 = 7x^6 \qquad\qquad \text{[by Theorem 10].}$$

Example 3

$$D_x 5x^8 = 5D_x x^8 \qquad\quad \text{[by Theorem 7]}$$
$$= 5(8x^7) \qquad\qquad \text{[by Theorem 10]}$$
$$= 40x^7.$$

Example 4

$$D_x(x^4 + x^3) = D_x x^4 + D_x x^3 \qquad \text{[by Theorem 6]}$$
$$= 4x^3 + 3x^2 \qquad \text{[by Theorem 10]}.$$

Example 5

$$D_x(3 + 5x - 4x^2 + x^3)$$
$$= D_x(3) + D_x(5x) - D_x(4x^2) + D_x(x^3) \qquad \text{[by Theorem 6]}$$
$$= D_x(3) + 5D_x x - 4D_x x^2 + D_x x^3 \qquad \text{[by Theorem 7]}$$
$$= 0 + 5 - 8x + 3x^2 \qquad \text{[by Theorems 4 and 10]}.$$

Example 6

$$D_x[(x^2 + 1)(3 + 5x^4)]$$
$$= (x^2 + 1)D_x(3 + 5x^4) + (3 + 5x^4)D_x(x^2 + 1) \qquad \text{[by Theorem 8]}$$
$$= (x^2 + 1)(20x^3) + (3 + 5x^4)(2x) \qquad \text{[by Theorems 6, 7, and 10]}$$
$$= 20x^5 + 20x^3 + 6x + 10x^5$$
$$= 30x^5 + 20x^3 + 6x.$$

Example 7

$$D_x[(x - 2)(x^2 + 5)]$$
$$= (x - 2)D_x(x^2 + 5) + (x^2 + 5)D_x(x - 2) \qquad \text{[by Theorem 8]}$$
$$= (x - 2)(2x) + (x^2 + 5)(1) \qquad \text{[by Theorems 4, 6, and 10]}$$
$$= 2x^2 - 4x + x^2 + 5$$
$$= 3x^2 - 4x + 5.$$

Example 8

$$D_x\left(\frac{5x^2}{x^3 + 1}\right) = \frac{(x^3 + 1)D_x(5x^2) - 5x^2 D_x(x^3 + 1)}{(x^3 + 1)^2} \qquad \text{[by Theorem 9]}$$
$$= \frac{(x^3 + 1)(10x) - 5x^2(3x^2)}{(x^3 + 1)^2} \qquad \text{[by Theorems 6, 7, and 10]}$$
$$= \frac{10x^4 + 10x - 15x^4}{(x^3 + 1)^2}$$
$$= \frac{10x - 5x^4}{(x^3 + 1)^2}, \qquad \text{provided } x \neq {}^-1.$$

Example 9

$$\dot{D}_x(2 + 3x - 5x^2 - 7x^3 + x^4 + 3x^5) = 3 - 10x - 21x^2 + 4x^3 + 15x^4.$$

Example 10

$$D_x\left(\frac{x+1}{x+2}\right) = \frac{(x+2)D_x(x+1) - (x+1)D_x(x+2)}{(x+2)^2} \quad \text{[by Theorem 9]}$$

$$= \frac{(x+2)(1) - (x+1)(1)}{(x+2)^2}$$

$$= \frac{x+2-x-1}{(x+2)^2}$$

$$= \frac{1}{(x+2)^2}, \quad \text{provided } x \neq {}^-2.$$

Theorems 4, 6, 7, and 10 enable us to compute the derivative of any polynomial function; Examples 4, 5, and 9 illustrate the procedure. Moreover, Theorems 8 and 9 enable us to compute the derivative of products and quotients of polynomials; Examples 6, 7, 8, and 10 illustrate the procedure. The restrictions in Examples 8 and 10 are to guarantee existence of the derivatives.

EXERCISE SET 8.4

I. Differentiate each of the following polynomial functions; i.e., compute $f'(x)$. What is the domain of f? What is the domain of f'?

1. $f(x) = 5 + x$ 2. $f(x) = 1 + 5x$

3. $f(x) = 3 + 2x - x^2$ 4. $f(x) = 3 - 2x + x^2$

5. $f(x) = x + x^2 - x^3 + 5x^4$ 6. $f(x) = x - x^2 + x^3 + 3x^4$

7. $f(x) = 3 - x + x^2 - x^3 + x^4 - x^5$

8. $f(x) = 2 - x + x^2 - x^3 + x^4 - x^5$

9. $f(x) = x^{10} - x^8 + 2x^6 - 3x^4 + x^2 - 5$

10. $f(x) = x^9 - x^7 + 3x^5 - 2x^3 + x$

II. Differentiate each of the following functions. Identify $\mathscr{D}(f)$ and $\mathscr{D}(f')$.

1. $f(x) = (x + 3)^2(2x - 1)^3$ 2. $f(x) = (x + 3)^3(2x - 1)^2$

3. $f(x) = (2x + 5)^2(3x^2 - 1)$ 4. $f(x) = (3x - 5)^2(3x^2 + 1)$

5. $f(x) = (x^4 + 1)(x^3 - 1)$ 6. $f(x) = (x^4 - 1)(x^3 + 1)$

7. $f(x) = \dfrac{x - 1}{x + 1}$ 8. $f(x) = \dfrac{x + 1}{x - 1}$

9. $f(x) = \dfrac{3x^2 + 5}{2x + 7}$ 10. $f(x) = \dfrac{3x^2 + 7}{2x + 5}$

III. In each of the following, determine a function f whose derivative is specified. How many functions exist in each case?

1. $f'(x) = 0$ 2. $f'(x) = 1$

3. $f'(x) = 2$ 4. $f'(x) = 2x$

5. $f'(x) = x$ 6. $f'(x) = 4x^3$

7. $f'(x) = 5x^4$

8. $f'(x) = nx^{n-1}$ [n is a positive integer]

9. $f'(x) = x^{n-1}$ [n is a positive integer]

10. $f'(x) = x^n$ [n is a positive integer]

8.5 MAXIMA AND MINIMA

We have learned that the slope of the tangent line to the graph of any polynomial function f at the point (x, y) is $f'(x)$. For example, the slopes of the three tangent lines shown in Fig. 8.7 are $f'(x_1)$, $f'(x_2)$, and $f'(x_3)$.

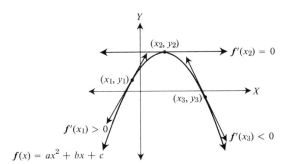

Fig. 8.7

The point (x_2, y_2) is the vertex of the parabola and hence the *highest* point on the curve. The slope of the tangent line appears to be 0. Since $f'(x_1) > 0$ for every x_1 to the left of x_2 and $f'(x_3) < 0$ for every x_3 to the right of x_2, it seems intuitively obvious that $f'(x_2) = 0$, provided it exists. Any point such as (x_2, y_2) is called a *relative maximum point*, and y_2 is called a *relative maximum* of f.

Similarly any point such as (x_2, y_2) in Fig. 8.8 is called a *relative minimum point*, and y_2 is called a *relative minimum* of f.

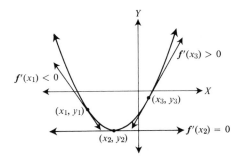

Fig. 8.8

Intuitively, a *relative maximum* of a function is the maximum value of the function in some neighborhood of a point, and a *relative minimum* of a function is the minimum value of the function in some neighborhood of a point. In Fig. 8.7 the relative maximum is an absolute maximum; in Fig. 8.8 the relative minimum is an absolute minimum. However, in Fig. 8.9, the relative minimum is not an absolute minimum, and the relative maximum is not an absolute maximum. In fact, f has neither an absolute maximum nor an absolute minimum because the graph extends indefinitely upward and downward.

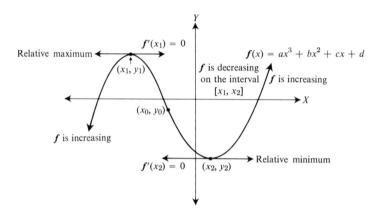

Fig. 8.9

In any interval in which $f'(x) > 0$ we say that f is *increasing*. In any interval in which $f'(x) < 0$ we say that f is *decreasing*. For example, the function in Fig. 8.9 is *increasing* in any open interval (a, x_1) in which $a < x_1$; *decreasing* in the open interval (x_1, x_2); and *increasing* in any open interval (x_2, b) in which $b > x_2$.

The tangent line at (x_2, y_2) to the cubical parabola in Fig. 8.10 is horizontal. Thus $f'(x_2) = 0$. However, (x_2, y_2) is neither a relative maximum nor a relative minimum point. We observe that f is increasing both to the left of x_2 and to the right of x_2. We say that f is *stationary* at $(x_2, f(x_2))$. Moreover, the tangent line at (x_2, y_2) crosses the graph at (x_2, y_2).

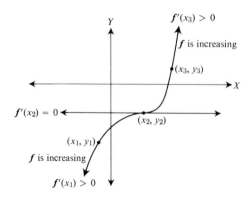

Fig. 8.10

Any point such as (x_2, y_2) in Fig. 8.10 is called a *point of inflection*. The tangent line to the curve at (x_2, y_2) in Fig. 8.10 is horizontal; that is, $f'(x_2) = 0$. However, there are points of inflection at which the tangent lines are not horizontal. For example, (x_0, y_0) in Fig. 8.9 is a point of inflection, but $f'(x_0) \neq 0$. The tangent line to the graph of f at (x_0, y_0) crosses the graph of f at (x_0, y_0).

Although a point of inflection of the type in Fig. 8.9 is of interest in a more advanced course, the only points of inflection of interest to us in a brief course are those of the type in Fig. 8.10.

We formalize the above discussion in the following definitions.

Definition 6. *The function f is said to be **decreasing at the point** x_1 if and only if $f'(x_1) < 0$. The function f is said to be **decreasing on the open interval (a, b)** if and only if $f'(x) < 0$ for each x in (a, b).*

Definition 7. *The function f is said to be **increasing at the point** x_1 if and only if $f'(x_1) > 0$. The function f is said to be **increasing on the open interval (a, b)** if and only if $f'(x) > 0$ for each x in (a, b).*

Definition 8. *The function f is said to be **stationary at the point** x_1 if and only if $f'(x_1) = 0$. The function f is said to be **stationary on the interval (a, b)** if and only if $f'(x) = 0$ for each x in (a, b).*

Figures 8.11 through 8.13 illustrate the fact that the terms *decreasing*, *increasing*, and *stationary* apply to linear functions as well as to polynomial functions of higher degree.

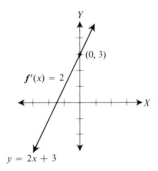

$f'(x) = 2$

$(0, 3)$

$y = 2x + 3$

The function f, which is equal to $\{(x, y): y = 2x + 3\}$, is *increasing* on R because $f'(x)$ is *positive* for every x in R.

Fig. 8.11

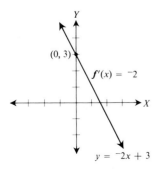

$(0, 3)$

$f'(x) = {}^-2$

$y = {}^-2x + 3$

The function f, which is equal to $\{(x, y): y = {}^-2x + 3\}$, is *decreasing* on R because $f'(x)$ is *negative* for every x in R.

Fig. 8.12

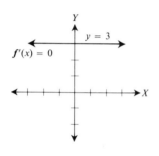

The function f, which is equal to $\{(x, y): y = 3\}$, is *stationary* on R because $f'(x) = 0$ for every x in R.

Fig. 8.13

Definition 9. *The polynomial function f is said to have a **relative minimum** at a point x_1 in an open interval (a, b) if and only if f is decreasing on the open interval (a, x_1) and increasing on the open interval (x_1, b). The point $\left(x_1, f(x_1)\right)$ is called a relative minimum point.*

Definition 10. *The polynomial function f is said to have a **relative maximum** at a point x_1 in an open interval (a, b) if and only if f is increasing on the open interval (a, x_1) and decreasing on the open interval (x_1, b). The point $\left(x_1, f(x_1)\right)$ is called a relative maximum point.*

Definition 11. *The point $\left(x_1, f(x_1)\right)$ of the polynomial function f is said to be a point of inflection if and only if the tangent line to the graph of f at $\left(x_1, f(x_1)\right)$ crosses the graph at $\left(x_1, f(x_1)\right)$.*

The following theorems, which we state without proof, provide a method of computing the relative minima, the relative maxima, and certain points of inflection (the type in Fig. 8.10) of any *continuous function f whose derivative is defined for every element of the domain of f.*

Theorem 11. *If a, b, and x_1 are any real numbers such that $a < x_1 < b$ and if f is any polynomial function such that $f'(x_1) = 0$, $f'(x) < 0$ for all x in the open interval (a, x_1), and $f'(x) > 0$ for all x in the open interval (x_1, b), then $\left(x_1, f(x_1)\right)$ is a relative minimum point and $f(x_1)$ is the minimum value of f in the open interval (a, b).*

Theorem 12. *If a, b, and x_1 are any real numbers such that $a < x_1 < b$ and if f is any polynomial function such that $f'(x_1) = 0$, $f'(x) > 0$ for all x in the open interval (a, x_1), and $f'(x) < 0$ for all x in the open interval (x_1, b), then $\left(x_1, f(x_1)\right)$ is a relative maximum point and $f(x_1)$ is the maximum value of f in the open interval (a, b).*

Theorem 13. *If a, b, and x_1 are any real numbers such that $a < x_1 < b$ and if f is any polynomial function such that $f'(x_1) = 0$ and $f'(x_1) > 0$ for all x in $(a, x_1) \cup (x_1, b)$ or $f'(x_1) < 0$ for all x in $(a, x_1) \cup (x_1, b)$, then $\left(x_1, f(x_1)\right)$ is a point of inflection and $f(x_1)$ is neither the minimum nor the maximum value of f in the open interval (a, b).*

The following examples illustrate the applications of Theorems 11, 12, and 13 to computation of minima, maxima, and points of inflection and to sketching the graphs of continuous functions.

Example 1. The function $f(x) = x^2 - 4x + 3$ has a relative minimum at 2; i.e., the point $(2, {}^{-}1)$ is a relative minimum point of $f(x) = x^2 - 4x + 3$, and $^{-}1$ is the minimum value of f, because of the following analysis:

$$f(x) = x^2 - 4x + 3,$$

$$f'(x) = 2x - 4,$$

$$2x_1 - 4 = 0,$$

$$x_1 = 2,$$

$$f(x_1) = 2^2 - 4(2) + 3 = {}^{-}1,$$

$$f'(1) = 2(1) - 4 = 2 - 4 = {}^{-}2 \quad \text{and} \quad {}^{-}2 < 0,$$

$$f'(3) = 2(3) - 4 = 6 - 4 = 2 \quad \text{and} \quad 2 > 0.$$

That is, $f'(2) = 0$, $1 < 2 < 3$, $f'(1) < 0$, $f'(3) > 0$; and $f'(x) < 0$ for any x in the open interval $(1, 2)^*$ and $f'(x) > 0$ for any x in the open interval $(2, 3)^*$. Hence, by Theorem 11, $(2, {}^{-}1)$ is a relative minimum point of f and $^{-}1$ is the minimum value of f in the open interval $(1, 3)$. Moreover, $^{-}1$ is the minimum value of f in any open interval (a, b) such that $a < 2 < b$, as the accompanying figure illustrates.

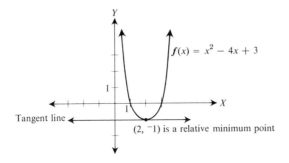

$f(x) = x^2 - 4x + 3$

Tangent line

$(2, {}^{-}1)$ is a relative minimum point

Example 2. The function $f(x) = 5 + 2x - x^2$ has a relative maximum at 1; i.e., the point $(1, 6)$ is a relative maximum point of $f(x) = 5 + 2x - x^2$,

---

*   The above results are consequences of the following analysis:

$f'(x) = 2x - 4,$	$f'(x) = 2x - 4,$
$2x - 4 < 0,$	$2x - 4 > 0,$
$2x < 4,$	$2x > 4,$
$x < 2,$	$x > 2.$

and 6 is the maximum value of f because of the following analysis:

$$f(x) = 5 + 2x - x^2,$$
$$f'(x) = 2 - 2x,$$
$$2 - 2x_1 = 0,$$
$$x_1 = 1,$$
$$f(x_1) = 5 + 2(1) - 1^2,$$
$$f(x_1) = 6,$$
$$f'(0) = 2 - 2(0) = 2 \quad \text{and} \quad 2 > 0,$$
$$f'(2) = 2 - 2(2) = {}^-2 \quad \text{and} \quad {}^-2 < 0.$$

That is, $f'(1) = 0$, $0 < 1 < 2$, $f'(0) > 0$, $f'(2) < 0$; and $f'(x) > 0$ for any x in the open interval $(0, 1)$ and $f'(x) < 0$ for any x in the open interval $(1, 2)$. Hence, by Theorem 12, $(1, 6)$ is a relative maximum point of f, and 6 is the maximum value of f in the open interval $(0, 2)$. Moreover, 6 is the maximum value of f in any open interval (a, b) such that $a < 1 < b$, as the accompanying figure illustrates.

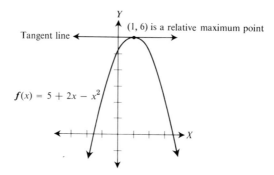

Tangent line $\longleftarrow$ $(1, 6)$ is a relative maximum point

$f(x) = 5 + 2x - x^2$

Example 3. The function $f(x) = x^3 + 2$ has a point of inflection at 0; i.e., $(0, 2)$ is a point of inflection of $f(x) = x^3 + 2$, because of the following analysis:

$$f(x) = x^3 + 2,$$
$$f'(x) = 3x^2,$$
$$3x_1^2 = 0,$$
$$x_1^2 = 0,$$
$$x_1 = 0,$$
$$f(x_1) = 0^3 + 2,$$
$$f(x_1) = 2,$$
$$f'({}^-1) = 3({}^-1)^2 = 3(1) = 3 \quad \text{and} \quad 3 > 0,$$
$$f'(1) = 3(1)^2 = 3(1) = 3 \quad \text{and} \quad 3 > 0.$$

That is, $f'(0) = 0$, $^-1 < 0 < 1$, $f'(^-1) > 0$, $f'(1) > 0$; and $f'(x) > 0$ for each x in the open interval $(^-1, 0)$ and $f'(x) > 0$ for each x in the open interval $(0, 1)$. Hence, by Theorem 13, $(0, 2)$ is a point of inflection. Moreover, f has no maximum or minimum, as the accompanying figure illustrates.

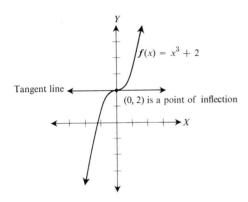

EXERCISE SET 8.5

I. Determine the relative maximum point, the relative minimum point, or the point of inflection of each of the following. Then sketch the graph of each.

1. $f(x) = x^2 - 3x + 2$ 2. $f(x) = x^2 - 5x + 4$
3. $f(x) = {}^-x^2 + 3x - 2$ 4. $f(x) = {}^-x^2 + 5x - 4$
5. $f(x) = x^2 - 9$ 6. $f(x) = x^2 - 4$
7. $f(x) = x^3 - 1$ 8. $f(x) = x^3 + 1$
9. $f(x) = 4 - x^2$ 10. $f(x) = 9 - x^2$

II. Each of the following has either a relative maximum or a relative minimum. Determine that point, and sketch the graph.

1. $f(x) = x^4$ 2. $f(x) = 2x^4$
3. $f(x) = \frac{1}{2}x^6$ 4. $f(x) = x^6$
5. $f(x) = 2 - x^6$ 6. $f(x) = 1 - x^6$
7. $f(x) = 1 - x^4$ 8. $f(x) = 2 - x^4$
9. $f(x) = x^4 - 2$ 10. $f(x) = x^4 - 1$

III. Each of the following has a point of inflection. Determine that point of inflection, and sketch the graph.

1. $f(x) = 2x^5$ 2. $f(x) = x^5$
3. $f(x) = 2 - x^5$ 4. $f(x) = 1 - 2x^5$
5. $f(x) = 1 - x^3$ 6. $f(x) = 2 - x^3$
7. $f(x) = 2 + x^3$ 8. $f(x) = 3 + x^3$
9. $f(x) = 1 + x^7$ 10. $f(x) = 1 - x^7$

8.6 APPLICATIONS

The derivative has extensive applications in the physical sciences, management science, industry, and other disciplines. Frequently one needs to maximize or minimize a given function. For example, in order to maximize profit, a manufacturer must minimize the cost. The following examples illustrate some of the simpler applications of the derivative.

Example 1. A farmer has 1000 ft of fencing to fence a *rectangular* field for cattle grazing. Since he wishes to enclose the largest possible region, he decides to take advantage of a river which adjoins his property and to use fencing on three sides only (the river side requires no fencing). What are the dimensions of the field of maximum area which he can enclose with the 1000 ft of fencing?

From the accompanying figure, we see that the area of the field is the value $f(x)$ of the function f defined by the formula $f(x) = x(1000 - 2x)$, in which $0 < x < 500$.

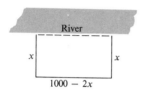

To compute the maximum area, we compute that x_1 such that $f'(x_1) = 0$ and then we compute $f(x_1)$:

$$f(x) = 1000x - 2x^2,$$
$$f'(x) = 1000 - 4x,$$
$$1000 - 4x_1 = 0,$$
$$x_1 = 250;$$
$$f(x_1) = 250(1000 - 500)$$
$$= 250(500)$$
$$= 125,000.$$

To determine that $f(x_1)$ is really a maximum, we may compute $f'(200)$ and $f'(300)$:

$$f'(200) = 1000 - 4(200) = 1000 - 800 = 200,$$
$$f'(300) = 1000 - 4(300) = 1000 - 1200 = {}^-200.$$

Since $f'(200) > 0$, $f'(300) < 0$, $f'(250) = 0$, $200 < 250 < 300$, and $f(x) > 0$ for every x in $[200, 250)$ and $f'(x) < 0$ for every x in $(250, 300]$, it follows from Theorem 12 that $(250, f(250))$ is a relative maximum point.

Hence the maximum area he can enclose with the 1000 ft of fencing is 125,000 square feet. The dimensions of the rectangular field are 250 ft and 500 ft. That is, the two sides perpendicular to the river should be 250 ft each, and the side parallel to the river should be 500 ft.

Example 2. From past experience a citrus farmer knows that 40 orange trees per acre will yield 20,000 oranges per acre, an average of 500 oranges per tree. If he increases the number of trees per acre above 40, the average yield per tree is reduced by 10 oranges for each additional tree. How many trees per acre should he plant in order to maximize his yield per acre?

Letting x be the number of trees per acre in excess of 40, we see that there are $40 + x$ trees per acre with an average yield of $500 - 10x$ oranges per tree. Thus the yield y per acre is the product; that is,

$$y = f(x) = (40 + x)(500 - 10x)$$

$$= 20,000 + 100x - 10x^2.$$

Then

$$f'(x) = 100 - 20x,$$

$$100 - 20x_1 = 0,$$

$$x_1 = 5;$$

$$f(x_1) = f(5) = (40 + 5)(500 - 50)$$

$$= 45(450)$$

$$= 20,250.$$

Thus the farmer increases the yield per acre by planting 5 extra trees per acre. That is, he should plant 45 trees per acre; the average yield will be 450 oranges per tree. The average yield will be 20,250 oranges per acre. We can actually verify that 20,250 is the maximum attainable yield per acre.

Example 3. Karl is standing on a platform 100 ft high and throws a baseball straight upward with an initial speed of 32 ft/sec. The motion of the ball is described by the function

$$f(t) = 100 + 32t - 16t^2,$$

in which t is the time in seconds after he has thrown the ball and $f(t)$ is the height of the ball in feet. When does the ball reach its maximum height?

$$f(t) = 100 + 32t - 16t^2,$$

$$f'(t) = 32 - 32t,$$

$$32 - 32t_1 = 0,$$

$$t_1 = 1;$$

$$f(t_1) = f(1) = 100 + 32(1) - 16(1^2)$$

$$= 100 + 32 - 16$$

$$= 116.$$

Thus the ball attains its maximum height 1 sec after it has been thrown. Then the ball begins to fall. The maximum height is 116 ft above ground.

EXERCISE SET 8.6

I.

1. Verify that the result of Example 1 is actually a maximum by computing $f'(225)$ and $f'(275)$ and proceeding as in Example 1.

2. Verify that the result of Example 2 is actually a maximum by computing $f'(4)$ and $f'(6)$ and proceeding as in Example 1.

3. Verify that the result of Example 3 is actually a maximum by computing $f'(0)$ and $f'(2)$ and proceeding as in Example 1. Sketch the graph of f.

II. The perimeter of a rectangle is 80 ft. The area is the maximum possible area of any rectangle whose perimeter is 80 ft. What are the dimensions? [*Hint:* Refer to the accompanying figure.]

III. A tinsmith wishes to make an open box by cutting a square region from each corner of a sheet of metal 12 in. square and turning up the sides. Compute the length of the side of each square region he must cut out so that the volume of the box will be maximum. [*Hint:* Refer to the accompanying figure. You will have to solve a quadratic equation by inspection.]

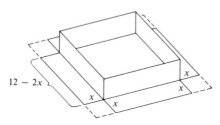

8.7 THE ANTIDERIVATIVES OF A FUNCTION

We have learned that $D_x x^n = nx^{n-1}$ for every positive integer n and that $D_x c = 0$ for any real number c.* Moreover, $D_x(x^n + 3) = nx^{n-1}$ and

$$D_x(x^n + c) = nx^{n-1}$$

for every positive integer n and every real number c. The inverse of differentiation, called *integration*, involves computing a function whose derivative is specified. Since $D_x(x^n + c) = nx^{n-1}$ for every real number c and each positive integer n,

---

*   The real number c, which does not depend on x, is usually called a *constant*.

and since there are infinitely many real numbers, it follows that there are infinitely many functions corresponding to each derivative.

Definition 12. *Any function F such that $F' = f$ is called an* **antiderivative of f**.

For example, $F(x) = x^n + c$ is an antiderivative of $f(x) = nx^{n-1}$. The following examples further illustrate the computation of the antiderivatives of a polynomial function.

Example 1. An antiderivative of $f(x) = 4x^3$ is $F(x) = x^4$ because $F'(x) = 4x^3$. However, another antiderivative of $f(x) = 4x^3$ is $G(x) = x^4 + c$ for any real number c because

$$G'(x) = D_x(x^4 + c) = D_x x^4 + D_x c = 4x^3 + 0 = 4x^3.$$

Hence there are infinitely many antiderivatives of $f(x) = 4x^3$.

Example 2. An antiderivative of $f(x) = x^5$ is $F(x) = \frac{1}{6}x^6$ because

$$F'(x) = 6(\tfrac{1}{6})x^5 = x^5.$$

Moreover, $G(x) = \frac{1}{6}x^6 + c$ is an antiderivative of $f(x) = x^5$ because $G'(x) = x^5$. Hence there are infinitely many antiderivatives of $f(x) = x^5$.

Example 3. An antiderivative of $f(x) = 1 + 2x + 3x^2$ is

$$F(x) = 1 + x + x^2 + x^3$$

because

$$F'(x) = 0 + 1 + 2x + 3x^2.$$

Moreover,

$$G(x) = c + x + x^2 + x^3$$

is an antiderivative of $f(x) = 1 + 2x + 3x^2$ because

$$G'(x) = 1 + 2x + 3x^2.$$

Hence there are infinitely many antiderivatives of

$$f(x) = 1 + 2x + 3x^2.$$

Example 4. An antiderivative of $f(x) = 0$ is $F(x) = 0$ because $F'(x) = 0$. Moreover, $G(x) = c$ is an antiderivative of $f(x) = 0$. The graphs of some of the antiderivatives are shown in the accompanying figure.

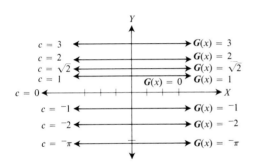

Example 5. An antiderivative of $f(x) = 2$ is $F(x) = 2x$ because $F'(x) = 2$. Moreover, $G(x) = 2x + c$ is an antiderivative of $f(x) = 2$ because $G'(x) = 2$. Hence there are infinitely many antiderivatives of $f(x) = 2$. The graphs of some of the antiderivatives are shown in the accompanying figure.

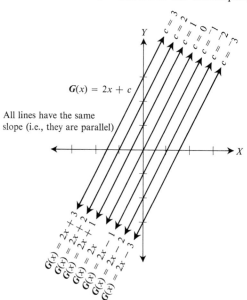

The above discussion and examples illustrate the fact that every polynomial function has infinitely many antiderivatives. Moreover, if F and G are any antiderivatives of f and if x is in the domain of F and the domain of G, then $F(x) - G(x)$ is a constant; i.e., the functional values of any two antiderivatives of a function differ by a constant. For example, if $G(x) = 2x + 3$ and $F(x) = 2x$, then $G(x) - F(x) = 3$ and both are antiderivatives of $f(x) = 2$. Consequently, it is customary to say that *the antiderivative of* $f(x) = 2$ *is* $F(x) = 2x + c$.

The above examples illustrate further that the antiderivative of $f(x) = x^n$ is

$$F(x) = \frac{x^{n+1}}{n+1} + c.$$

The next theorem follows from Theorem 10.

Theorem 14. *If n is any counting number, then the antiderivative of $f(x) = x^n$ is*

$$F(x) = \frac{x^{n+1}}{n+1} + c.$$

Proof

$$F'(x) = D_x\left(\frac{x^{n+1}}{n+1} + c\right)$$

$$= (n+1)\frac{x^{n+1} - 1}{n+1} + 0$$

$$= x^n. \quad \text{(QED)}$$

In Example 5 we learned that the antiderivative of $f(x) = 2$ is $G(x) = 2x + c$. That is, if $y' = 2$, then $y = 2x + c$. In general, if $y' = a$, then $y = ax + b$. But the graph of $y = ax + b$ is a line, as illustrated in Example 5. Moreover, the slope is a. Hence we may determine the *equation* of a line (i.e., the formula defining a linear function) if we know the slope and a point on the line. The following examples illustrate the procedure.

Example 6. The slope of a line is 5. The line contains the point $(3, 4)$. What is the equation of the line?

$$y' = 5,$$

$$y = 5x + b,$$

$$4 = 5(3) + b,$$

$$4 = 15 + b,$$

$$4 - 15 = b,$$

$$b = {}^-11.$$

Therefore,

$$y = 5x + {}^-11.$$

Hence the equation of the line is $y = 5x - 11$. The slope is 5 and the y-intercept is $^-11$.

Example 7. The point $(2, {}^-7)$ is on a line, and the slope of the line is $^-3$. What is the equation of the line?

$$y' = {}^-3,$$

$$y = {}^-3x + b,$$

$${}^-7 = {}^-3(2) + b,$$

$${}^-7 + 6 = b,$$

$$b = {}^-1.$$

Therefore,

$$y = {}^-3x + {}^-1.$$

Hence the equation of the line is $y = {}^-3x - 1$. The slope is $^-3$ and the y-intercept is $^-1$.

The above examples illustrate that the constant b, which we determine by substituting the coordinates of the given point for x and y in the formula defining the antiderivative, is the y-intercept of the line. Since the slope (y') is given, the particular point on the line determines the y-intercept but not the slope. For example, any line such that $y' = {}^-3$ has slope $^-3$. In particular, that line through $(2, {}^-7)$ is parallel to the line through $(3, 2)$; i.e., the slope of each is $^-3$, but the y-intercepts are different.

EXERCISE SET 8.7

I. Determine the antiderivative of each of the following functions. [For example, the antiderivative of $f(x) = x^2$ is $F(x) = \frac{1}{3}x^3 + c$.]

1. $f(x) = 3x^2$ 2. $f(x) = 4x^3$
3. $f(x) = 4x^3 - 3x^2$ 4. $f(x) = 4x^3 + 3x^2$
5. $f(x) = 3x + 2$ 6. $f(x) = 2x + 3$
7. $f(x) = 9x^8$ 8. $f(x) = 10x^9$
9. $f(x) = 10x^9 - 9x^8$ 10. $f(x) = 9x^8 - 10x^9$

II. Derive the equation of the line which has the following slope and which passes through the following indicated point.

1. Slope $= 5$, point is $(2, 3)$ 2. Slope $= 5$, point is $(3, 2)$
3. Slope $= 4$, point is $({}^-3, 2)$ 4. Slope $= 4$, point is $(2, {}^-3)$
5. Slope $= {}^-7$, point is $(4, {}^-2)$ 6. Slope $= {}^-7$, point is $({}^-5, 2)$
7. Slope $= {}^-4$, point is $(0, 4)$ 8. Slope $= {}^-4$, point is $(4, 0)$
9. Slope $= 0$, point is $(1, 3)$ 10. Slope $= 0$, point is $(3, 1)$

III.

1. If $F'(x) = 3x^2 - 2x + 2$ and $F(1) = 2$, compute $F(x)$ and $F({}^-3)$.
2. If $F'(x) = 3x^2 - 2x + 5$ and $F(1) = {}^-3$, compute $F(x)$ and $F(2)$.
3. If $F'(x) = 4x^3 - 3x^2 + 2$ and $F(0) = 5$, compute $F(x)$ and $F(1)$.
4. If $F'(x) = 4x^3 + 3x^2 - 2$ and $F(0) = 3$, compute $F(x)$ and $F(1)$.

8.8 THE INTEGRAL

The antiderivative of a function is useful in the computation of the area bounded by the continuous nonnegative function f, the x-axis, and the vertical lines $x = a$ and $x = b$. For example, if we wish to compute the area of the metal plate represented by the region in Fig. 8.14, we consider the upper edge to be part of the graph of f, the lower edge to be the interval $[a, b]$ on the X-axis, the left edge to be part of the line $x = a$, and the right edge to be part of the line $x = b$. If the plate were a rectangular one, its area would be the product of its base and its altitude. For example, if the top edge were the horizontal line $y = f(a)$, indicated in Fig. 8.14, the area would be $(b - a)f(a)$. Of course, the area of the metal plate is greater than $(b - a)f(a)$.

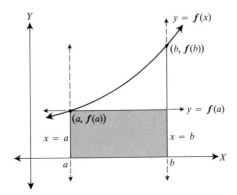

Fig. 8.14

We can partition the interval $[a, b]$ by its midpoint x_1 into two intervals and construct two rectangles as indicated in Fig. 8.15. Since the base of each rectangle is $(b - a)/2$, the sum of the areas of the two rectangular regions is

$$\frac{b - a}{2} f(a) + \frac{b - a}{2} f(x_1),$$

which is still less than the area of the plate.

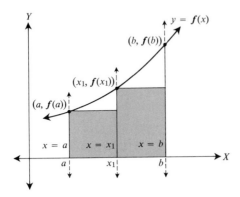

Fig. 8.15

In order to obtain a better approximation to the area of the plate, we can partition the interval $[a, b]$ into four intervals and construct four rectangles of equal base, as indicated in Fig. 8.16. Since the base of each rectangle is $(b - a)/4$, the sum of the areas of the rectangular regions is

$$\frac{b - a}{4} f(a) + \frac{b - a}{4} f(x_1) + \frac{b - a}{4} f(x_2) + \frac{b - a}{4} f(x_3),$$

which is still less than the area of the plate.

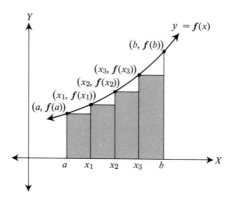

Fig. 8.16

We can obtain a better approximation to the area of the plate by partitioning further. For example, we can partition $[a, b]$ into eight intervals and construct eight rectangles of equal base, as indicated in Fig. 8.17. Since the base of each rectangle is $(b - a)/8$, the sum of the areas of the eight rectangular regions is

$$\frac{b - a}{8}\left[f(a) + f(x_1) + f(x_2) + f(x_3) + f(x_4) + f(x_5) + f(x_6) + f(x_7)\right],$$

which is still less than the area of the plate.

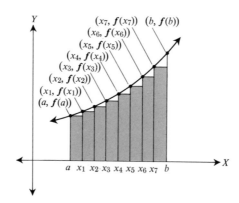

Fig. 8.17

We can partition still further. For example, we can construct 16 rectangles or 32 rectangles, or any larger number of rectangles of equal base. It seems intuitively clear that the sum of the areas of the rectangular regions approaches the area of the plate as the number of rectangles increases and the bases of the rectangles decrease.

Although the above limit is not the same type of limit that we previously studied, it does exist under the conditions in which we are interested. Since the proof is somewhat tedious and difficult for an introductory course, we state the following theorem without proof.

Theorem 15. *If f is a nonnegative polynomial function and $a < b$, then*

$$\lim_{n \to \infty} \frac{b - a}{n} \left[f(a) + f(x_1) + f(x_2) + \cdots + f(x_{n-1}) \right]$$

exists.

We follow established convention and denote the limit in Theorem 15 by the symbol

$$\text{``} \int_a^b f \text{''} \qquad \text{or} \qquad \text{``} \int_a^b f(x) \, dx \text{''}$$

and we call it *the integral of f from a to b.* Thus

$$\int_a^b f = \int_a^b f(x) \, dx = \lim_{n \to \infty} \frac{b - a}{n} \left[f(a) + f(x_1) + \cdots + f(x_{n-1}) \right].$$

Because of Theorem 15, we make the following definition.

Definition 13. *The **area** of the region bounded by the graph of the nonnegative polynomial function f, the X-axis, and the vertical lines $x = a$ and $x = b$, in which $a < b$, is $\int_a^b f$.*

Although Definition 13 specifies the area of the plate exactly, it does not afford a simple method of computing the area.   The *fundamental theorem of integral calculus,* whose proof is beyond the scope of the text, relates $\int_a^b f$ to the antiderivative of f in a manner which simplifies the computation of the area.

Theorem 16 (Fundamental Theorem of Integral Calculus). *If f is a nonnegative polynomial function, if $a < b$, and if F is an antiderivative of f, then*

$$\int_a^b f = F(b) - F(a).$$

The following examples illustrate the computation of the area of a region of the type in Fig. 8.14 by means of the fundamental theorem of integral calculus.

Example 1. The area of the region bounded by $f(x) = x$, the X-axis, and the vertical lines $x = 2$ and $x = 5$ is $\int_2^5 x \, dx$. By the fundamental theorem,

$$\int_2^5 x \, dx = F(5) - F(2),$$

in which F is an antiderivative of f. Thus $F'(x) = f(x) = x$. Hence $F(x) = x^2/2$.

Thus

$$\int_2^5 x \, dx = F(5) - F(2)$$

$$= \frac{5^2}{2} - \frac{2^2}{2}$$

$$= \frac{25}{2} - \frac{4}{2}$$

$$= \frac{21}{2}.$$

Hence the area of the region is $\frac{21}{2}$ units². The region is illustrated in the accompanying figure.

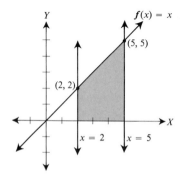

The reader may check the above by recognizing that the area of the larger triangular region is $\frac{25}{2}$ and the area of the smaller triangular region is 2, and hence the area of the shaded region is $\frac{25}{2} - 2$.

Example 2. The area of the region bounded by $f(x) = x^2$, the X-axis, and the vertical lines $x = 1$ and $x = 4$ is $\int_1^4 x^2 \, dx$. By the fundamental theorem,

$$\int_1^4 x^2 \, dx = F(4) - F(1),$$

in which F is an antiderivative of f. Thus $F'(x) = f(x) = x^2$. Hence $F(x) = x^3/3$. Thus

$$\int_1^4 x^2 \, dx = F(4) - F(1)$$

$$= \frac{4^3}{3} - \frac{1^3}{3}$$

$$= \frac{64}{3} - \frac{1}{3}$$

$$= \frac{63}{3}.$$

Hence the area of the region is $\frac{63}{3}$ units^2. The region is illustrated in the accompanying figure.

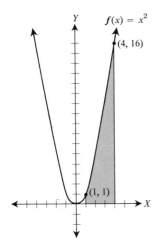

Although we required the polynomial function to be nonnegative, we could have permitted it to be negative outside of the interval $[a, b]$. In fact, by modifying the theorems and definitions, we can permit the graph of the polynomial function to cross the X-axis in the interval $[a, b]$.

The following example illustrates the computation of the area of such a region.

Example 3. The area of the region bounded by $f(x) = x^3$, the X-axis, and the vertical lines $x = {}^-1$ and $x = 2$ is

$$\left| \int_{-1}^{0} x^3 \, dx \right| + \int_{0}^{2} x^3 \, dx.$$

By the modified fundamental theorem,

$$\int_{-1}^{0} x^3 \, dx = F(0) - F({}^-1),$$

in which F is an antiderivative of f. Thus $F'(x) = f(x) = x^3$, and hence $F(x) = x^4/4$. Thus

$$\int_{-1}^{0} x^3 \, dx = F(0) - F({}^-1)$$

$$= \frac{0^4}{4} - \frac{({}^-1)^4}{4}$$

$$= 0 - \frac{1}{4}$$

$$= \frac{{}^-1}{4}.$$

Hence

$$\left| \int_{-1}^{0} x^3 \, dx \right| = \left| \frac{^-1}{4} \right| = \frac{1}{4}.$$

Similarly,

$$\int_{0}^{2} x^3 \, dx = \frac{2^4}{4} - \frac{0^4}{4}$$

$$= 4.$$

Hence

$$\left| \int_{-1}^{0} x^3 \, dx \right| + \int_{0}^{2} x^3 \, dx = \frac{1}{4} + 4 = \frac{17}{4}.$$

Thus the area is $\frac{17}{4}$ units^2. The region is illustrated in the accompanying figure.

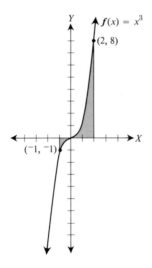

The reason for the absolute value is that the area cannot be negative. If we fail to consider the region *below* the X-axis and the region *above* the X-axis separately, the result will *not* be the area. That is,

$$\int_{-1}^{2} x^3 \, dx = \frac{15}{4};$$

however, the area of the shaded region is $\frac{17}{4}$.

The above treatment of integrals and areas can be extended to functions which are not polynomial functions, but the extension is beyond the scope of the text.

EXERCISE SET 8.8

I. Explain how the area in Example 1 can be checked.

II. Explain why $\int_{-1}^{2} x^3 \, dx$ is not the area in Example 3.

III. Compute the area of the region bounded by f, the X-axis, and the vertical lines $x = a$ and $x = b$ in each of the following.

$f(x)$	a	b
1. x	0	5
2. x	1	2
3. x^2	$^-1$	2
4. x^2	$^-2$	1
5. x^3	0	4
6. x^3	0	3
7. x^3	$^-1$	3
8. x^3	$^-2$	2
9. $x + x^2$	1	3
10. $x + x^2$	0	2
11. $1 + x^3$	0	3
12. $2 + x^3$	0	2
13. $x + x^3$	1	3
14. $x + x^3$	0	2
15. $x - x^2$	0	1
16. $x - x^2$	0	$\frac{1}{2}$
17. $x - x^3$	0	$\frac{1}{2}$
18. $x - x^3$	0	1
19. $x^2 - x^3$	0	1
20. $x^2 - x^4$	0	1

IV. The shaded region in the accompanying figure is the region bounded by the graphs of $f(x) = x$ and $g(x) = x^2$. Compute the area of the shaded region. [*Hint:* Compute the difference of two areas.]

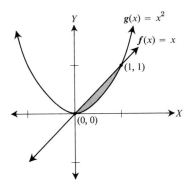

V. The shaded region in the accompanying figure is the region bounded by the graphs of $f(x) = x$ and $g(x) = x^3$. Compute the area of the shaded region. [*Hint:* Employ the hint of Exercise IV, and observe that the area of the region in the third quadrant is equal to the area of the region in the first quadrant.]

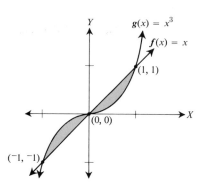

VI. Compute the area of the shaded region in the accompanying figure.

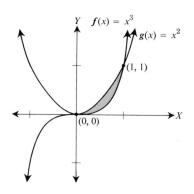

VII. Compute the area of the shaded region in the accompanying figure.

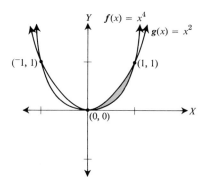

VIII. The average value of the function f on the closed interval $[a, b]$ is

$$\frac{1}{b - a} \int_a^b f.$$

The speed of a falling body t sec after it begins to fall is $16t^2$ ft/sec.

1. Compute the average speed during the 3-sec time interval from 1 sec to 4 sec.
2. Compute the average speed during the 3-sec time interval from 3 sec to 6 sec.

Pierre-Simon de Laplace was born in Beaumont-en-Auge on March 23, 1749. His parents were peasants, but very little else is known of his childhood and youth, largely because of his own snobbishness. He was so ashamed of his humble parents that he did everything in his power to conceal his peasant background.

Laplace showed remarkable talent in the village school and especially excelled in mathematics and theological debates. Through the efforts of wealthy neighbors, he was admitted to a military academy in Beaumont.

Laplace's estimate of his intelligence was high, and with justified self-confidence he moved to Paris at the age of 18 to master the world of mathematics. Laplace attempted to meet with D'Alembert, who refused to see him despite letters of recommendation from influential and wealthy people. Laplace then sent D'Alembert a personal letter explaining his views on the general principles of mechanics. The letter impressed D'Alembert so much that he secured for Laplace an appointment as Professor of Mathematics at the Military School of Paris. Laplace then devoted most of his time to the detailed application of the Newtonian law of gravitation to the entire solar system. During the 26 years following his appointment to the Military School of Paris, Laplace published numerous papers on the mathematics of astronomy, which he later incorporated in his masterpiece, *Mécanique céleste*.

In 1785, at the age of 36, Laplace was promoted to full membership in the Academy of Sciences. In that same year, he interviewed Napoleon Bonaparte, who was then a 16-year-old candidate for the Military School.

During the French Revolution, which began with the storming of the Bastille on July 14, 1789, Laplace became involved in politics and remained active in politics throughout the remainder of his life. Although he was commonly considered a brazen opportunist, Laplace was of strong character and stood by his friends in times of political disfavor; he even opposed the Emperor Napoleon on certain issues. He considered politics a necessary evil and cooperated with every political party in control so that he would be allowed to continue his mathematical work without governmental interference.

LAPLACE
(1749–1827)

Although he was better known for his great contributions in mathematical astronomy (he was known as "the Newton of France"), he contributed more to the theory of probability than had any other mathematician. From 1774 to 1812 he wrote many memoirs, which he embodied in his classic publication, *Théorie analytique des probabilités*.

Laplace spent his last years in peaceful retirement at his country estate at Arcueil, near Paris. After a brief illness, he died on March 5, 1827.

Chapter 9

Finite Probability

9.1 SAMPLE SPACE, EVENTS, AND OUTCOMES

The theory of probability, which began in the seventeenth century as an aid to gamblers, has become an essential science today. Probability plays a role in practically every facet of our lives. For example, probability is important in the biomedical sciences, the physical sciences, the management sciences, and the behavorial sciences. Even the weather reporter uses simple probability language in his reports, and the meteorologist who forecasts the weather uses simple probability theory to predict weather conditions.

The true developers of the mathematical theory of probability were Blaise Pascal (1623–1662) and Pierre de Fermat (1601–1665). However, Pierre-Simon de Laplace (1749–1827) was probably the greatest contributor to the theory of probability prior to the twentieth century. The progression of probability from its humble beginning to its prominence in mathematical science is summarized by the following remark made by Laplace in the nineteenth century:

> We see . . . that the theory of probabilities is at bottom only common sense reduced to calculation; it makes us appreciate with exactitude what reasonable minds feel by a sort of instinct, often without being able to account for it. . . . It is remarkable that this science, which originated in the consideration of games of chance, should have become the most important object of human knowledge.

Although the theory of probability is quite profound and involves deep results from analysis (including integration theory), we present a simple intuitive introduction which requires no more background than two years of high school mathematics. In doing so, we avoid the formal logical content and the significant applications. The reader who is fascinated by the simple introduction we present may refer to any of the well-known texts on probability for a more complete treatment of the subject.

The theory of probability gains an intuitive meaning and a practical significance from such real (or imaginary) experiments as the following:

1. Tossing a coin
2. Rolling a pair of dice (or one die)
3. Shuffling a deck of cards
4. Playing bridge
5. Playing poker
6. Playing roulette
7. Observing the life span of an isotope
8. Observing common traits in a selected group of people
9. Observing the phenotypes of the offspring of a white French poodle and a black French poodle
10. Predicting the future number of calls on a given telephone
11. Predicting random noise in a communication system
12. Controlling the quality of production of a given product
13. Observing and predicting the frequency of accidents at a given place
14. Predicting the weather conditions in a given location
15. Predicting the winner of a given race.

Because of the vagueness of the above descriptions, we must agree on the meaning of the possible results or outcomes of a given observation or experiment. *Mathematical probability is a mathematical model which provides a universal means of expressing the likelihood of occurrence in a given experiment.*

When one tosses a coin, the possible *outcomes* [that is, the results of the experiment] are *heads, tails, edge,* and *disappearance.* However, since the most frequent and usual outcomes are *heads* and *tails,* we agree that *heads* and *tails* are the only possible outcomes. Since such agreement simplifies the theory without destroying its applicability, it is common practice to *idealize* experiments by ignoring such results as *edge* and *disappearance* and considering only the most practical outcomes, *heads* and *tails.*

Denoting the two possible outcomes of the toss of a coin by "*h*" (for *heads*) and "*t*" (for *tails*), we see that the *sample space* [i.e., the set of possible outcomes of the experiment (of tossing a coin)] is $\{h, t\}$. We assume that each outcome (heads or tails) is *equally likely* to occur; i.e., intuitively, we assume that neither heads nor tails are favored on any given toss.

Definition 1

  a) *Any result [real or conceptual] of an experiment or observation is called an* **outcome** *of the experiment or observation.*

  b) *The set S of all outcomes of an experiment or observation is called a* **sample space** *[or* **universal set***].*

c) *Any subset E of the sample space of an experiment or observation is called an **event** of the experiment or observation.*

d) *Any event consisting of exactly one element of the sample space is called a **simple** [or **elementary**] **event**.*

e) *Any event consisting of two or more elements is called a **compound event**.*

f) *Any event consisting of no elements [i.e., the empty set] is called the **empty** [or **null** or **impossible**] **event**.*

g) *The event consisting of all elements of the sample space is called the **certain event**.*

A sample space of an experiment is a universal set; it is not an absolute set but is relative to the experiment and to the results in which we are interested. For example, in the roll of a die, the sample space is

$$\{1, 2, 3, 4, 5, 6\}$$

if we are interested in all possible outcomes of the roll. However, if we are interested only in knowing whether the outcome is a perfect square, the sample space is

$$\{a, b\},$$

in which a is 1 or 4 and b is 2, 3, 5, or 6. The sample space $\{a, b\}$ is really the sample space $\{\{1, 4\}, \{2, 3, 5, 6\}\}$. That is, the sample space is a set of sets. The outcome a [i.e., the event $\{1, 4\}$] occurs if and only if the outcome is either 1 or 4. If the sample space of an experiment is not specified, we assume that the most obvious sample space is intended. For example, in the roll of a die we assume that the sample space is $\{1, 2, 3, 4, 5, 6\}$, and in the toss of a coin we assume that the sample space is $\{h, t\}$, unless we specify other sample spaces.

The following examples further illustrate sample space, events, and outcomes of an experiment.

Example 1. A nickel and a dime are tossed. There are four possible outcomes, as indicated in the accompanying table.

Nickel	Dime	(Nickel, Dime)
h	h	(h, h)
h	t	(h, t)
t	h	(t, h)
t	t	(t, t)

The ordered pair (h, t) indicates that the nickel shows *heads* and the dime shows *tails*, whereas (t, h) indicates that the nickel shows *tails* and the dime shows *heads*. The *sample space S* is

$$\{(h, h), (h, t), (t, h), (t, t)\}.$$

The four outcomes are

$$(h, h), \quad (h, t), \quad (t, h), \quad \text{and} \quad (t, t).$$

The *events* of the experiment are the 16 subsets of the sample space. The empty set [which is a subset of the sample space] is the *empty* or *null* event. The *simple events* are

$$\{(h, h)\}, \quad \{(h, t)\}, \quad \{(t, h)\}, \quad \text{and} \quad \{(t, t)\}.$$

Some *compound events* are

$$\{(h, h), (h, t)\} \quad \text{and} \quad \{(h, t), (t, h), (t, t)\}.$$

There are nine other *compound events*, one of which is the certain event S.

Example 2. A die is rolled and a dime is tossed. There are 12 possible outcomes, as indicated in the accompanying table.

Die	1	1	2	2	3	3	4	4	5	5	6	6
Dime	h	t	h	t	h	t	h	t	h	t	h	t

The *sample space* S is

$$\{(1, h), (1, t), (2, h), (2, t), (3, h), (3, t), (4, h), (4, t), (5, h), (5, t), (6, h), (6, t)\}.$$

The twelve *outcomes* are

$$(1, h), \quad (1, t), \quad (2, h), \quad (2, t), \quad (3, h), \quad (3, t),$$

$$(4, h), \quad (4, t), \quad (5, h), \quad (5, t), \quad (6, h), \quad \text{and} \quad (6, t).$$

The *events* are the 2^{12} subsets of the sample space. Two *simple events* are $\{(2, h)\}$ and $\{(5, t)\}$, and two *compound events* are $\{(2, h), (5, t), (6, h)\}$ and S itself. Of course, there are many other compound events.

Since an *event* is a *set*, we frequently describe an event by a clause or sentence. In Example 1 we may describe the event $\{(h, h), (h, t)\}$ by the sentence, "The nickel shows heads." In general, we may describe any event E [which is really a subset of the sample space S] by the sentence, "*The event E occurs,*" or by the sentence, "$e \in E$," in which e is an outcome of the experiment.

The reader should observe that any compound event is the union of simple events. For example, the compound event

$$\{(2, h), (5, t), (6, h)\}$$

of Example 2 is equal to

$$\{(2, h)\} \cup \{(5, t)\} \cup \{(6, h)\}.$$

As we have indicated previously, the sample space of an experiment functions as the universal set for the experiment. Recalling the definition of the *complement* of any set A [denoted by "$\tilde{A}$"] as the set of all elements (of U) not in A, we define the *complement* of any event of an experiment.

Definition 2. *The set of all elements of a sample space S of an experiment which are not elements of the event E is called the **complement of E** or the **complementary event of E** and is denoted by "$\tilde{E}$." That is, $\tilde{E} = \{s: s \in S \text{ and } s \notin E\}$.*

For example, in the roll of a die, $S = \{1, 2, 3, 4, 5, 6\}$. If $E = \{1, 3, 5\}$, then $\tilde{E} = \{2, 4, 6\}$. From Chapter 2 we recall that $E \cup \tilde{E} = S$ and $E \cap \tilde{E} = \varnothing$ for any experiment.

Since modern probability theory depends on set theory, we employ set language, set notation, and set operations in probability theory. The definitions, laws, and properties of Chapter 2 are applicable to the study of probability. In Fig. 9.1 we relate certain terms of probability theory to the corresponding terms of set theory. The sample space is indicated by "S," any event by "E," and any outcome by "s."

Set Theory	Probability Theory
$s \in S$	s is an outcome
$E \subset S$	E is an event
$s \in E$	E occurs
$\tilde{E} \subset S$	$\tilde{E}$ is the complementary event of E
$E_1 \cup E_2$	E_1 or E_2
$E_1 \cap E_2$	E_1 and E_2
$s \in E_1 \cup E_2$	E_1 or E_2 occurs
$s \in E_1 \cap E_2$	E_1 and E_2 occur
$E = S$	E is certain
$E = \varnothing$	E is impossible [E does not occur]

Fig. 9.1

EXERCISE SET 9.1

I. Two dice are rolled, one red and the other blue. The ordered pair (r, b) represents an outcome of the experiment if and only if r appears on the red die and b appears on the blue die. For example $(2, 3)$, indicates that 2 appears on the red die and 3 appears on the blue die.

1. What is the sample space?

2. What is the event E that the sum of the coordinates is 2?

3. What is the event E that the sum of the coordinates is 3?

4. What is the event E that the sum of the coordinates is 4?

5. What is the event E that the sum of the coordinates is 5?

6. What is the event E that the sum of the coordinates is 6?

7. What is the event E that the sum of the coordinates is 7?

8. What is the event E that the sum of the coordinates is 8?

9. What is the event E that the sum of the coordinates is 9?

10. What is the event E that the sum of the coordinates is 10?

11. What is the event E that the sum of the coordinates is 11?

12. What is the event E that the sum of the coordinates is 12?

13. What is the event E that the sum of the coordinates is 13?

14. What is the event E that the sum of the coordinates is 1?

15. What is the event E that the sum of the coordinates is less than 13?

16. What is the event E that the sum of the coordinates is a perfect square?

17. What is the event E that the sum of the coordinates is odd?

18. What is the event E that the sum of the coordinates is even?

19. What is the event E that the sum of the coordinates is a multiple of 3?

20. What is the event E that the sum of the coordinates is a multiple of 5?

II. Specify a sample space for each of the following experiments.

1. A penny, a nickel, and a dime are tossed.

2. A red marble, a white marble, and a blue marble are drawn from a box one at a time.

3. A card is drawn from a standard deck of 52 cards.

4. A card is drawn from the 13 spades of a standard deck.

5. A card is drawn from the 13 hearts of a standard deck.

6. A card is drawn from the four aces.

7. Two cards are drawn from the four aces.

8. Three cards are drawn from the four aces.

9. A heart is drawn from a standard deck of cards.

10. A club is drawn from a standard deck of cards.

III. Two coins are tossed.

1. What is the sample space?

2. What is the event that exactly two tails occur?

3. What is the event that exactly two heads occur?

4. What is the event that exactly one head occurs?

5. What is the event that exactly one tail occurs?

6. What is the event that at least one head occurs?

7. What is the event that at least one tail occurs?

8. What is the event that no more than one tail occurs?

9. What is the event that no more than one head occurs?

10. What is the event that no more than two heads occur?

11. What is the event that no more than two tails occur?

12. What is the event that no tails occur?

13. What is the event that no heads occur?

14. What is the event that neither heads nor tails occurs?

IV. Three coins are tossed.

 1. What is the sample space?
 2. What is the event that exactly two heads occur?
 3. What is the event that at least two heads occur?
 4. What is the event that at least two tails occur?
 5. What is the event that exactly two tails occur?
 6. What is the event that exactly three tails occur?
 7. What is the event that exactly three heads occur?
 8. What is the event that no more than two heads occur?
 9. What is the event that at least one tail occurs?
10. What is the event that no more than one tail occurs?

 V. What is the complement of each event in Exercise IV?

VI. A gardener has 3 flower bulbs. One bulb produces a red flower, one bulb produces a white flower, and one bulb produces a blue flower. An experiment consists of choosing a bulb at random and planting it. Let r, w, and b, respectively, represent the three bulbs.

 1. What is the sample space?
 2. What are the simple events?
 3. What are the compound events?
 4. What is the impossible event?
 5. What is the certain event?
 6. What is the event that the planted bulb does not produce a blue flower?
 7. What is the event that the planted bulb does not produce a white flower?
 8. What is the event that the planted bulb does not produce a red flower?
 9. What is the event that the planted bulb does not produce either a red flower or a blue flower?
10. What is the event that the planted bulb does produce either a red flower or a blue flower?

VII. A gardener has 3 flower bulbs as described in Exercise VI. An experiment consists of choosing *two* bulbs at random for planting. The sample space is
$\{(r, w), (r, b), (w, b)\}$.

 1. What is the certain event?
 2. What are the simple events?
 3. What are the compound events?
 4. What is the event that neither planted bulb produces a blue flower?
 5. What is the event that one of the planted bulbs produces a blue flower?
 6. What is the event that the planted bulbs do not produce either a blue flower or a white flower?
 7. What is the event that the planted bulbs produce either a white flower or a blue flower?

8. What is the event that the planted bulbs produce a white flower and a blue flower?

9. What is the event that the planted bulbs produce two red flowers?

10. What is the event that the planted bulbs do not produce two red flowers?

VIII. An experiment consists of tossing a coin once and then either tossing it again or rolling a die. If the outcome of the first toss is tails, then the coin is tossed again; if, instead, the outcome of the first toss is heads, then the die is rolled.

1. List the elements of the sample space.

2. List the elements of the event E that the outcome of the roll of the die is an odd number.

3. List the elements of the event E that the outcome of the roll of the die is an even number.

4. What is the event that no heads occur?

5. What is the event that two heads occur?

6. What is the event that two heads do not occur?

7. What is the event that two tails do not occur?

8. What is the event that the coin is tossed twice?

9. What is the event that the coin is not tossed twice?

10. What is the event that the die is not rolled?

IX. An experiment consists of drawing a card from a standard deck and then tossing a dime. List the 104 elements of the sample space. [*Hint:* Use the three-dots notation and designate the 52 cards by the numbers 1, 2, 3, . . . , 52.]

X. An experiment consists of tossing a dime and then drawing a card from a standard deck. List the 104 elements of the sample space. Compare with Exercise IX. List the elements of the event E that a *head* occurs on each toss. List the elements of $\tilde{E}$. Describe the event $\tilde{E}$.

9.2 THE PROBABILITY OF AN EVENT

When the weather reporter states that the probability of rain is $\frac{3}{10}$ [or 3 chances in 10], he is assigning a numerical measure to the likelihood of rain. If the probability of rain is $\frac{9}{10}$, we are surprised if it does not rain. If the probability of rain is $\frac{1}{10}$, we are somewhat surprised if it does rain. The probability measure makes more precise a statement such as "We may expect some scattered thundershower activity this afternoon." The reader will recall that the probability of rain is never less than 0 (no rain expected) and never more than 1 (rain is certain).

A rigorous definition of *probability* without logical or other difficulties is beyond the scope of the text. Hence we restrict the definition to events which are subsets of *finite sample spaces*, and we overlook the logical difficulties.

Definition 3. *A function P which assigns a real number $P(E)$ to each event E of a finite sample space S of an experiment is called a **probability function** if and only if* *the following conditions are satisfied:*

a) *If* $s_i \in S$, *then* $0 \le P(\{s_i\}) \le 1$.

b) *If* $E = \{s_1\} \cup \{s_2\} \cup \cdots \cup \{s_k\}$, *then*
$$P(E) = P(\{s_1\}) + P(\{s_2\}) + \cdots + P(\{s_k\}).$$

c) $P(S) = 1$.

The real number $P(E)$ *is called the* **probability of E** [*or the* **probability measure of E**].

Definition 3 does not *specify* the probability of E but *restricts* the probability of E to be a real number no less than 0 and no greater than 1. If the probability of E is 0, then E is the impossible event; if $P(E) = 1$, then E is the certain event. Actually, the probability of an event is undefined; Definition 3 constitutes a set of axioms which prescribe the relationships of events to each other and impose upper and lower bounds on the probability of any event.

It follows from Definition 3 that $P(\varnothing) = 0$ and $P(E) > 0$ if $E \neq \varnothing$.

The case in which all simple events are equally likely is especially simple. In that case, the probability function assigns the same real number to all simple events. For example, in the roll of an unloaded unbiased die, all of the six faces are equally likely. Intuitively, we observe that the probability of each of the six faces is $\frac{1}{6}$; i.e., any of the six faces

$$[1, 2, 3, 4, 5, \text{ or } 6]$$

has one chance in six of occurring.

Definition 4. *The probability function which assigns the same real number to all simple events is called the* **equiprobable measure** [*or* **uniform probability function**].

Theorem 1. *If* $S = \{s_1\} \cup \{s_2\} \cup \cdots \cup \{s_k\}$ *and* P *is the equiprobable measure, then*
$$P(\{s_1\}) = P(\{s_2\}) = \cdots = P(\{s_k\}) = \frac{1}{k}.$$

Proof

$$P(\{s_1\}) = P(\{s_2\}) = \cdots = P(\{s_k\})\qquad \text{[by hypothesis]}.$$

Moreover,

$$P(\{s_1\}) + P(\{s_2\}) + \cdots + P(\{s_k\}) = 1 \qquad \text{[by Definition 3]}.$$

Hence

$$P(\{s_k\}) + P(\{s_k\}) + \cdots + P(\{s_k\}) = 1 \qquad [k \text{ summands}].$$

Thus

$$kP(\{s_k\}) = 1.$$

Hence

$$P(\{s_k\}) = \frac{1}{k}. \quad \text{(QED)}$$

According to Theorem 1, if all simple events of an experiment whose sample space contains exactly k elements are equally likely to occur, then the probability of any simple event is $1/k$. For example, the probability of *heads* on a single toss of an ordinary coin is $\frac{1}{2}$, and the probability of *tails* is also $\frac{1}{2}$.

The following examples further illustrate the equiprobable measure.

Example 1. A card is drawn at random from a deck of playing cards. What is the probability that it is the ace of spades?

Since there are 52 cards in the deck, the sample space is

$$\{C_1, C_2, C_3, \ldots, C_{52}\},$$

in which each C_i represents a card. Moreover, any card is as probable as any other card. Hence, by Theorem 1, the probability that the card drawn is the ace of spades is $\frac{1}{52}$.

Example 2. A card is drawn at random from the 13 spades of a deck of playing cards. What is the probability that it is the ace of spades?

Since there are 13 spades, the sample space is $\{s_1, s_2, \ldots, s_{13}\}$, in which each s_i represents a spade. Moreover, any spade is as probable as any other spade. Hence, by Theorem 1, the probability that the card drawn is the ace of spades is $\frac{1}{13}$.

Example 3. What is the probability of drawing (at random) the white poker chip from a box containing three chips—one red, one white, and one blue?

The sample space is $\{r, w, b\}$, in which each letter represents one of the chips. By Theorem 1, the probability of drawing the white chip is $\frac{1}{3}$.

Intuitively, it appears that the probability of drawing a white chip from a box containing 3 white chips, 1 red chip, and 1 blue chip should be $\frac{3}{5}$. We generalize and formalize the above observation in the following theorem. The reader should supply the proof.

> **Theorem 2.** *If S is a finite sample space of an experiment, if E is an event of the experiment, and if P is the equiprobable measure, then*
>
> $$P(E) = \frac{number\ of\ elements\ of\ E}{number\ of\ elements\ of\ S} = \frac{n(E)}{n(S)}.$$

The following examples illustrate Theorem 2.

Example 4. There are three burned bulbs and 17 good bulbs on a string of series-wired Christmas tree lights in a department store. Since any burned bulb breaks the circuit, all lights are out. To detect the burned bulbs, the clerk unscrews one bulb, tests it in the bulb tester, replaces it if necessary, and continues the procedure until he has replaced all burned bulbs. What is the probability that the first bulb he tests is burned? What is the probability that the first bulb he tests is good?

Since there are 20 bulbs on the string, the sample space S contains 20 elements. The event E that a bulb is burned contains 3 elements. Hence

$$P(E) = \frac{n(E)}{n(S)} = \frac{3}{20}.$$

Moreover,

$$P(\tilde{E}) = \frac{n(\tilde{E})}{n(S)} = \frac{17}{20}.$$

Hence the probability that the first bulb he tests is burned is $\frac{3}{20}$, and the probability that it is good is $\frac{17}{20}$. We observe that $P(\tilde{E}) = 1 - P(E)$.

Example 5. What is the probability that a number greater than 2 results from a single roll of a die?

The sample space S is $\{1, 2, 3, 4, 5, 6\}$. The event E that a number greater than 2 results is $\{3, 4, 5, 6\}$. Hence

$$P(E) = \frac{n(E)}{n(S)} = \frac{4}{6} = \frac{2}{3}.$$

The following theorems, which follow from the preceding definitions and theorems, simplify the computations of probabilities. In each case the sample space S of the experiment is finite. However, the results (but not the proof) are valid for infinite sample spaces.

Theorem 3. *If A and B are events of an experiment with sample space S and $A \cap B = \emptyset$, then*

$$P(A \cup B) = P(A) + P(B).$$

Proof. Since A and B are finite, there exist counting numbers k and m such that

$$A = \{a_1, a_2, \ldots, a_k\} \quad \text{and} \quad B = \{b_1, b_2, \ldots, b_m\}.$$

Then

$$A \cup B = \{a_1, a_2, \ldots, a_k, b_1, b_2, \ldots, b_m\}$$

and

$$n(A \cup B) = k + m \quad [\text{since } A \cap B = \emptyset].$$

Hence

$$\begin{aligned}
P(A \cup B) &= P(\{a_1\}) + \cdots + P(\{a_k\}) \\
&\quad + P(\{b_1\}) + P(\{b_2\}) + \cdots + P(\{b_m\}) \\
&= [P(\{a_1\}) + P(\{a_2\}) + \cdots + P(\{a_k\})] \\
&\quad + [P(\{b_1\}) + P(\{b_2\}) + \cdots + P(\{b_k\})] \\
&= P(A) + P(B). \quad \text{(QED)}
\end{aligned}$$

Theorem 4. *The probability of the impossible event is 0; that is $P(\emptyset) = 0$.*

Proof. Now $S \cap \emptyset = \emptyset$. Hence

$$P(S \cup \emptyset) = P(S) + P(\emptyset) \quad [\text{by Theorem 3}].$$

But $S \cup \emptyset = S$. Hence $P(S \cup \emptyset) = P(S)$. Thus $P(S) + P(\emptyset) = P(S)$.

Hence

$$P(\emptyset) = 0. \quad \text{(QED)}$$

Theorem 5. *If E is any event of an experiment and $\tilde{E}$ is the complementary event of E, then $P(E) + P(\tilde{E}) = 1$.*

Proof. Now $E \cap \tilde{E} = \emptyset$. Hence

$$P(E \cup \tilde{E}) = P(E) + P(\tilde{E}) \qquad \text{[by Theorem 3]}.$$

Moreover, $E \cup \tilde{E} = S$. Thus $P(E \cup \tilde{E}) = P(S)$. Hence $P(E) + P(\tilde{E}) = P(S)$. But

$$P(S) = 1 \qquad\qquad\qquad \text{[by Definition 3]}.$$

Thus

$$P(E) + P(\tilde{E}) = 1. \quad \text{(QED)}$$

The following theorem, which is sometimes called *the general law of addition*, is stated without proof. The reader should formulate the proof.

Theorem 6 **(General Law of Addition).** *If E_1 and E_2 are any events of an experiment, then*

$$P(E_1 \cup E_2) = P(E_1) + P(E_2) - P(E_1 \cap E_2).$$

The reader will observe that Theorem 6 reduces to Theorem 3 if

$$E_1 \cap E_2 = \emptyset.$$

The following examples illustrate the above theorems.

Example 6. A card is drawn at random from a standard deck of playing cards. What is the probability that it is the ace of spades or any king?

The sample space S is the set of the 52 playing cards. The event E_1 that the card drawn is the ace of spades is $\{a_s\}$, in which a_s is the ace of spades. The event E_2 that the card drawn is a king is $\{k_c, k_d, k_h, k_s\}$.

$$P(E_1) = \frac{n(E_1)}{n(S)} = \frac{1}{52} \qquad\qquad \text{[by Theorem 2]},$$

$$P(E_2) = \frac{n(E_2)}{n(S)} = \frac{4}{52} \qquad\qquad \text{[by Theorem 2]},$$

$$E_1 \cap E_2 = \emptyset,$$

$$P(E_1 \cup E_2) = P(E_1) + P(E_2) \qquad \text{[by Theorem 3]}$$

$$= \tfrac{1}{52} + \tfrac{4}{52}$$

$$= \tfrac{5}{52}.$$

Hence the probability that the card is the ace of spades or a king is $\tfrac{5}{52}$.

Example 7. A card is drawn at random from a standard deck of playing cards. What is the probability that it is a black card or an ace?

The sample space S is the set of the 52 playing cards. The event E_1 that the card is a black card is the set of the 26 black cards, $\{b_1, b_2, b_3, \ldots, b_{26}\}$; and the event E_2 that the card is an ace is the set of four aces, $\{a_c, a_d, a_h, a_s\}$.

$$P(E_1) = \frac{n(E_1)}{n(S)} = \frac{26}{52} \qquad\qquad \text{[by Theorem 2],}$$

$$P(E_2) = \frac{n(E_2)}{n(S)} = \frac{4}{52} \qquad\qquad \text{[by Theorem 2],}$$

$$E_1 \cap E_2 = \{a_c, a_s\},$$

$$P(E_1 \cap E_2) = \frac{n(E_1 \cap E_2)}{n(S)} = \frac{2}{52} \qquad\qquad \text{[by Theorem 2],}$$

$$P(E_1 \cup E_2) = P(E_1) + P(E_2) - P(E_1 \cap E_2) \qquad \text{[by Theorem 6]}$$

$$= \tfrac{26}{52} + \tfrac{4}{52} - \tfrac{2}{52}$$

$$= \tfrac{28}{52}$$

$$= \tfrac{7}{13}.$$

Hence the probability that it is a black card or an ace is $\tfrac{7}{13}$.

Example 8. The weatherman reports that the probability that it will rain during the weekend is $\tfrac{3}{10}$. What is the probability that it will not rain?

If E is the event that it will rain, then $\tilde{E}$ is the event that it will not rain.

$$P(E) + P(\tilde{E}) = 1 \qquad \text{[by Theorem 5]}.$$

Hence

$$P(\tilde{E}) = 1 - P(E)$$

$$= 1 - \tfrac{3}{10}$$

$$= \tfrac{7}{10}.$$

Hence the probability that it will not rain is $\tfrac{7}{10}$.

Example 9. A single die is rolled. What is the probability that the outcome is both 4 and 5 simultaneously?

The sample space S is $\{1, 2, 3, 4, 5, 6\}$. The event E that the outcome is both 4 and 5 is the intersection of the event E_1 that the outcome is 4 and the event E_2 that the outcome is 5.

$$E = E_1 \cap E_2$$

$$= \{4\} \cap \{5\}$$

$$= \varnothing.$$

Hence

$$P(E) = 0 \quad [\text{by Theorem 4}].$$

Thus the event E is impossible.

EXERCISE SET 9.2

I. Two dice are rolled, one red and the other blue. The ordered pair (r, b) represents
an outcome of the experiment if and only if r appears on the red die and b appears
on the blue die. For example, $(2, 3)$ indicates that 2 appears on the red die and 3
appears on the blue die.

1. What is the probability of the event E that the sum of the coordinates is 2?
2. What is the probability of the event E that the sum of the coordinates is 3?
3. What is the probability of the event E that the sum of the coordinates is 5?
4. What is the probability of the event E that the sum of the coordinates is 7?
5. What is the probability of the event E that the sum of the coordinates is 8?
6. What is the probability of the event E that the sum of the coordinates is 11?
7. What is the probability of the event E that the sum of the coordinates is 12?
8. What is the probability of the event E that the sum of the coordinates is 13?
9. What is the probability of the event E that the sum of the coordinates is a perfect
   square?
10. What is the probability of the event E that the sum of the coordinates is even?

II. Two coins are tossed.
1. What is the probability that exactly one head occurs?
2. What is the probability that exactly two heads occur?
3. What is the probability that exactly one head does not occur?
4. What is the probability that exactly two heads do not occur?
5. What is the probability that no heads occur?
6. What is the probability that at least one tail occurs?
7. What is the probability that no more than one tail occurs?
8. What is the probability that no tails occur?
9. What is the probability that either two heads or two tails occur?
10. What is the probability that neither two heads nor two tails occur?

III. A card is drawn at random from a standard deck of 52 playing cards.
1. What is the probability that the card is an honor card (*ten, jack, queen, king,* or *ace*)?
2. What is the probability that the card is not an honor card?
3. What is the probability that the card is either a red ace or a black queen?
4. What is the probability that the card is either an honor card or a heart?
5. What is the probability that the card is a ten or a red jack or the ace of spades?

6. What is the probability that the card is the two of spades or the ten of diamonds or a club?

7. What is the probability that the card is either a red card or a black card?

8. What is the probability that the card is both a red card and a black card?

9. What is the probability that the card has a face value less than 10 and is an honor card?

10. What is the probability that the card has a face value less than 10 or is an honor card?

IV. A gardener has 3 flower bulbs. One bulb produces a red flower, one bulb produces a white flower, and one bulb produces a blue flower. An experiment consists of choosing two bulbs at random and planting them.

1. What is the probability that neither planted bulb produces a blue flower?

2. What is the probability that one of the planted bulbs produces a blue flower?

3. What is the probability that the planted bulbs do not produce either a blue flower or a white flower?

4. What is the probability that the planted bulbs produce either a white flower or a blue flower?

5. What is the probability that the planted bulbs produce a white flower and a blue flower?

6. What is the probability that the planted bulbs produce two red flowers?

7. What is the probability that the planted bulbs do not produce two red flowers?

8. What is the probability that the planted bulbs produce at least one blue flower?

V. An experiment consists of tossing a coin once and then either tossing it again or rolling a die. If the outcome of the first toss is tails, then the coin is tossed again; if, instead, the outcome of the first toss is heads, then the die is rolled. The sample space is $\{(t, t), (t, h), (h, 1), (h, 2), (h, 3), (h, 4), (h, 5), (h, 6)\}$. Although we may be tempted to assume the equiprobable measure, and assign a probability of $\frac{1}{8}$ to each simple event, more careful analysis reveals that we should assign weighted probabilities. Accordingly, we assume that

$$P(\{(t, t)\}) = \tfrac{1}{4}, \qquad P(\{(t, h)\}) = \tfrac{1}{4},$$
$$P(\{(h, 1)\}) = \tfrac{1}{12}, \qquad P(\{(h, 2)\}) = \tfrac{1}{12},$$
$$P(\{(h, 3)\}) = \tfrac{1}{12}, \qquad P(\{(h, 4)\}) = \tfrac{1}{12},$$
$$P(\{(h, 5)\}) = \tfrac{1}{12}, \quad \text{and} \quad P(\{(h, 6)\}) = \tfrac{1}{12}.$$

1. What is the probability that two tails occur?

2. What is the probability that a tail and a head occur?

3. What is the probability that a head and an odd number occur?

4. What is the probability that a head and an even number occur?

5. What is the probability that exactly one head occurs?

6. What is the probability that no heads occur?

7. What is the probability that a head does occur and an even number does not occur?

8. What is the probability that a tail does occur and an odd number does not occur?

9. What is the probability that two heads occur?

10. What is the probability that two heads do not occur?

11. What is the probability that at least one tail occurs?

12. What is the probability that no more than one tail occurs?

VI. Prove that if A and B are any two events of an experiment with sample space S and if $A \subset B$, then $P(A) \leq P(B)$.

VII. Prove Theorem 6. [*Hint:* Assume $\mathbf{n}(A \cup B) = \mathbf{n}(A) + \mathbf{n}(B) - \mathbf{n}(A \cap B)$.]

VIII. Prove that if $S = \{a_1, a_2, a_3, \ldots, a_k\}$, if $P(\{a_i\}) = 1/k$ for each simple event, and if A is any event, then

$$P(A) = \frac{\mathbf{n}(A)}{k}.$$

[*Hint:* Employ Theorems 1, 2, and 3.]

IX. Prove each of the following.

1. If A and B are any events, then $P(A \cup B) \leq P(A) + P(B)$.

2. If A and B are any events, then $P(\widetilde{A \cup B}) < P(\tilde{A}) + P(\tilde{B})$.

9.3 PERMUTATIONS AND COUNTING

Before developing probability theory further, we consider several problems concerned with counting and permutations. In the next section we shall apply the theory of counting and permutations to problems involving combinations.

While driving to class one morning a student observes that either one of two roads at a given intersection leads to school. Taking one of the roads, he observes that it leads to three other roads, each of which leads to school. The next day he decides to take the second road. To his surprise, he notices that it, too, leads to three other roads, each of which leads to school. How many possible roads can he take to school? The problem is represented schematically by the diagram—called a *tree* diagram—in Fig. 9.2.

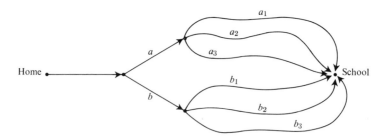

Fig. 9.2

From the tree diagram we observe that there are two possible routes [a and b] and for each route there are three branches [subroutes] to school.

That is, there are 2×3 possible routes from home to school. Of course, we can count the branches to verify that there are actually six routes.

If there were 25 roads near home and 17 roads for each of the 25, the tree diagram would be somewhat complicated and confusing. Moreover, constructing the diagram would be tedious and time-consuming. Consequently, we state the following principle, known as the *fundamental counting law*.

> **Fundamental Counting Law.** *If there are k_1 possible ways of making a first choice, and for each of the k_1 possible ways there are k_2 possible ways of making a second choice, then there are $k_1 \times k_2$ possible ways of making the two choices.*

The fundamental counting law can be generalized to any number of choices. The following examples illustrate the fundamental counting law.

Example 1. There are 7 air routes from City X to City Y and 5 air routes from City Y to City Z, but there are no direct air routes from City X to City Z. How many air routes are there from City X to City Z?

By the fundamental counting law, there are 7×5 different air routes from City X to City Z.

Example 2. A mathematics club consists of 25 members. No member may hold more than one office. In how many ways can the offices of President, Vice-President, Recording Secretary, Corresponding Secretary, and Treasurer be filled?

There are 25 candidates available for the first office; i.e., there are 25 ways of making the first choice (*President*). After the President has been chosen, there are 24 ways of making the second choice (*Vice-President*). After the Vice-President has been chosen, there are 23 ways of making the third choice (*Recording Secretary*). After the Recording Secretary has been chosen, there are 22 ways of making the fourth choice (*Corresponding Secretary*). After the Corresponding Secretary has been chosen, there are 21 ways of making the fifth choice (*Treasurer*). Hence, by the fundamental counting law, there are

$$25 \times 24 \times 23 \times 22 \times 21 = 6{,}375{,}600$$

ways of filling the five offices.

Example 3. How many seven-digit telephone numbers can be assigned by a telephone company in a city if the first three digits are 446 and 447?

There is one way of making the first choice, one way of making the second choice, two ways of making the third choice, ten ways of making the fourth choice, ten ways of making the fifth choice, ten ways of making the sixth choice, and ten ways of making the seventh choice. By the fundamental counting law, there are

$$1 \times 1 \times 2 \times 10 \times 10 \times 10 \times 10$$

ways of making all the choices. That is, the telephone company can assign 20,000 telephone numbers in the city. If the city needs more than 20,000 telephones, the telephone company must use more prefixes than 446 and 447.

Example 4. What is the probability that a telephone number chosen at random from the telephone directory of the city of Example 3 is in the sequence 447-9060 through 447-9089?

There are 30 telephone numbers in the sequence, and 20,000 possible telephone numbers in the city. Hence the probability that a given number is in the given sequence is 30/20,000 [or 3/2000].

In Section 6.2 we studied permutations on 3 symbols and permutations on 4 symbols. In particular, we learned that there are $1 \times 2 \times 3$ permutations on 3 symbols and $1 \times 2 \times 3 \times 4$ permutations on 4 symbols. In general, even if $k > 4$, then there are $1 \times 2 \times 3 \times \cdots \times k$ permutations on k symbols. Now that we know the fundamental counting law, we can easily prove that there are $1 \times 2 \times 3 \times 4$ permutations on 4 symbols and $1 \times 2 \times 3 \times \cdots \times k$ permutations on k symbols. For example, there are four ways to choose the first symbol; for each of the four choices, there are three ways to choose the second symbol; for each of the three choices, there are two ways to choose the third symbol; and for each of the two choices, there is one way to choose the last (fourth) symbol. Hence, by the fundamental counting law, there are $4 \times 3 \times 2 \times 1$ ways to choose all of the four symbols. That is, there are 24 permutations on 4 symbols.

In an analogous manner, we can prove that there are

$$1 \times 2 \times 3 \times \cdots \times k$$

permutations on k symbols. Since the product $1 \times 2 \times 3 \times \cdots \times k$ occurs so frequently in mathematics, it is customary to denote it by the special symbol "$k!$" and call it k-*factorial*, as indicated in the following definition.

Definition 5. *The* **factorial** *of any counting number k [denoted by "$k!$" and called* **k-factorial**] *is defined as follows:*

a) $k! = 1 \times 2 \times \cdots \times k$ *if* $k \geq 2$,

b) $1! = 1$,

c) $0! = 1$.

For example,

$$2! = 1 \times 2 = 2 \times 1 = 2;$$

$$3! = 1 \times 2 \times 3 = 3 \times 2 \times 1 = 6;$$

and

$$4! = 1 \times 2 \times 3 \times 4 = 4 \times 3 \times 2 \times 1 = 24.$$

Using the factorial notation, we can indicate the number of permutations on k symbols more briefly than previously. There are 4! permutations on 4 symbols, 5! permutations on 5 symbols, 6! permutations on 6 symbols, ..., $k!$ permutations on k symbols.

The definition of 1! probably seems natural, but the definition of 0! may seem artificial to the reader. We define 0! to be 1 so that we can avoid exceptions in certain formulas. Moreover, the definition does not contradict any other results.

The following examples illustrate the use of the factorial notation in the solution of problems involving the fundamental counting law.

Example 5. In how many ways can the manager of a major league baseball team assign the batting order of the 9 players?

He may assign any one of the 9 members to bat first, any one of the 8 remaining members to bat second, any one of the 7 remaining members to bat third, etc. By the fundamental counting law, there are

$$9 \times 8 \times 7 \times 6 \times 5 \times 4 \times 3 \times 2 \times 1$$

possible batting orders. That is, the manager can assign the batting order in 9! ways. [9! = 362,880.]

Example 6. In how many ways can the manager of a major league baseball team assign the batting order of the 9 players if the pitcher must bat last?

Since the pitcher must bat last, the batting order of the remaining 8 players must be assigned. Hence the manager can assign the batting order in 8! ways.

The preceding examples pertain to the number of permutations of k distinct elements (taken k at a time). Frequently we must compute the number of permutations of m elements taken k at a time, in which $k < m$. The following examples illustrate a method of computation and motivate a theorem which simplifies the computation.

Example 7. Susan has seven crayons (of different colors) to use in coloring a map. By experimentation, she discovers that four colors are sufficient for coloring the map without having adjacent regions of the same color. In how many different ways can she color the map if she uses exactly four colors each time?

Susan may choose any one of the 7 crayons for the first color, any one of the 6 remaining crayons for the second color, any one of the 5 remaining crayons for the third color, and any one of the 4 remaining crayons for the fourth color. By the fundamental counting law, there are

$$7 \times 6 \times 5 \times 4$$

ways to color the map. We observe that

$$
\begin{aligned}
7 \times 6 \times 5 \times 4 &= 7 \times 6 \times 5 \times 4 \times \frac{3 \times 2 \times 1}{3 \times 2 \times 1} \\
&= \frac{7 \times 6 \times 5 \times 4 \times 3 \times 2 \times 1}{3 \times 2 \times 1} \\
&= \frac{7!}{3!} \\
&= \frac{7!}{(7-4)!}.
\end{aligned}
$$

Example 8. Paula has 8 filing-cabinet drawers available for filing. Her supervisor instructs her to select 3 drawers for filing 3 sets of special correspondence. In how many ways can she select the 3 drawers?

Paula may choose any one of the 8 drawers for the first set, any one of the remaining 7 drawers for the second set, and any one of the remaining 6 drawers for the third set. By the fundamental counting law, there are

$$8 \times 7 \times 6$$

ways in which she can select the 3 drawers. We observe that

$$
\begin{aligned}
8 \times 7 \times 6 &= 8 \times 7 \times 6 \times \frac{5 \times 4 \times 3 \times 2 \times 1}{5 \times 4 \times 3 \times 2 \times 1} \\
&= \frac{8 \times 7 \times 6 \times 5 \times 4 \times 3 \times 2 \times 1}{5 \times 4 \times 3 \times 2 \times 1} \\
&= \frac{8!}{5!} \\
&= \frac{8!}{(8 - 3)!}.
\end{aligned}
$$

In Example 7, we observed that the number of permutations of 7 elements taken 4 at a time is $7!/(7 - 4)!$. According to Example 8, the number of permutations of 8 elements taken 3 at a time is $8!/(8 - 3)!$. In an analogous manner, we can prove that the number of permutations of m elements taken k at a time is $m!/(m - k)!$, provided, of course, that $k \leq m$. If $k = m$, then

$$\frac{m!}{(m - k)!} = \frac{m!}{0!} = \frac{m!}{1} = m! = k!;$$

that is, the number of permutations of m elements taken m at a time is $m!$, as we concluded previously.

We state the above result in the following theorem. The reader should formulate a proof. The notation "$P(m : k)$" denotes the number of permutations of m elements taken k at a time.*

Theorem 7. *If $k \leq m$, then the number of permutations of m elements taken k at a time is $m!/(m - k)!$. That is,*

$$P(m : k) = \frac{m!}{(m - k)!}.$$

To illustrate Theorem 7 again, we compute the number of ways in which *win*, *place*, and *show* can be assigned in a 10-horse race. Since there are 3 positions

---

*   There are several notations for the number of permutations of m elements taken k at a time. The notation "$P(m : k)$" is self-explanatory and should not be confusing to the beginner.

to be assigned from a set of 10 horses, we see that the correct answer is the number of permutations of 10 elements taken 3 at a time. Thus

$$P(10:3) = \frac{10!}{(10-3)!} = \frac{10!}{7!} = 720.$$

EXERCISE SET 9.3

I. The fundamental counting law can be generalized to include any number of choices. For example, if there are k_1 ways of making a first choice, and for each of the k_1 ways of making a first choice there are k_2 ways of making a second choice, and for each of the k_2 ways of making a second choice there are k_3 ways of making a third choice, then there are

$k_1 \times k_2 \times k_3$

ways of making the three choices.

State the *generalized fundamental counting law* for a sequence of *m* choices, and employ it to solve each of the following.

1. A coed purchases 3 dresses, 2 pairs of shoes, and 3 handbags, any of which can be worn with the others. How many outfits (1 dress, 1 pair of shoes, and 1 purse) can she select from the above wardrobe?

2. A housing contractor will build a house with 2, 3, or 4 bedrooms, 2 or 3 bathrooms, and a single or double garage. How many basic choices does he offer?

3. There are 3 routes from Chicago to Gotham City and two routes from Gotham City to Metropolis. In how many ways can Batman make the trip from Chicago to Metropolis via Gotham City? In how many ways can he make the trip from Metropolis to Chicago via Gotham City? In how many ways can he make the round trip from Chicago to Metropolis via Gotham City?

4. A fisherman discovers that there are 3 navigable streams from the boat dock to Lake A and 4 navigable streams from Lake A to Lake B. How many routes can he travel from the boat dock to Lake B via Lake A? How many routes can he travel from Lake B to the boat dock via Lake A? How many round-trip routes can he travel from the boat dock to Lake B via Lake A?

II.

1. A command pilot, a first assistant, and a second assistant for a flight to Mars are chosen from a group of 20 astronauts. In how many ways can the 3 men be chosen for the 3 positions?

2. A command aquanaut and an assistant for a scheduled trip to the ocean floor in the South Atlantic are to be chosen from a group of 10 aquanauts. In how many ways can the men be chosen for the 2 positions?

3. A command pilot, a first assistant, and a second assistant for an interplanetary flight are chosen from a group of 20 astronauts—15 military personnel and 5 civilian personnel. The command pilot is to be a civilian and the two assistants are to be military personnel. In how many ways can the 3 men be chosen for the 3 positions?

4. A command pilot, a first assistant, and a second assistant for an interplanetary flight are chosen from a group of 20 astronauts—15 military personnel and 5 civilian personnel. The command pilot is to be a military person, and the two assistants are to be civilians. In how many ways can the 3 men be chosen for the 3 positions?

5. In how many ways can the second runner-up, the first runner-up, and the winner of the Miss America Pageant be chosen from 55 contestants?

6. In how many ways can the Navy choose 3 officers from 10 available officers to be first, second, and third in command of an operation?

7. In how many ways can the letters of the word *word* be arranged?

8. In how many ways can the letters of the word *study* be arranged?

III. The number of ways in which the letters of the word *earth* can be arranged is $P(5 : 5)$. To compute the number of arrangements in the word *moon*, the reader should exercise caution, because if the second and third letters of the word *moon* are interchanged, the two arrangements are indistinguishable. If the 4 letters were distinct, then the number of arrangements would be $P(4 : 4)$, which is 4!. Since there are 2! ways of arranging the two *o*'s of the word *moon*, we see that $P(4 : 4)/2!$ is the number of *distinguishable* arrangements of the 4 letters of the word *moon*. Similarly, the number of distinguishable arrangements of the letters of the word *Mississippi* is $P(11 : 11)/4! \, 4! \, 2!$, because the *i* appears 4 times, the *s* appears 4 times, and the *p* appears twice. Compute the number of distinguishable arrangements of the letters of each of the following words.

1. *probabilities*   2. *calculus*

3. *arrangement*   4. *mathematics*

5. *topology*   6. *geometry*

7. *algebra*   8. *Apollo*

9. *Mars*   10. *space*

11. *differentiate*   12. *integrate*

13. *analysis*   14. *statistics*

IV. In a typical 10-horse race the results are *win*, *place*, and *show* [for *first*-, *second*-, and *third*-place winners]. If the set of horses in a given race is
$\{h_1, h_2, h_3, h_4, h_5, h_6, h_7, h_8, h_9, h_{10}\}$,
then the three winners constitute an ordered triple (h_w, h_p, h_s). Let
$$E_1 = \{(h_{10}, h_5, h_2)\}, \qquad E_2 = \{(h_3, h_1, h_2)\}, \qquad \text{and} \qquad E_3 = \{(h_1, h_6, h_4)\}.$$
Moreover, let
$$P(E_1) = \tfrac{1}{10}, \qquad P(E_2) = \tfrac{1}{100}, \qquad \text{and} \qquad P(E_3) = \tfrac{1}{1000}.$$

1. Describe the sample space.

2. Describe the event E_1.

3. Describe the event E_2.

4. Describe the event E_3.

5. Describe the event E_1 or E_2.

6. Describe the event E_1 or E_3.

7. Describe the event E_2 or E_3.

8. Compute the probability that E_1 or E_2 occurs.

9. Compute the probability that E_1 or E_3 occurs.

10. Compute the probability that E_2 or E_3 occurs.

11. Compute the probability that E_1 or E_2 or E_3 occurs.

12. Compute the probability that E_1 does not occur.

13. Compute the probability that E_2 does not occur.

14. Compute the probability that E_3 does not occur.

15. Compute the probability that neither E_1 nor E_2 occurs.

16. Compute the probability that neither E_1 nor E_3 occurs.

17. Compute the probability that neither E_2 nor E_3 occurs.

18. Compute the probability that E_1 does not occur, E_2 does not occur, and E_3 does not occur.

19. How many simple events does the sample space contain?

20. Is it possible to compute the probability of (h_{10}, h_1, h_4) from the given information?

9.4 COMBINATIONS

In Section 9.3 we learned that the number of *permutations* of m distinct elements taken k at a time is $m!/(m - k)!$ for any k which is less than or equal to m. In other words, the formula

$$P(m : k) = \frac{m!}{(m - k)!}$$

enables us to compute the number of *ordered* sets, each of order k, which are subsets of a given set of order m. The word *ordered* in the above sentence is important. For example, the number of permutations of 4 elements taken 2 at a time is $4!/2!$; i.e., the number of *ordered* subsets (each of order 2) of $\{1, 2, 3, 4\}$ is 12. However, the number of *subsets* (each of order 2) of $\{1, 2, 3, 4\}$ is 6. The ordered subsets are shown in Fig. 9.3(a), and the subsets are shown in Fig. 9.3(b).

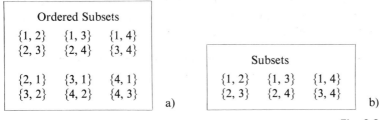

a)

b)

Fig. 9.3

The *ordered subsets* represent the *permutations* of 4 elements taken 2 at a time; the *subsets* represent the *combinations* of 4 elements taken 2 at a time.

From Fig. 9.3 we see that the number of combinations of 4 elements taken 2 at a time is less than the number of permutations of 4 elements taken 2 at a time.

To further illustrate the distinction between a *permutation* and a *combination*, in Fig. 9.4 we list the 10 *combinations* of 5 elements taken 3 at a time. That is, we list the 10 subsets of order 3 of the set $\{1, 2, 3, 4, 5\}$.

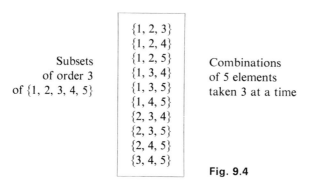

Subsets
of order 3
of $\{1, 2, 3, 4, 5\}$

$\{1, 2, 3\}$
$\{1, 2, 4\}$
$\{1, 2, 5\}$
$\{1, 3, 4\}$
$\{1, 3, 5\}$
$\{1, 4, 5\}$
$\{2, 3, 4\}$
$\{2, 3, 5\}$
$\{2, 4, 5\}$
$\{3, 4, 5\}$

Combinations
of 5 elements
taken 3 at a time

Fig. 9.4

The reader should list the 60 *permutations* [i.e., the ordered sets of order 3] of the 5 elements taken 3 at a time. Each *subset* [i.e., each combination] generates 3! *ordered* subsets [i.e., permutations]. Hence there are 3! times as many permutations of 5 elements taken 3 at a time as there are combinations. Since there are $P(5 : 3)$ *permutations* of 5 elements taken 3 at a time, it follows that there are $P(5 : 3)/3!$ *combinations* of 5 elements taken 3 at a time. Since

$$\frac{P(5 : 3)}{3!} = \frac{5!/(5-3)!}{3!} = \frac{5!}{(5-3)!\,3!} = \frac{5!}{3!\,2!},$$

we see that the number of *combinations* of 5 elements taken 3 at a time is

$$\frac{5!}{3!\,2!}.$$

In the following theorem, we generalize the above result to represent the number of *combinations* of m elements taken k at a time. The reader should supply the proof. We employ the notation "$C(m : k)$" to represent the number of *combinations* of m elements taken k at a time.

Theorem 8. *If $k \leq m$, then the number of combinations of m elements taken k at a time is $m!/k!\,(m-k)!$. That is,*

$$C(m : k) = \frac{m!}{k!\,(m-k)!}.$$

The following examples illustrate Theorem 8.

Example 1. A subcommittee of 4 members is to be appointed from a committee of 7 members. In how many ways can the committee be appointed?

The number of different 4-member subcommittees which can be appointed from the 7-member committee is $C(7:4)$.

$$C(7:4) = \frac{7!}{4!\,3!}$$

$$= \frac{1 \times 2 \times 3 \times 4 \times 5 \times 6 \times 7}{(1 \times 2 \times 3 \times 4) \times (1 \times 2 \times 3)}$$

$$= 5 \times 7$$

$$= 35.$$

Thus there are 35 possible 4-member subcommittees which can be appointed from a 7-member committee.

Example 2. On a final examination in American history a student must answer 20 questions from a set of 22 questions. In how many ways can he make his choice?

$$C(22:20) = \frac{22!}{20!\,2!}$$

$$= \frac{1 \times 2 \times 3 \times \cdots \times 20 \times 21 \times 22}{(1 \times 2 \times 3 \times \cdots \times 20) \times (1 \times 2)}$$

$$= \frac{21 \times 22}{2}$$

$$= 21 \times 11$$

$$= 231.$$

Thus the student may choose the 20 questions in 231 ways. That is, there are 231 subsets of order 20 of any set of order 22.

Example 3. How many distinct lines are determined by 10 distinct points, no three of which are collinear?

Since two distinct points determine a unique line, we must compute the number of combinations of 10 elements (points) taken two at a time.

$$C(10:2) = \frac{10!}{2!\,8!}$$

$$= \frac{1 \times 2 \times 3 \times 4 \times 5 \times 6 \times 7 \times 8 \times 9 \times 10}{(1 \times 2) \times (1 \times 2 \times 3 \times 4 \times 5 \times 6 \times 7 \times 8)}$$

$$= \frac{9 \times 10}{2}$$

$$= 45.$$

Hence 45 distinct lines are determined. Some of the lines are indicated in the accompanying figure (page 264). The reader should draw the remaining lines and count them. Since the line through P_1 and P_2 is the same line as the line through P_2 and P_1, it is easy to understand why we compute the number of *combinations* rather than the number of *permutations*.

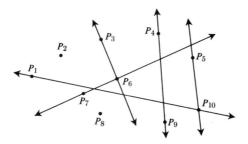

Example 4. An experiment consists of drawing two marbles at random from a box which contains six red marbles and 4 blue marbles. What is the probability that two red marbles are drawn?

The number of elements in the sample space S is the number of combinations of 10 things taken 2 at a time. Since

$$C(10:2) = \frac{10!}{2!\,8!} = \frac{9 \times 10}{1 \times 2} = 45,$$

we see that there are 45 elements in the sample space. That is, there are 45 possible ways to choose 2 marbles out of 10 marbles. The event E that two red marbles are drawn contains 15 elements because

$$C(6:2) = \frac{6!}{2!\,4!} = \frac{5 \times 6}{1 \times 2} = 15.$$

That is, there are 15 possible ways to choose 2 marbles out of 6 marbles.

$$P(E) = \frac{\mathbf{n}(E)}{\mathbf{n}(S)} \quad \text{[by Theorem 2]}$$

$$= \frac{15}{45}$$

$$= \frac{1}{3}.$$

Hence the probability that two red marbles are drawn is $\frac{1}{3}$.

EXERCISE SET 9.4

   I.

   1. How many bridge hands are there in a standard deck of playing cards?

   2. How many 5-card poker hands are there in a standard deck of playing cards?

   3. In how many ways can 5 fraternity pledges be selected from a group of 20 pledges?

4. In how many ways can a committee of 10 senators be chosen from the U.S. Senate?

5. There are 6 nominees for best actor of the year and 5 nominees for best actress of the year. In how many ways can the best actor be chosen? In how many ways can the best actress be chosen? In how many ways can the best pair (actor and actress) be chosen?

6. There are 10 boys nominated for *Most Popular Boy* on campus and 12 girls nominated for *Most Popular Girl* on campus. In how many ways can the boy be selected? In how many ways can the girl be selected? In how many ways can the *Most Popular Couple* consisting of the *Most Popular Boy* and the *Most Popular Girl* be selected?

7. In Exercise 5, an actor and his wife are both nominees for the awards. What is the probability that they will both be chosen? [Assume equiprobable measure.]

8. In Exercise 6, John Brown and Jane Smith are nominated for *Most Popular Boy* and *Most Popular Girl*. What is the probability that they will both be chosen? [Assume equiprobable measure.]

II.

1. In how many ways can a student select exactly 20 questions to answer on a mathematics examination consisting of 25 questions?

2. In how many ways can a student select exactly 20 questions to answer on a mathematics examination consisting of 30 questions?

3. In how many ways can a student select exactly 20 questions to answer on a physics examination consisting of 25 questions, if he must select the first five questions?

4. In how many ways can a student select exactly 20 questions to answer on a chemistry examination consisting of 30 questions, if he must select the first 10 questions?

III. A box contains 3 white marbles and 5 black marbles. Three marbles are drawn at random from the box.

1. What is the probability of the event that three black marbles are drawn?

2. What is the probability of the event that three white marbles are drawn?

3. What is the probability of the event that at least one white marble is drawn?

4. What is the probability of the event that at least one black marble is drawn?

5. What is the probability of the event that 2 white marbles and one black marble are drawn?

6. What is the probability of the event that 2 black marbles and one white marble are drawn?

IV. Compute each of the following.

1. $C(0 : 0)$	2. $C(1 : 0)$
3. $C(1 : 1)$	4. $C(2 : 0)$
5. $C(2 : 1)$	6. $C(2 : 2)$
7. $C(3 : 0)$	8. $C(3 : 1)$
9. $C(3 : 2)$	10. $C(3 : 3)$

V.

1. Construct a quadrilateral and determine the number of diagonals.

2. Construct a pentagon and determine the number of diagonals.

3. Construct a hexagon and determine the number of diagonals.

4. Construct an octagon and determine the number of diagonals.

5. Construct an 11-gon (an 11-sided polygon) and determine the number of diagonals.

6. Construct a 10-gon and determine the number of diagonals.

VI. Since the number of segments determined by m distinct points, no three of which are collinear, is $C(m:2)$ and the number of sides of an m-gon is m, it follows that the number of diagonals of an m-gon is $C(m:2) - m$. Use the expression $C(m:2) - m$ for the number of diagonals of an m-gon to verify each result in Exercise V.

VII. Prove each of the following.

1. $C(m:0) = 1$ 2. $C(m:m) = 1$

3. $C(m:1) = m$ 4. $C(m:m-1) = m$

5. $C(m:k) = C(m:m-k)$

6. $C(m:k) + C(m:k+1) = C(m+1:k+1)$

9.5 THE BINOMIAL THEOREM

In Section 7.4 we studied polynomials and polynomial functions. For example, we learned that $2 + 3x - 5x^2 + 7x^4$ is a fourth-degree polynomial in x over the field of real numbers, and the numerical coefficients are 2, 3, $^-5$, 0, and 7. The expression $2 + 3x + 4y - 5xy + y^3$ is a polynomial in x and y. Similarly, $x + y$ is a polynomial in x and y. The latter expression contains two *terms*, whereas the expression $x^2 + 2xy + y^2$ contains three *terms*. In general, the *terms* of the expression $t_1 + t_2 + \cdots + t_k$ are $t_1, t_2, \ldots,$ and t_k. We give a special name to a polynomial which has exactly two terms.

Definition 6. *Any polynomial consisting of exactly two terms is called a **binomial**.*

For example, $x^2 + 2$ is a binomial and $x + 2y$ is a binomial. Although $x^2 + 2xy + y^2$ is not a binomial, it is the square of the binomial $x + y$. The reader may verify the following formulas by application of the laws of exponents and the field laws. In each case, the power of the binomial $x + y$ is expressed as a polynomial, called an *expansion* of the binomial.

$(x + y)^0 = 1$

$(x + y)^1 = x + y$

$(x + y)^2 = x^2 + 2xy + y^2$

$(x + y)^3 = x^3 + 3x^2y + 3xy^2 + y^3$

$(x + y)^4 = x^4 + 4x^3y + 6x^2y^2 + 4xy^3 + y^4$

$(x + y)^5 = x^5 + 5x^4y + 10x^3y^2 + 10x^2y^3 + 5xy^4 + y^5$

$(x + y)^6 = x^6 + 6x^5y + 15x^4y^2 + 20x^3y^3 + 15x^2y^4 + 6xy^5 + y^6$

We observe certain patterns in the above expansions. For example, the number of terms in the expansion of $(x + y)^2$ is 3 and the number of terms in $(x + y)^5$ is 6. Moreover, the sum of the exponents in any term of $(x + y)^4$ is 4. We list the above observations and others in the following general list. The exponent m is a counting number, and k is a counting number less than or equal to m.

1. The expansion of $(x + y)^m$ contains $m + 1$ terms.

2. The first term of the expansion of $(x + y)^m$ is x^m.

3. The last term of the expansion of $(x + y)^m$ is y^m.

4. In any other term of the expansion of $(x + y)^m$, the sum of the exponents is m.

5. The term involving $x^{m-k} y^k$ is the $(k + 1)$th term of the expansion of $(x + y)^m$.

6. In the expansion of $(x + y)^m$, the exponent of x successively decreases by 1, and the exponent of y successively increases by 1.

7. The numerical coefficients of the terms in the expansion of $(x + y)^m$ follow the pattern indicated in Fig. 9.5. The array of coefficients in Fig. 9.5(b) is known as *Pascal's triangle.** The indicated powers of $x + y$ are shown in Fig. 9.5(a).

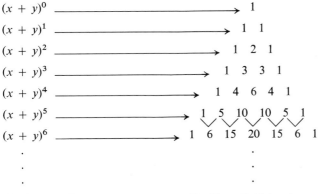

$(x + y)^0$ ⟶ 1

$(x + y)^1$ ⟶ 1 1

$(x + y)^2$ ⟶ 1 2 1

$(x + y)^3$ ⟶ 1 3 3 1

$(x + y)^4$ ⟶ 1 4 6 4 1

$(x + y)^5$ ⟶ 1 5 10 10 5 1

$(x + y)^6$ ⟶ 1 6 15 20 15 6 1

a) Power of $x + y$ b) Pascal's Triangle   **Fig. 9.5**

The reader should study and analyze Pascal's triangle so that he can comprehend the pattern and complete several more lines of it. He should observe that each entry (except 1) in any given line is the sum of the two entries in the line above. For example, in the last line shown in Fig. 9.5(b) [i.e., in the line of

---

*   *Pascal's triangle* is named for Blaise Pascal (1623–1662) because he made such ingenious use of it in probability theory. However, the triangle was known before Pascal's birth.

coefficients in the expansion of $(x + y)^6$], the entries are

1, 6, 15, 20, 15, 6, and 1.

Moreover,

$$6 = 1 + 5,$$

$$15 = 5 + 10,$$

$$20 = 10 + 10,$$

$$15 = 10 + 5,$$

and

$$6 = 5 + 1,$$

as we have indicated by the " $\vee$ " markings in Fig. 9.5(b).

The reader should verify that Pascal's triangle can be expressed in combinatorial notation as shown in Fig. 9.6.

$(x + y)^0$ ────────────────────────→ $C(0:0)$

$(x + y)^1$ ──────────────────→ $C(1:0)$ $C(1:1)$

$(x + y)^2$ ────────────────→ $C(2:0)$ $C(2:1)$ $C(2:2)$

$(x + y)^3$ ──────────────→ $C(3:0)$ $C(3:1)$ $C(3:2)$ $C(3:3)$

$(x + y)^4$ ──────────→ $C(4:0)$ $C(4:1)$ $C(4:2)$ $C(4:3)$ $C(4:4)$

$(x + y)^5$ ──────→ $C(5:0)$ $C(5:1)$ $C(5:2)$ $C(5:3)$ $C(5:4)$ $C(5:5)$

$(x + y)^6$ ──→ $C(6:0)$ $C(6:1)$ $C(6:2)$ $C(6:3)$ $C(6:4)$ $C(6:5)$ $C(6:6)$

.

.

.

Pascal's Triangle in Combinatorial Notation   **Fig. 9.6**

The numbers in Fig. 9.6 are the coefficients in the expansion of $(x + y)^m$. For example, the numbers indicated in the last line shown are the coefficients in the expansion of $(x + y)^6$. The advantage of the combinatorial notation is that the first number of the ordered pair is m and the second number is the exponent of y. For example, $C(5:2)$ is the coefficient of that term in the expansion of $(x + y)^5$, which contains y^2 as a factor; that is, $C(5:2)$ is the coefficient of x^3y^2 (since the sum of the exponents is 5).

The reader may wonder whether the pattern of Pascal's triangle is general and provides a set of coefficients in the expansion of $(x + y)^m$ for any counting number m. In the partial form of Pascal's triangle, we have indicated the coefficients for $m \leq 6$. Theorem 9, which we state without proof, provides a general formula for the expansion of $(x + y)^m$ for any counting number m. Theorem 9 is known as the *binomial theorem*.

Theorem 9 (Binomial Theorem). *If m is any counting number, then*

$$(x + y)^m = C(m:0)x^m y^0 + C(m:1)x^{m-1}y^1 + C(m:2)x^{m-2}y^2$$
$$+ C(m:3)x^{m-3}y^3 + \cdots + C(m:k)x^{m-k}y^k$$
$$+ \cdots + C(m:m-1)x^1 y^{m-1} + C(m:m)x^0 y^m.$$

Of course, $C(m:0) = 1$, $C(m:m) = 1$, $x^0 = 1$, $y^0 = 1$, $0! = 1$, and $1! = 1$. Moreover, we may express $C(m:k)$, for each k in $\{0, 1, 2, \ldots, m\}$, in the *factorial notation*. Hence we may restate the binomial theorem in the following form.

Theorem 10 (Binomial Theorem). *If m is any counting number, then*

$$(x + y)^m = \frac{m!}{0!\,m!} x^m y^0 + \frac{m!}{1!\,(m-1)!} x^{m-1}y^1 + \frac{m!}{2!\,(m-2)!} x^{m-2}y^2$$

$$+ \frac{m!}{3!\,(m-3)!} x^{m-3}y^3 + \cdots + \frac{m!}{k!\,(m-k)!} x^{m-k}y^k$$

$$+ \cdots + \frac{m!}{(m-1)!\,1!} x^1 y^{m-1} + \frac{m!}{m!\,0!} x^0 y^m.$$

The reader will observe from Theorem 10 that the first coefficient is the same as the last coefficient, the second coefficient is the same as the second-to-last coefficient, etc., and that the binomial theorem agrees with Pascal's triangle.

The following examples illustrate the binomial theorem.

Example 1. Expand $(x + y)^5$.

By the binomial theorem

$$(x + y)^5 = \frac{5!}{0!\,5!} x^5 y^0 + \frac{5!}{1!\,4!} x^4 y^1 + \frac{5!}{2!\,3!} x^3 y^2 + \frac{5!}{3!\,2!} x^2 y^3$$

$$+ \frac{5!}{4!\,1!} x^1 y^4 + \frac{5!}{5!\,0!} x^0 y^5$$

$$= x^5 + 5x^4 y + 10x^3 y^2 + 10x^2 y^3 + 5xy^4 + y^5.$$

Example 2. Expand $(x + y)^6$.

By the binomial theorem

$$(x + y)^6 = \frac{6!}{0!\,6!} x^6 y^0 + \frac{6!}{1!\,5!} x^5 y^1 + \frac{6!}{2!\,4!} x^4 y^2 + \frac{6!}{3!\,3!} x^3 y^3$$

$$+ \frac{6!}{4!\,2!} x^2 y^4 + \frac{6!}{5!\,1!} x^1 y^5 + \frac{6!}{6!\,0!} x^0 y^6$$

$$= x^6 + 6x^5 y + 15x^4 y^2 + 20x^3 y^3 + 15x^2 y^4 + 6xy^5 + y^6.$$

Example 3. Compute the seventh term in the expansion of $(x + y)^{11}$.

The seventh term is the term involving $x^{11-6}y^6$. Hence we compute

$$\frac{m!}{k!\,(m-k)!}\,x^{m-k}y^k,$$

in which $m = 11$ and $k = 6$.

$$\frac{11!}{6!\,5!}\,x^{11-6}y^6 = \frac{1 \times 2 \times 3 \times 4 \times 5 \times 6 \times 7 \times 8 \times 9 \times 10 \times 11}{(1 \times 2 \times 3 \times 4 \times 5 \times 6) \times (1 \times 2 \times 3 \times 4 \times 5)}\,x^5 y^6$$

$$= \frac{7 \times 8 \times 9 \times 10 \times 11}{1 \times 2 \times 3 \times 4 \times 5}\,x^5 y^6$$

$$= 462x^5 y^6.$$

Thus the seventh term of the expansion of $(x + y)^{11}$ is $462x^5 y^6$.

In Theorems 9 and 10 we indicated the first four terms of the expansion of $(x + y)^m$, then we indicated the $(k + 1)$th term, next we indicated the second-to-last term, and finally we indicated the last term. Of course, if $m < 6$, then we have indicated too many terms. In such a formulation, we assume that the reader will make the necessary adjustment if the number of terms is less than indicated. For example, if $m = 3$, then there are exactly 4 terms in the expansion; hence we must adjust the formula accordingly.

We can avoid the above difficulty by means of the *compact summation notation*, in which we indicate the sum of terms by the capital Greek letter "Σ" (called *sigma* and associated with the letter "S" for *sum*). For example,

$$\sum_{i=1}^{5} x_i = x_1 + x_2 + x_3 + x_4 + x_5,$$

and

$$\sum_{k=1}^{20} kx^k = 1x^1 + 2x^2 + 3x^3 + \cdots + 20x^{20}.$$

The notation

$$\sum_{i=1}^{m} x_i$$

is read

"the sum of all x_i as i varies from 1 to m inclusive."

In the compact summation notation we may restate the binomial theorem as in Theorem 11.

Theorem 11 (Binomial Theorem). *If m is any counting number, then*

$$(x + y)^m = \sum_{k=0}^{m} \frac{m!}{k!\,(m-k)!}\,x^{m-k}y^k.$$

For example,

$$(x + y)^4 = \sum_{k=0}^{4} \frac{4!}{k!\,(4 - k)!}$$

$$= \frac{4!}{0!\,(4 - 0)!}\,x^{4-0}y^0 + \frac{4!}{1!\,(4 - 1)!}\,x^{4-1}y^1$$

$$+ \frac{4!}{2!\,(4 - 2)!}\,x^{4-2}y^2 + \frac{4!}{3!\,(4 - 3)!}\,x^{4-3}y^3$$

$$+ \frac{4!}{4!\,(4 - 4)!}\,x^{4-4}y^4$$

$$= x^4 + 4x^3y + 6x^2y^2 + 4xy^3 + y^4.$$

EXERCISE SET 9.5

I. Employ *Pascal's triangle* to expand each of the following.

1. $(x + y)^7$ 2. $(x + y)^8$ 3. $(x + y)^{10}$
4. $(x + y)^9$ 5. $(x + y)^5$ 6. $(x - y)^6$
7. $(2x - y)^5$ 8. $(x - 2y)^5$ 9. $(x + b)^6$
10. $(a + y)^6$

II. Employ the *binomial theorem* to expand each of the following.

1. $(x + y)^8$ 2. $(x + y)^7$ 3. $(x + y)^9$
4. $(x + y)^{10}$ 5. $(x - y)^6$ 6. $(x - y)^5$
7. $(x - 2y)^5$ 8. $(2x - y)^5$ 9. $(a + 2y)^4$
10. $(2x + b)^4$

III. Compute the fifth term in the expansion of each of the following.

1. $(x + h)^9$ 2. $(x + y)^8$ 3. $(x + y)^5$
4. $(x + y)^4$ 5. $(x + y)^6$ 6. $(x + y)^7$
7. $(x - y)^7$ 8. $(x - y)^6$ 9. $(2x + y)^9$
10. $(x + 2y)^9$

IV.

1. Compute the coefficient of x^5y^7 in the expansion of $(x + y)^{12}$.
2. Compute the coefficient of x^7y^5 in the expansion of $(x + y)^{12}$.
3. Compute the coefficient of x^8y^4 in the expansion of $(x + y)^{12}$.
4. Compute the coefficient of x^4y^8 in the expansion of $(x + y)^{12}$.
5. Compute the coefficient of xy^7 in the expansion of $(x + y)^8$.
6. Compute the coefficient of x^7y in the expansion of $(x + y)^8$.
7. Compute the coefficient of $x^{10}y^7$ in the expansion of $(x + y)^{17}$.

8. Compute the coefficient of x^7y^{10} in the expansion of $(x + y)^{17}$.

9. Compute the coefficient of x^4y^3 in the expansion of $(x - 2y)^7$.

10. Compute the coefficient of x^4y^3 in the expansion of $(2x - y)^7$.

V. Compute the sum of the coefficients in the expansion of each of the following.

1. $(x + y)^1$ 2. $(x + y)^2$ 3. $(s + t)^3$

4. $(s + t)^4$ 5. $(h + y)^5$ 6. $(h + y)^6$

7. $(h + t)^7$ 8. $(h + t)^8$ 9. $(h + t)^9$

10. $(h + t)^{10}$

VI. Compute each of the following and compare with the corresponding part of Exercise V.

1. 2^1 2. 2^2 3. 2^3

4. 2^4 5. 2^5 6. 2^6

7. 2^7 8. 2^8 9. 2^9

10. 2^{10}

VII. Express in *exponential form* with base 2 the sum of the coefficients in the expansion of each of the following. [*Hint:* Refer to Exercise VI.]

1. $(x + y)^{20}$ 2. $(x + y)^{25}$ 3. $(x + y)^{50}$

4. $(x + y)^{45}$ 5. $(h + t)^{60}$ 6. $(h + t)^{75}$

7. $(h + t)^{100}$ 8. $(h + t)^{90}$ 9. $(h + y)^{500}$

10. $(h + y)^{499}$

VIII. Prove that the sum of the coefficients in the expansion of $(x + y)^m$ is 2^m.

[*Hint:* $2^m = (1 + 1)^m = C(m : 0) 1^m 1^0 + C(m : 1)1^{m-1}1^1 + \cdots + C(m : m)1^0 1^m.$]

IX. An experiment consists of tossing a coin three times and observing the outcomes (*heads* or *tails*). Since there are two possible outcomes for each toss and there are three tosses, it follows that there are 2^3 possible outcomes, as follows:

$(h, h, h),$ $(h, h, t),$ $(h, t, h),$ $(h, t, t),$

$(t, h, h),$ $(t, h, t),$ $(t, t, h),$ $(t, t, t).$

We observe that *two heads and one tail* can occur in *three* possible ways; namely, $(h, h, t), (h, t, h), (t, h, h).$

Moreover, $(h + t)^3 = h^3 + 3h^2t + 3ht^2 + t^3$, and the coefficient of h^2t [representing 2 *heads* and 1 *tail*] is 3. Thus, the number of ways in which 2 *heads and 1 tail* can occur is the coefficient of h^2t in the expansion of $(h + t)^3$. Similarly, the number of ways in which 3 *tails* can occur is the coefficient of t^3 in the expansion of $(h + t)^3$. In general, the number of ways in which k *heads and* $m - k$ *tails* can occur in m tosses of a coin is the coefficient of $h^k t^{m-k}$ in the expansion of $(h + t)^m$. That is, there are $C(m : m - k)$ ways in which k *heads and* $m - k$ *tails* can occur in m tosses of a coin. Since there are 2^m possible outcomes, we see that the probability of the event that k *heads and* $m - k$ *tails* occur is $C(m : m - k)/2^m$.

In Exercise VII.5 in Section 9.4, we observed that $C(m : m - k) = C(m : k)$. Hence the probability of the event that k *heads occur* in m tosses is $C(m : k)/2^m$. Compute the probability of each of the following events.

1. In 10 tosses of a coin, 7 heads and 3 tails occur.
2. In 10 tosses of a coin, 3 heads and 7 tails occur.
3. In 10 tosses of a coin, 6 heads and 4 tails occur.
4. In 10 tosses of a coin, 4 heads and 6 tails occur.
5. In 10 tosses of a coin, 5 heads and 5 tails occur.
6. In 12 tosses of a coin, 6 heads and 6 tails occur.
7. In 13 tosses of a coin, 2 heads and 11 tails occur.
8. In 11 tosses of a coin, 1 head and 10 tails occur.
9. In 13 tosses of a coin, 13 heads occur.
10. In 11 tosses of a coin, 11 tails occur.
11. In 11 tosses of a coin, no heads occur.
12. In 13 tosses of a coin, no tails occur.

9.6 CONDITIONAL PROBABILITY

The probability problems considered in the preceding sections have been *unconditional* in the sense that each experiment was assigned a sample space and the probability of a given event was computed unconditionally—i.e., without knowledge of any additional information which might affect the probability of the event. For example, if the experiment consists of rolling a single die and observing the outcome, then the sample space S is $\{1, 2, 3, 4, 5, 6\}$ and the probability of the event E that the outcome is 4 is $\frac{1}{6}$, because $E = \{4\}$ and

$$n(E)/n(S) = \tfrac{1}{6}.$$

On the other hand, if we know in advance that the outcome is even, then the *reduced* sample space S_r is $\{2, 4, 6\}$ [rather than $\{1, 2, 3, 4, 5, 6\}$], and the probability of E is $\frac{1}{3}$, because $E = \{4\}$ and $n(E)/n(S_r) = \frac{1}{3}$. The latter probability is known as a *conditional probability* because of the additional condition imposed on the experiment. Since

$$\frac{n(E)}{n(S_r)} = \frac{n(E)/n(S)}{n(S_r)/n(S)} = \frac{P(E)}{P(S_r)},$$

we make the following definition.

Definition 7. *The **conditional probability** of the event E_1, given that the nonempty event E_2 of an experiment has occurred, is denoted by "$P(E_1 \mid E_2)$" and is equal to $P(E_1 \cap E_2)/P(E_2)$. That is,*

$$P(E_1 \mid E_2) = \frac{P(E_1 \cap E_2)}{P(E_2)}.$$

*The notation "$P(E_1 \mid E_2)$" is read briefly "$P(E_1)$ **given** E_2."*

The reader should observe from Definition 7 that E_2 serves as a reduced sample space of the experiment and that $E_1 \cap E_2$ is that subset of the event E_1 which is common to E_2.

The following examples illustrate Definition 7.

Example 1. Two dice (one red die and one green die) are rolled. The outcome of one of the dice is 5; i.e., 5 occurs on one of the dice. What is the probability that the sum is 8?

The sample space contains 36 ordered pairs. However, the event E_2 that the outcome of one die is 5 [the reduced sample space] consists of 11 ordered pairs as follows:

$$E_2 = \{(1, 5), (2, 5), (3, 5), (4, 5), (5, 5), (6, 5),$$
$$(5, 1), (5, 2), (5, 3), (5, 4), (5, 6)\}.$$

The event E_1 that the sum is 8 consists of 5 ordered pairs as follows:

$$E_1 = \{(2, 6), (3, 5), (4, 4), (5, 3), (6, 2)\}.$$

Hence $E_1 \cap E_2 = \{(3, 5), (5, 3)\}$. Thus

$$P(E_1 \mid E_2) = \frac{P(E_1 \cap E_2)}{P(E_2)} = \frac{2/36}{11/36} = \frac{2}{11}.$$

In Example 1, we computed the conditional probability to be $\frac{2}{11}$. A common error is to reason that the probability of obtaining a sum of 8 is $\frac{1}{6}$ because 5 has already occurred on one die and the probability of 3 occurring on the second die is $\frac{1}{6}$. The fallacy is due to the fact that the ordered pair (5, 5) [for 5 on the red die and 5 on the green die], which is an element of E_2, is a *single* outcome which occurs *once* rather than *twice*. If we counted (5, 5) twice, then we would conclude *erroneously* that E_2 contains 12 elements rather than 11. Then we would compute the conditional probability *erroneously* as follows:

$$P(E_1 \mid E_2) = \frac{P(E_1 \cap E_2)}{P(E_2)} = \frac{2/36}{12/36} = \frac{1}{6}. \qquad [\text{ERROR}]$$

Example 2. A light-bulb manufacturer knows that 15% of the bulbs he produces are 60-watt bulbs and 5% of all bulbs he produces are 60-watt bulbs which are defective. What is the probability that a 60-watt bulb selected at random is defective?

The probability that a randomly selected 60-watt bulb is defective is the conditional probability of the event that a bulb is defective if we know that it is a 60-watt bulb. If E_2 is the event that the bulb is a 60-watt bulb and E_1 is the event that the bulb is defective, then $E_1 \cap E_2$ is the event that the bulb is a 60-watt bulb which is defective.

$$P(E_1 \mid E_2) = \frac{P(E_1 \cap E_2)}{P(E_2)} = \frac{.05}{.15} = \frac{1}{3}.$$

Hence the probability that any given 60-watt bulb is defective is $\frac{1}{3}$. Thus the manufacturer should initiate more rigid quality-control procedures.

We may employ the conditional probability formula of Definition 7 to prove the following theorem, which is usually known as the *theorem on compound probabilities.*

Theorem 12 (Theorem on Compound Probabilities). *If E_1 and E_2 are non-empty events of an experiment, then*

$$P(E_1 \cap E_2) = P(E_1)P(E_2 \mid E_1).$$

Proof. Interchanging the roles of E_1 and E_2 in Definition 7, we obtain the formula

$$P(E_2 \mid E_1) = \frac{P(E_2 \cap E_1)}{P(E_1)}$$

for the conditional probability of E_2 given E_1. Now $E_2 \cap E_1 = E_1 \cap E_2$. Hence

$$P(E_2 \mid E_1) = \frac{P(E_1 \cap E_2)}{P(E_1)}.$$

Thus

$$P(E_1)P(E_2 \mid E_1) = P(E_1 \cap E_2).$$

Hence

$$P(E_1 \cap E_2) = P(E_1)P(E_2 \mid E_1). \quad \text{(QED)}$$

The following examples illustrate Theorem 12.

Example 3. A box contains 3 red checkers and 2 black checkers. Marcella draws one checker at random, and without noting its color she draws another one at random. What is the probability that both checkers are red?

If E_1 is the event that the first checker is red and E_2 is the event that the second checker is red, then $E_1 \cap E_2$ is the event that both checkers are red, and $P(E_1 \cap E_2)$ is the probability that both checkers are red.

Now $P(E_1) = \frac{3}{5}$ [since 3 of the 5 checkers are red]. Moreover,

$$P(E_2 \mid E_1) = \tfrac{2}{4} = \tfrac{1}{2}$$

[since 2 of the remaining 4 checkers are red]. Hence

$$P(E_1 \cap E_2) = P(E_1)P(E_2 \mid E_1)$$
$$= \tfrac{3}{5} \times \tfrac{1}{2}$$
$$= \tfrac{3}{10}.$$

Hence the probability that both checkers are red is $\frac{3}{10}$.

Example 4. Box A contains 3 white chips and 4 blue chips. Box B contains 4 white chips, 5 blue chips, and 2 red chips. Karen selects a box at random and draws one chip at random from that box. What is the probability that she selects a white chip?

The probability of selecting Box A is $\frac{1}{2}$, and the probability of selecting Box B is $\frac{1}{2}$. The conditional probability of drawing a white chip given that Box A is selected is $\frac{3}{7}$ [since 3 of the 7 chips in Box A are white].

The conditional probability of drawing a white chip given that Box B is selected is $\frac{4}{11}$ [since 4 of the 11 chips in Box B are white].

If E_1 is the event that Box A is selected and E_2 is the event that a white chip is drawn, then

$$P(E_1 \cap E_2) = P(E_1)P(E_2 \mid E_1)$$
$$= \tfrac{1}{2} \times \tfrac{3}{7}$$
$$= \tfrac{3}{14}.$$

That is, the probability of selecting Box A and drawing a white chip is $\frac{3}{14}$.

If E_3 is the event that Box B is selected and E_2 is the event that a white chip is drawn, then

$$P(E_3 \cap E_2) = P(E_3)P(E_2 \mid E_3)$$
$$= \tfrac{1}{2} \times \tfrac{4}{11}$$
$$= \tfrac{2}{11}.$$

That is, the probability of selecting Box B and drawing a white chip is $\frac{2}{11}$.

Since the desired event is the *union* of $E_1 \cap E_2$ and $E_3 \cap E_2$, it follows that the desired probability is the *sum* of $P(E_1 \cap E_2)$ and $P(E_3 \cap E_2)$:

$$P(E_1 \cap E_2) + P(E_3 \cap E_2) = \frac{3}{14} + \frac{2}{11}$$
$$= \frac{33 + 28}{154}$$
$$= \frac{61}{154}.$$

Hence the probability that she draws a white chip is $\frac{61}{154}$ [approximately 40%].

The above discussion is summarized in the accompanying tree diagram.

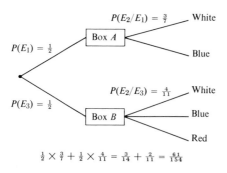

$\frac{1}{2} \times \frac{3}{7} + \frac{1}{2} \times \frac{4}{11} = \frac{3}{14} + \frac{2}{11} = \frac{61}{154}$

Two events E_1 and E_2 of an experiment may be so related that the occurrence of E_1 influences the occurrence of E_2, or vice versa. The probability of E_1 given E_2 is the conditional probability $P(E_1 \mid E_2)$.

If the occurrence of E_2 does not influence the occurrence of E_1, then $P(E_1 \mid E_2) = P(E_1)$; that is, the conditional probability of E_1 given that E_2 has occurred is the same as the unconditional probability, $P(E_1)$.

Definition 8. *The events E_1 and E_2 are said to be **independent** if and only if $P(E_1 \mid E_2) = P(E_1)$. The events E_1 and E_2 are said to be **dependent** if and only if $P(E_1 \mid E_2) \neq P(E_1)$.*

The following theorem, which follows from Definition 8 and Theorem 12, is useful in determining the probability of the intersection of any two independent events.

Theorem 13. *The nonempty events E_1 and E_2 are independent if and only if $P(E_1 \cap E_2) = P(E_1)P(E_2)$.*

Proof. $P(E_1 \cap E_2) = P(E_1)P(E_2 \mid E_1)$ [by Theorem 12]. But $P(E_2 \mid E_1) = P(E_2)$ if and only if E_1 and E_2 are independent [by Definition 8]. Hence

$$P(E_1 \cap E_2) = P(E_1)P(E_2)$$

if and only if E_1 and E_2 are independent. (QED)

The following examples illustrate Definition 8 and Theorem 13.

Example 5. A coin is tossed twice. What is the probability of the event E_2 that the outcome of the second toss is tails, given the event E_1 that the outcome of the first toss is heads?

If the sample space S is $\{(h, h), (h, t), (t, h), (t, t)\}$, the event E_1 is $\{(h, h), (h, t)\}$, and the event E_2 is $\{(h, t), (t, t)\}$, then

$$E_1 \cap E_2 = \{(h, t)\}, \qquad P(E_1 \cap E_2) = \tfrac{1}{4}, \qquad P(E_1) = \tfrac{2}{4} = \tfrac{1}{2},$$

and

$$P(E_2) = \tfrac{2}{4} = \tfrac{1}{2}.$$

Hence $P(E_1 \cap E_2) = P(E_1)P(E_2)$. But

$$P(E_1 \cap E_2) = P(E_1)P(E_2 \mid E_1) \qquad \text{[by Theorem 12].}$$

Hence

$$P(E_2 \mid E_1) = P(E_2) = \tfrac{1}{2}.$$

The events E_1 and E_2 are *independent*.

Example 6. A nickel and a dime are tossed. Is the event E_1 that the coins match independent of the event E_2 that head occurs on (at least) one of the coins?

If the sample space S is $\{(h, h), (h, t), (t, h), (t, t)\}$, the event E_1 is $\{(h, h), (t, t)\}$, and the event E_2 is $\{(h, t), (t, h), (h, h)\}$, then

$$E_1 \cap E_2 = \{(h, h)\}, \qquad P(E_1 \cap E_2) = \tfrac{1}{4}, \qquad P(E_1) = \tfrac{2}{4} = \tfrac{1}{2},$$

and

$$P(E_2) = \tfrac{3}{4}.$$

Thus

$$P(E_1)P(E_2) = \tfrac{1}{2} \times \tfrac{3}{4} = \tfrac{3}{8}.$$

Hence

$$P(E_1 \cap E_2) \neq P(E_1)P(E_2).$$

Thus E_1 and E_2 are *dependent* events.

EXERCISE SET 9.6

I. A white die and a blue die are rolled.

1. What is the probability of the event E_1 that the sum is greater than 8, given the event E_2 that 4 occurs on the blue die?

2. What is the probability of the event E_1 that the sum is less than 8, given the event E_2 that 4 occurs on the blue die?

3. What is the probability of the event E_1 that the sum is 7, given the event E_2 that 5 occurs on the white die?

4. What is the probability of the event E_1 that the sum is 12, given the event E_2 that 6 occurs on the white die?

II. Box A contains 3 red poker chips, 2 white poker chips, and 1 blue poker chip; Box B contains 2 red poker chips, 1 white poker chip, and 3 blue poker chips. A box is selected at random, and a chip is drawn from the box.

1. What is the probability of the event E that a blue chip is drawn?

2. What is the probability of the event E that a white chip is drawn?

3. What is the probability of the event E that a red chip is drawn?

4. What is the probability of the event E that a white chip is not drawn?

5. What is the probability of the event E that a blue chip or a white chip is drawn?

6. What is the probability of the event E that a red chip or a blue chip is drawn?

7. What is the probability of the event E that a red chip or a white chip is drawn?

8. What is the probability of the event E that a red chip or a white chip or a blue chip is drawn?

9. What is the probability of the event E that a blue chip is not drawn?

10. What is the probability of the event E that a red chip is not drawn?

III. Forty percent of all cars manufactured by Company X are X-1 models. Twenty percent of all models are X-1 models with defective steering. What is the probability of the event E_1 that a car has defective steering, given the event E_2 that it is an X-1 model?

IV. Thirty percent of all airplanes manufactured by Company A are A-506 models. It is discovered that 20% of the A-506 models have defective frames. What is the probability of the event E that a randomly chosen plane manufactured by Company A is an A-506 model with a defective frame?

V. An experiment consists of rolling a die twice. Determine whether each of the following pairs of events is *independent* or *dependent*.

1. The outcome of the first roll is 3, and the outcome of the second roll is 4.

2. The outcome of the first roll is 5, and the outcome of the second roll is an odd number.

3. The outcome of the first roll is 3, and the sum of the outcomes of the two rolls is 7.

4. The outcome of the first roll is an even number, and the sum of the outcomes of the two rolls is an odd number.

VI. An experiment consists of drawing a card at random from a standard deck of playing cards. Let E_1 be the event that the card is a heart, E_2 be the event that the card is a king, E_3 be the event that the card is an ace, and E_4 be the event that the card is a red card. Determine which of the following pairs of events are independent.

1. E_1, E_2 2. E_1, E_3

3. E_2, E_3 4. $E_1, (E_2 \cup E_3)$

5. $E_2, (E_1 \cup E_3)$ 6. $E_3, (E_1 \cup E_2)$.

VII. A *short deck* of playing cards consists of the 20 honor cards in a standard deck. An experiment consists of drawing 1 card from each of 2 short decks.

1. What is the probability of drawing 2 aces?

2. What is the probability of drawing an ace and a king?

3. What is the probability of drawing a black card and a heart?

4. What is the probability of drawing a red card and a club?

5. What is the probability of drawing 2 black cards?

6. What is the probability of drawing 2 red cards?

7. What is the probability of drawing a heart and a club?

8. What is the probability of drawing a spade and a diamond?

9. What is the probability of drawing a king and a red queen?

10. What is the probability of drawing a jack and a black queen?

VIII. A *short deck* of playing cards consists of the 20 honor cards in a standard deck. An experiment consists of drawing 2 cards from a short deck.

1. What is the probability that the second card is an ace, given that the first card is an ace?

2. What is the probability that the second card is a jack, given that the first card is a jack?

3. What is the probability that the second card is an ace, given that the first card is the ace of hearts?

4. What is the probability that the second card is a queen, given that the first card is the queen of spades?

5. What is the probability that the second card is an ace, given that the first card is a red ace?

6. What is the probability that the second card is not an ace, given that the first card is an ace?

PUZZLE PROBLEMS

1. There are 30 men at a luncheon. What is the probability that two men have the same birthday (not necessarily the same year)? [*Hint:* First compute the probability of the complementary event that no two have the same birthday.]

2. A woman wrote three letters and addressed the three corresponding envelopes, and asked her daughter to insert the letters into the envelopes and seal them. Later she learned that her daughter had dropped the letters and envelopes onto the floor and picked them up and inserted them into the envelopes at random. What is the probability that she inserted all three letters into the proper envelopes? What is the probability that she inserted exactly two letters into the proper envelopes? What is the probability that she inserted exactly one letter into the proper envelope? What is the probability that she inserted no letter into the proper envelope?

Answers to Selected Exercises

Exercise Set 1.1

1. Statement	3. Statement
5. Open sentence	7. Statement
9. Neither	11. Open sentence
13. Open sentence	15. Open sentence
17. Open sentence	19. Open sentence
21. Neither	23. Neither

Exercise Set 1.2

I.

1. All	3. Some	5. Some
7. All	9. All	11. Some, No
13. All	15. Some	

II.

1. No quantifier	3. Implied
5. No quantifier	7. No quantifier
9. No quantifier	

III.

1. All	3. All	5. Some
7. All	9. All	11. Some
13. All	15. All	

IV.

1. $\forall x, x + x = 2x$; true
   $\exists x, x + x = 2x$; true
   There is no $x, x + x = 2x$; false

3. $\forall t, 5 + t = 5$; false
   $\exists t, 5 + t = 5$; true
   There is no t, $5 + t = 5$; false

5. $\forall x, 7 + x = x$; false
   $\exists x, 7 + x = x$; false
   There is no x, $7 + x = x$; true

7. $\forall t, t + 6 = 6$; false
   $\exists t, t + 6 = 6$; true
   There is no t, $t + 6 = 6$; false

9. $\forall b, b + 6 = 5$; false
   $\exists b, b + 6 = 5$; false
   There is no b, $b + 6 = 5$; true

Exercise Set 1.3

I.

1. Simple

3. Compound; not

5. Compound; and

7. Compound; or

9. Compound; if-then

11. Compound; if and only if

13. Compound; if-then, not

15. Compound; not

17. Compound; if-then, not

19. Compound; if-then, not, and

21. Compound; if-then

II.

1. Compound
   p: Gary is in college
   q: he is living with his family
   $p \rightarrow {\sim}q$

3. Simple
   p: x is greater than zero
   p

5. Compound
   p: $\frac{1}{2} + \frac{1}{3} = \frac{1}{6}$
   q: $\frac{1}{3} + \frac{1}{4} = \frac{1}{12}$
   $p \rightarrow q$

7. Compound
   p: $3 + 4 = 7$
   ${\sim}({\sim}p)$

9. Compound
   p: mathematics is a science
   $p \vee {\sim}p$

11. Compound
    p: $4 + 6 = 5$
    q: $3 + 6 = 9$
    $p \vee {\sim}q$

13. Compound
    p: $4 + 7 = 8$
    q: $2 + 3 = 1$
    $p \rightarrow q$

15. Simple
    p: $a + 0 = a \times 0$
    p

Exercise Set 1.4

I.

1. The moon is not a planet.

3. $3 + 4 \neq 7$.

5. Some number is not positive.

7. $2 + 4 \neq 6$.

9. Some number is even.
11. No numbers are not even. (All numbers are even.)
13. There is no x, x is less than 5.
15. No numbers are greater than 25.
17. $\exists x$, $x + 1$ is not greater than x.
19. $\exists y$, y^2 is negative.

II.

1. False; true	3. True; false
5. False; true	7. True; false
9. False; true	11. True; false
13. True; false	15. True; false
17. True; false	19. True; false

Exercise Set 1.5

1. T	3. F	5. T	7. F
9. T	11. T	13. F	15. T
17. F	19. T		

Exercise Set 1.6

1. T	3. T	5. T	7. T
9. F	11. T	13. T	15. F
17. T	19. F	21. T	

Exercise Set 1.7

I.

1.

p	q	$p \vee q$	$p \to (p \vee q)$
T	T	T	T
T	F	T	T
F	T	T	T
F	F	F	T

3.

p	q	$p \vee q$	$(p \vee q) \to p$
T	T	T	T
T	F	T	T
F	T	T	F
F	F	F	T

5.

p	q	$p \lor q$	$p \leftrightarrows (p \lor q)$
T	T	T	T
T	F	T	T
F	T	T	F
F	F	F	T

7.

p	q	$p \to q$	$q \to p$	$(p \to q) \leftrightarrows (q \to p)$
T	T	T	T	T
T	F	F	T	F
F	T	T	F	F
F	F	T	T	T

9.

p	q	$\sim p$	$\sim q$	$p \to q$	$\sim q \to \sim p$	$(p \to q) \leftrightarrows (\sim q \to \sim p)$
T	T	F	F	T	T	T
T	F	F	T	F	F	T
F	T	T	F	T	T	T
F	F	T	T	T	T	T

11.

p	q	$\sim p$	$\sim q$	$p \to q$	$\sim p \to \sim q$	$(p \to q) \to (\sim p \to \sim q)$
T	T	F	F	T	T	T
T	F	F	T	F	T	T
F	T	T	F	T	F	F
F	F	T	T	T	T	T

13.

p	q	$\sim q$	$p \land \sim q$	$\sim(p \land \sim q)$	$p \to q$	$\sim(p \land \sim q) \leftrightarrows (p \to q)$
T	T	F	F	T	T	T
T	F	T	T	F	F	T
F	T	F	F	T	T	T
F	F	T	F	T	T	T

15.

p	q	$\tilde{}p$	$\tilde{}q$	$p\leftrightarroweq q$	$\tilde{}(p\leftrightarroweq q)$	$p\wedge\tilde{}q$	$q\wedge\tilde{}p$	$(p\wedge\tilde{}q)\vee(q\wedge\tilde{}p)$	$\tilde{}[p\leftrightarroweq q]\leftrightarroweq[(p\wedge\tilde{}q)\vee(q\wedge\tilde{}p)]$
T	T	F	F	T	F	F	F	F	T
T	F	F	T	F	T	T	F	T	T
F	T	T	F	F	T	F	T	T	T
F	F	T	T	T	F	F	F	F	T

II. (1), (2), (9), (12), (13), (14), and (15) are logical truths.

III.

1.

p	q	$p\vee q$	$q\vee p$	$(p\vee q)\leftrightarroweq(q\vee p)$
T	T	T	T	T
T	F	T	T	T
F	T	T	T	T
F	F	F	F	T

3.

p	q	r	$(p\wedge q)$	$q\wedge r$	$(p\wedge q)\wedge r$	$p\wedge(q\wedge r)$	$[(p\wedge q)\wedge r]\leftrightarroweq[p\wedge(q\wedge r)]$
T	T	T	T	T	T	T	T
T	T	F	T	F	F	F	T
T	F	T	F	F	F	F	T
T	F	F	F	F	F	F	T
F	T	T	F	T	F	F	T
F	T	F	F	F	F	F	T
F	F	T	F	F	F	F	T
F	F	F	F	F	F	F	T

5.

p	$p\wedge p$	$(p\wedge p)\leftrightarroweq p$
T	T	T
F	F	T

7. Since $(2+3=5)$ is true and $[(2+3)+4=5+4]$ is true, $[2+3=5]$ $\leftrightarroweq[(2+3)+4=5+4]$ is true.

9.

p	q	$\tilde{}p$	$\tilde{}q$	$p \wedge \tilde{}q$	$q \wedge \tilde{}p$	$(p \wedge \tilde{}q) \vee (q \wedge \tilde{}p)$
T	T	F	F	F	F	F
T	F	F	T	T	F	T
F	T	T	F	F	T	T
F	F	T	T	F	F	F

$p \to q$	$(p \to q) \to (q \wedge \tilde{}p)$	$[(p \wedge \tilde{}q) \vee (q \wedge \tilde{}p)] \leftrightarrows [(p \to q) \to (q \wedge \tilde{}p)]$
T	F	T
F	T	T
T	T	T
T	F	T

IV.

1. $(3 + 4 = 8$ and $2 + 0 \neq 0) \vee (2 + 0 = 0$ and $3 + 4 \neq 8)$.

3. (A triangle is equilateral and it is not equiangular) $\vee$ (A triangle is equiangular and it is not equilateral).

5. $4 + 5 = 8$ and $6 + 2 \neq 8$.   7. $(p \vee q) \wedge \tilde{}p$.

9. $[\tilde{}(p \to q) \wedge \tilde{}(p \wedge \tilde{}q)] \vee [(p \wedge \tilde{}q) \wedge (p \to q)]$.

Exercise Set 1.8

I.

1. *Converse:* If Tommy earns less than $1000 per year, then Tommy earns less than $6000 per year.
   Inverse: If Tommy does not earn less than $6000 per year, then Tommy does not earn less than $7000 per year.
   Contrapositive: If Tommy does not earn less than $7000 per year, then Tommy does not earn less than $6000 per year.

3. *Converse:* If $\triangle ABC$ is isosceles, then $\triangle ABC$ is equilateral.
   Inverse: If $\triangle ABC$ is not equilateral, then $\triangle ABC$ is not isosceles.
   Contrapositive: If $\triangle ABC$ is not isosceles, then $\triangle ABC$ is not equilateral.

5. *Converse:* If a^2 is an odd number, then a is an odd number.
   Inverse: If a is not an odd number, then a^2 is not an odd number.
   Contrapositive: If a^2 is not an odd number, then a is not an odd number.

7. *Converse:* If $ABCD$ is a rectangle, then $ABCD$ is a parallelogram.
   Inverse: If $ABCD$ is not a parallelogram, then $ABCD$ is not a rectangle.
   Contrapositive: If $ABCD$ is not a rectangle, then $ABCD$ is not a parallelogram.

9. *Converse:* If Johnnie is a girl, then Johnnie is a person.
   Inverse: If Johnnie is not a person, then Johnnie is not a girl.
   Contrapositive: If Johnnie is not a girl, then Johnnie is not a person.

II.
  1. *T*   3. *T*   5. *T*   7. *F*   9. *F*

III.
  1. *F*   3. *F*   5. *T*   7. *T*   9. *T*

IV.
  1. *F*   3. *F*   5. *T*   7. *T*   9. *T*

V.
  1. *T*   3. *T*   5. *T*   7. *F*   9. *F*

VI.
  1. *T*   3. *T*   5. *T*   7. *T*   9. *T*
  11. *T*

VII.
  1. *Converse:* $r \to (p \wedge q)$
     Inverse: $\sim(p \wedge q) \to r$
     Contrapositive: $\sim r \to \sim(p \wedge q)$
  3. *Converse:* $(p \to q) \to (\sim p \vee q)$
     Inverse: $\sim(\sim p \vee q) \to \sim(p \to q)$
     Contrapositive: $\sim(p \to q) \to \sim(\sim p \vee q)$
  5. *Converse:* $(\sim q \vee r) \to (p \vee q)$
     Inverse: $\sim(p \vee q) \to \sim(\sim q \vee r)$
     Contrapositive: $\sim(\sim q \vee r) \to \sim(p \vee q)$

Exercise Set 1.9

  I.

   p: Quadrilateral *ABCD* is a rectangle
   q: Quadrilateral *ABCD* is a parallelogram
   ($p \Rightarrow q$ and since p is true, q is true)

p	q	$p \to q$	$(p \to q) \wedge p$	$[(p \to q) \wedge p] \to q$
T	*T*	*T*	*T*	*T*
T	*F*	*F*	*F*	*T*
F	*T*	*T*	*F*	*T*
F	*F*	*T*	*F*	*T*

   Therefore $[(p \to q) \wedge p] \to q$ is a logical truth; that is, $[(p \to q) \wedge p] \Rightarrow q$.

  II.

  1. p: $2 + 5 = 9$
     q: $8 + 6 = 14$

     $p \to q$ is true
     q is true
     p is *not true;* that is, $[(p \to q) \wedge p] \not\Rightarrow p$.

III. $p: 2 + 1 = 3$
$q: 6 + 1 = 7$
$r: 2 + 2 = 4$

H1: $2 + 1 = 3$
H2: $[(2 + 1 = 3) \wedge (6 + 1 \neq 7)] \to [(2 + 2 = 4) \wedge (2 + 2 \neq 4)]$
C : $6 + 1 = 7$

p	q	r	$\sim q$	$\sim r$	$p \wedge \sim q$	$r \wedge \sim r$	$(p \wedge \sim q) \to (r \wedge \sim r)$
T	T	T	F	F	F	F	T
T	T	F	F	T	F	F	T
T	F	T	T	F	T	F	F
T	F	F	T	T	T	F	F
F	T	T	F	F	F	F	T
F	T	F	F	T	F	F	T
F	F	T	T	F	F	F	T
F	F	F	T	T	F	F	T

$p \wedge [(p \wedge \sim q) \to (r \wedge \sim r)]$	$\left(p \wedge [(p \wedge \sim q) \to (r \wedge \sim r)]\right) \to q$
T	T
T	T
F	T
F	T
F	T
F	T
F	T
F	T

IV.

1. Let a be an odd number. By definition of an odd number there exists some counting number k such that $a = 2k + 1$. Thus $a^2 = 4k^2 + 4k + 1 = 2(2k^2 + 2k) + 1$. Since k is a counting number, $2k^2 + 2k$ is a counting number. Let $t = 2k^2 + 2k$. Then $a^2 = 2t + 1$. Therefore a^2 is an odd number. (QED)

3. (Indirect method.) Assume a is not an odd number. Then a is an even number. By (2) above, a^2 is an even number. This contradicts our hypothesis which states that a^2 is an odd number. Therefore our assumption is false, and thus a is an odd number. (QED)

V.

1. Let A and B be two angles of an equilateral triangle. The measures of angle A and angle B are the same, but A and B are *not vertical angles*.

3. Let $\triangle ABC$ be a right triangle whose sides measure 3 ft., 4 ft., and 5 ft. $\triangle ABC$ is a right *triangle*, but $\triangle ABC$ is *not isosceles*.

VI. Besides proving that the arguments are valid by use of truth tables, a second method which is sometimes known as analysis will be given.

1.

p	q	$\sim p$	$p \vee q$	$(p \vee q) \wedge \sim p$	$[(p \vee q) \wedge \sim p] \to q$
T	T	F	T	F	T
T	F	F	T	F	T
F	T	T	T	T	T
F	F	T	F	F	T

Therefore $[(p \vee q) \wedge \sim p] \Rightarrow q$.

Second method. By H1, $p \vee q$ is true. Thus p is true or q is true (or both). By H2, $\sim p$ is true. Thus p is false. Since $p \vee q$ is true, the truth of q follows.

3.

p	q	$p \leftrightarrows q$	$(p \leftrightarrows q) \wedge q$	$[(p \leftrightarrows q) \wedge q] \to p$
T	T	T	T	T
T	F	F	F	T
F	T	F	F	T
F	F	T	F	T

Therefore $[(p \leftrightarrows q) \wedge q] \Rightarrow p$.

Second method. By H1, $(p \leftrightarrows q)$ is true. Thus p and q are both true, or p and q are both false. By H2, q is true. Therefore p is true.

5.

p	q	$\sim p$	$\sim q$	$(\sim p \vee \sim q)$	$(\sim p \vee \sim q) \wedge p$	$[(\sim p \vee \sim q) \wedge p] \to \sim q$
T	T	F	F	F	F	T
T	F	F	T	T	T	T
F	T	T	F	T	F	T
F	F	T	T	T	F	T

Therefore $[(\sim p \vee \sim q) \wedge p] \Rightarrow \sim q$.

Second method. By H1, $\sim p \vee \sim q$ is true. Thus $\sim p$ is true or $\sim q$ is true (or both). By H2, p is true. Thus $\sim p$ is false. Hence $\sim q$ is true.

7.

p	q	r	$p \leftrightarrows q$	$p \to r$	$(p \leftrightarrows q) \wedge (p \to r) \wedge q$	$[(p \leftrightarrows q)$ $\wedge (p \to r) \wedge g] \to r$
T	T	T	T	T	T	T
T	T	F	T	F	F	T
T	F	T	F	T	F	T
T	F	F	F	F	F	T
F	T	T	F	T	F	T
F	T	F	F	T	F	T
F	F	T	T	T	F	T
F	F	F	T	T	F	T

Therefore $[(p \leftrightharpoons q) \wedge (p \rightarrow r) \wedge q] \Rightarrow r$.

Second method. By H1, $p \leftrightharpoons q$ is true. Thus p and q are both true or p and q are both false. By H3, q is true. Thus p is true. By H2, $p \rightarrow r$ is true. Since the truth of p has been established, the truth of r must follow.

9.

p	q	r	s	$\tilde{~}q$	$\tilde{~}s$	$p \rightarrow q$	$q \rightarrow r$	$r \rightarrow s$
T	T	T	T	F	F	T	T	T
T	T	T	F	F	T	T	T	F
T	T	F	T	F	F	T	F	T
T	T	F	F	F	T	T	F	T
T	F	T	T	T	F	F	T	T
T	F	T	F	T	T	F	T	F
T	F	F	T	T	F	F	T	T
T	F	F	F	T	T	F	T	T
F	T	T	T	F	F	T	T	T
F	T	T	F	F	T	T	T	F
F	T	F	T	F	F	T	F	T
F	T	F	F	F	T	T	F	T
F	F	T	T	T	F	T	T	T
F	F	T	F	T	T	T	T	F
F	F	F	T	T	F	T	T	T
F	F	F	F	T	T	T	T	T

$(p \rightarrow q) \wedge (q \rightarrow r) \wedge (r \rightarrow s) \wedge \tilde{~}s$	$[(p \rightarrow q) \wedge (q \rightarrow r) \wedge (r \rightarrow s) \wedge \tilde{~}s] \rightarrow \tilde{~}q$
F	T
F	T
F	T
F	T
F	T
F	T
F	T
F	T
F	T
F	T
F	T
F	T
F	T
F	T
F	T
T	T

Therefore $[(p \rightarrow q) \wedge (q \rightarrow r) \wedge (r \rightarrow s) \wedge \tilde{~}s] \Rightarrow \tilde{~}q$.

Second method. By H4, $\tilde{~}s$ is true. Thus s is false. By H3, $r \rightarrow s$ is true. Thus r is false. By H2, $q \rightarrow r$ is true. Thus q is false. Therefore $\tilde{~}q$ is true.

Exercise Set 2.1

I.

1. The set of all tall humans.
   The set of all large numbers.
   The set of all old people.

5. $\{1, 2, 3\}$

II.

1. $1 \in A$ 3. $13 \in A$ 5. $99 \notin A$

7. $0 \notin A$ 9. $1000 \in A$

Exercise Set 2.2

I.

1. $\{1, 3, 5, 7, \ldots\}$

3. $\{1, 2, 3, 4, 6, 7, 8, 9, 11, 12, 13, 14, 16, 17, 18, 19, 21, \ldots\}$

5. $\{\ \}$ 7. U 9. $\{1, 2, 3, 4, \ldots\}$

II.

1. $A \setminus B = \{1, 5, 7, 11, 13, 17, 19\}$
   $B \setminus A = \{6, 12, 18\}$
   $\tilde{A} = \{2, 4, 6, 8, 10, 12, 14, 16, 18, 20\}$
   $\tilde{B} = \{1, 2, 4, 5, 7, 8, 10, 11, 13, 14, 16, 17, 19, 20\}$

3. $A \setminus B = \{5, 15\}$
   $B \setminus A = \{\ \}$
   $\tilde{A} = \{1, 2, 3, 4, 6, 7, 8, 9, 11, 12, 13, 14, 16, 17, 18, 19\}$
   $\tilde{B} = \{1, 2, 3, 4, 5, 6, 7, 8, 9, 11, 12, 13, 14, 15, 16, 17, 18, 19\}$

5. $A \setminus B = A$
   $B \setminus A = B$
   $\tilde{A} = B$
   $\tilde{B} = A$

7. $A \setminus B = \varnothing$
   $B \setminus A = \varnothing$
   $\tilde{A} = \tilde{B} = \{1, 2, 3, 5, 6, 7, 9, 10, 11, 13, 14, 15, 17, 18, 19\}$

9. $A \setminus B = \varnothing$
   $B \setminus A = B$
   $\tilde{A} = U$
   $\tilde{B} = \{1, 2, 3, 4, 6, 7, 8, 9, 11, 12, 13, 14, 16, 17, 18, 19\}$

III.

1. $\{1, 2\}, \{1\}, \{2\}, \varnothing$ 3. $\{1\}, \{2\}, \varnothing$ 5. 2^k

IV.

1. The set of all negative counting numbers.

2. The set of all even prime numbers greater than 3.

3. The set of all nonzero counting numbers that are divisible by counting numbers greater than themselves.

4. The set of all negative integers that are squares of integers.

5. The set of all mountains that are 50,000 ft high.

6. The set of all cars that travel 2000 mph.

7. The set of all American League Baseball players who won the 1969 World Series.

8. The set of all NFL football players who won the 1969 Superbowl.

9. The set of all statements p such that $p \wedge \sim p$ is true.

10. The set of all statements q such that $q \vee \sim q$ is false.

Exercise Set 2.3

I.

1. $A = \{1, 2, 3, 4, 5\}$ $A = \{1, 2, 3, 4, 5\}$

   $B = \{2, 4, 6, 8, 10\}$ $B = \{2, 4, 6, 8, 10\}$

II.

1. $A \approx B$ 3. $A \not\approx B$ 5. $A \not\approx B$ 7. $A \not\approx B$ 9. $A \approx B$

III.

1. Consider the set $\{4, 8, 12, 16, \ldots\}$. This set is a proper subset of $\{2, 4, 6, 8, \ldots\}$. Also, $\{4, 8, 12, 16, \ldots\} \approx \{2, 4, 6, 8, \ldots\}$. Therefore $\{2, 4, 6, 8, \ldots\}$ is an infinite set.

3. The proper subsets of $\{2, 4, 6\}$ are $\varnothing$, $\{2\}$, $\{4\}$, $\{6\}$, $\{2, 4\}$, $\{2, 6\}$, and $\{4, 6\}$. None of these proper subsets is equivalent to $\{2, 4, 6\}$. Therefore the set $\{2, 4, 6\}$ is not infinite. Hence $\{2, 4, 6\}$ is finite.

5. No

IV. (The following answers include only the odd-numbered relations.)
   (1), (5), and (9) are equivalence relations.

3. Does not satisfy reflexive and symmetric properties.

7. Does not satisfy transitive property.

Exercise Set 2.4

I.

1. $A \cup B = \{$Walter, Dorinne, Sonny, Clark, Tommy$\}$.
   $A \cap B = \{$Dorinne$\}$.

3. $A \cup B = \{$John, Eleanore, Vincent, Drue, David, Alicia, Leigh, Jeffrey, Jeanne, Karen$\}$.
   $A \cap B = \varnothing$.

5. $A \cup B = \{$Vera, Emil, Milton, Diana, May$\}$.
   $A \cap B = \varnothing$.

7. $(A \cup B) \cup C = \{$Toby, Elvina, Gladys, Elizabeth, Jennifer, Jeanette$\}$.
   $(A \cap B) \cap C = \varnothing = \{\ \}$.

9. $A \cup (B \cup C) = \{$Anthony, Roselind, Lorraine, Jacqueline, Barbara, Peter$\}$.
   $A \cap (B \cap C) = \{$Anthony$\}$.
   $A \cap B = \{$Anthony$\}$.
   $A \cup B = \{$Anthony, Roselind, Lorraine, Jacqueline$\}$.
   $A \cap C = \{$Anthony$\}$.

II.

1. $A \cup B = \{a, x, y\}$.
   $A \cap B = \{a, x, y\}$.

3. $A \cup B = \emptyset$.
   $A \cap B = \emptyset$.

5. $A \cup B = \{1, 2, 3, 4, 5, \ldots, 100\}$.
   $A \cap B = \emptyset$.

7. $A \cup B = \{x: x$ is a human with blue eyes or red hair$\}$.
   $A \cap B = \{x: x$ is a human with blue eyes and red hair$\}$.

9. $A \cup B = \{0, 1, 2, 3, \ldots\} = A$.
   $A \cap B = \emptyset = B$.

Exercise Set 2.5

I.

1. $\widetilde{A \cap B}$ is shaded

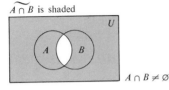

$A \cap B \neq \emptyset$

3. $\tilde{A} \cup \tilde{B}$ is shaded

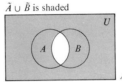

$A \cap B \neq \emptyset$

II.

1. 4180   3. 270   5. 70   7. 50

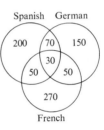

III.

1. $\overbrace{A \cup B \cup C}$ 3. A 5. C

7. $B \cap C \cap \tilde{A}$ 9. $(B \cap C) \cup C = C$

Exercise Set 2.6

I.

1. $A \cap B = \{2, 4, 6, 8, 10\}$.

3. $A \cup C = \{0, 1, 2, 3, 4, 5, 6, 8, 10\}$.

5. $(B \cup C) \cup A = \{0, 1, 2, 3, 4, 5, 6, 7, 8, 9, 10\}$.

7. $A \cap (B \cup C) = \{2, 4, 6, 8, 10\}$.

9. $\widetilde{A \cup B} = \{11, 12, 13, 14, \ldots\}$.

11. $\widetilde{A \cup U} = \emptyset$.

13. $\tilde{B} \cap C = \emptyset$.

15. $\tilde{C} = \{0, 2, 6, 7, 8, \ldots\}$.

II.

1. False   3. True   5. True   7. True   9. False

III.

1. If $x \in A \setminus B$, then $x \in A$ and $x \notin B$. Hence $x \in \tilde{B}$. Therefore $x \in A \cap \tilde{B}$. It follows that $A \setminus B \subset A \cap \tilde{B}$.
If $x \in A \cap \tilde{B}$, then $x \in A$ and $x \in \tilde{B}$. Hence $x \notin B$. Therefore $x \in A$ and $x \notin B$. It follows that $x \in A \setminus B$. Thus $A \cap \tilde{B} \subset A \setminus B$. Since $A \setminus B \subset A \cap \tilde{B}$ and $A \cap \tilde{B} \subset A \setminus B$, it follows that $A \setminus B = A \cap \tilde{B}$.

3. Consult standard dictionary.

Exercise Set 2.7

I.

1. $A \times B = \{(1, 3), (1, 5), (1, 7), (2, 3), (2, 5), (2, 7)\}$
$X \times Y = \{(1, 1), (1, 3), (1, 5), (1, 7), (2, 1), (2, 3), (2, 5), (2, 7), (3, 1), (3, 3), (3, 5), (3, 7)\}$
Since $(1, 3), (1, 5), (1, 7), (2, 3), (2, 5),$ and $(2, 7)$ are all elements in $X \times Y$, $A \times B \subset X \times Y$.

II. $A \times B = \{(6, 10), (7, 10), (8, 10), (9, 10), (10, 10), (11, 10), (12, 10), (13, 10), (14, 10)\}$
$B \times A = \{(10, 6), (10, 7), (10, 8), (10, 9), (10, 10), (10, 11), (10, 12), (10, 13), (10, 14)\}$

III.

1. $\{(0, 0), (0, 1), (0, 2), (0, 3), \ldots$
$(1, 0), (1, 1), (1, 2), (1, 3), \ldots$
$(2, 0), (2, 1), (2, 2), (2, 3) \ldots$
$\vdots$
$\ldots\}$

IV.

1. $A \times B \times C = \{(a, b, c): a \in A \wedge b \in B \wedge c \in C\}$

V.

1. $A = \{1, 2, 3, 4, 5\}, B = \{2\}$ 3. $A = \{0\}, B = \{1, 2, 3, \ldots\}$
5. $A = \{0\}, B = \{1\}$

VI.

1. $\{(1, 2), (2, 2)\}$; yes; no   3. $\{(0, 1), (0, 2), (0, 3), (0, 4), \ldots\}$; yes; no
5. $\{(0, 1)\}$; yes; no

VII.

1. $A \times B = \{1, 2), (1, 4), (1, 6), (1, 8), (2, 2), (2, 4), (2, 6), (2, 8), (3, 2), (3, 4), (3, 6), (3, 8)\}$
$\updownarrow \quad \updownarrow \quad \updownarrow \quad \updownarrow \quad \updownarrow \quad \updownarrow \quad \updownarrow \quad \updownarrow \quad \updownarrow \quad \updownarrow \quad \updownarrow \quad \updownarrow$
$B \times A = \{(2, 1), (4, 1), (6, 1), (8, 1), (2, 2), (4, 2), (6, 2), (8, 2), (2, 3), (4, 3), (6, 3), (8, 3)\}$

Since $A \times B$ is in a one-to-one correspondence with $B \times A$ as shown above, $A \times B \approx B \times A$.

5. $A \times B = \emptyset, B \times A = \emptyset$. Since $A \times B = B \times A, A \times B \approx B \times A$.

Exercise Set 3.1

I.

1. $A \neq \emptyset$ and $A \subset C_0$ (set of counting numbers). Thus A contains exactly one element which is the least element in A. This element is 0.

3. $A \cup B \neq \emptyset$ and $A \cup B \subset C_0$ (set of counting numbers). Thus $A \cup B$ contains exactly one element which is the least element in $A \cup B$. This element is 0.

II.

1. k can be any element in $\{x: x \geq 4\}$.
3. k can be any element in $\{x: x \geq 31\}$.
5. k can be any element in $\{x: x \geq 17\}$.
7. k can be any element in $\{x: x \geq 2\}$.
9. k can be any element in $\{x: x \geq 100\}$.

III.

1. $n(A \times B) = n(B \times A) = 2$ 3. $n(A \times B) = n(B \times A) = 0$

IV.

1. Commutative law for addition   3. Commutative law for addition
5. Distributive law   7. Distributive law
9. Definition of addition
11. Definition of multiplication, commutative law for multiplication

V.

1. Let $A = \{6, 8, 9, 10\}$ and $B = \{1, 3, 4\}$.
   $A \cap B = \emptyset$,
   $n(A) = 4$, $n(B) = 3$,
   $A \cup B = \{6, 8, 9, 10, 1, 3, 4\}$,
   $n(A \cup B) = 7$.
   Therefore $4 + 3 = 7$.

3. Let $A = \{1, 2, 3, 4, 5\}$ and $B = \{\triangle\}$.
   $A \cap B = \emptyset$, $n(A) = 5$, $n(B) = 1$,
   $A \cup B = \{1, 2, 3, 4, 5, \triangle\}$,
   $n(A \cup B) = 6$.
   Therefore $5 + 1 = 6$.

5. Let $A = \{1, 2, 3\}$, and $B = \{5, 6, 7, 8\}$.
   $A \cap B = \emptyset$, $n(A) = 3$, $n(B) = 4$,
   $A \cup B = \{1, 2, 3, 5, 6, 7, 8\}$,
   $n(A \cup B) = 7$.
   Therefore $3 + 4 = 7$.

9. Let $A = \emptyset$ and $B = \emptyset$.
   $A \cap B = \emptyset$, $n(A) = 0$, $n(B) = 0$,
   $A \cup B = \emptyset$,
   $n(A \cup B) = n(\emptyset) = 0$.
   Therefore $0 + 0 = 0$.

VI.

1. Let $A = \{1, 2, 3, 4\}$ and $B = \{1, 2, 5\}$.
   $\mathbf{n}(A) = 4$, $\mathbf{n}(B) = 3$,
   $A \times B = \{(1, 1), (1, 2), (1, 5), (2, 1), (2, 2), (2, 5), (3, 1), (3, 2), (3, 5), (4, 1), (4, 2),$
   $(4, 5)\}$,
   $\mathbf{n}(A \times B) = 12$.
   Therefore $4 \times 3 = 12$.

3. Let $A = \{90, 94, 96, 98, 100\}$ and $B = \{1000\}$.
   $\mathbf{n}(A) = 5$, $\mathbf{n}(B) = 1$,
   $A \times B = \{(90, 1000), (94, 1000), (96, 1000), (98, 1000), (100, 1000)\}$,
   $\mathbf{n}(A \times B) = 5$.
   Therefore $5 \times 1 = 5$.

5. Let $A = \{1, 2\}$ and $B = \{1, 2, 3\}$.
   $\mathbf{n}(A) = 2$, $\mathbf{n}(B) = 3$,
   $A \times B = \{(1, 1), (1, 2), (1, 3), (2, 1), (2, 2), (2, 3)\}$,
   $\mathbf{n}(A \times B) = 6$.
   Therefore $2 \times 3 = 6$.

9. Let $A = \emptyset$ and $B = \emptyset$.
   $\mathbf{n}(A) = 0$, $\mathbf{n}(B) = 0$,
   $A \times B = \emptyset$,
   $\mathbf{n}(A \times B) = 0$.
   Therefore $0 \times 0 = 0$.

VII. (1), (3), (5), (7), (9), and (11): Commutative law for addition.

VIII. (1), (3), (5), (7), (9), and (11): Commutative law for multiplication.

IX.

1. $(4 + 6) \times 4 = 4 \times (4 + 6)$ [Commutative law for multiplication]
   $\qquad\qquad\quad = (4 \times 4) + (4 \times 6)$ [Distributive law]
   $\qquad\qquad\quad = 16 + 24$ [Definition 3]
   $\qquad\qquad\quad = 40$.   [Definition 2]

3. $32a = (12 + 20)a$ [Definition 2]
   $\quad\;\; = a(12 + 20)$ [Commutative law for multiplication]
   $\quad\;\; = a \times 12 + a \times 20$ [Distributive law]
   $\quad\;\; = 12 \times a + 20 \times a$ [Commutative law for multiplication]
   $\quad\;\; = (4 \times 3)a + (5 \times 4)a$ [Definition 3]
   $\quad\;\; = 4(3a) + 5(4a)$.   [Associative law for multiplication]

X.

1. True   3. True   5. True

7. False   9. False

Exercise Set 3.2

I.

1. XXVI, $\cap\cap$ IIIIII

3. CDVII, $?\,?\,?\,?$ IIIIIII

5. CMXCIX, 999999999∩∩∩∩∩∩∩∩∩|||||||||

7. CI, 9|

9. DCCXLIX, 9999999∩∩∩|||||||||

11. MCMLXXI, ⚱999999999∩∩∩∩∩∩∩|

II.

1. ∩|||(∩|+∩∩|||||||) = (∩|||×∩|) + (∩|||×∩∩|||||||)

Exercise Set 3.3

I.

1.

Digit	2	7	5	3
Face Value	two	seven	five	three
Place Value	one thousand	one hundred	ten	one
Traditional Name	thousands digit	hundreds digit	tens digit	units digit

5.

Digit	1	0	0	9
Face Value	one	zero	zero	nine
Place Value	one million	one hundred thousand	ten thousand	one thousand
Traditional Name	millions digit	hundred thousands digit	ten thousands digit	thousands digit

9	0	1
nine	zero	one
one hundred	ten	one
hundreds digit	tens digit	units digit

II.

1. 9   3. 999   5. 99,999

III.

1. 0   3. 100   5. 10,000

Exercise Set 3.4

I.

1. $54 = 5(10^1) + 4(10^0)$

3. $4216 = 4(10^3) + 2(10^2) + 1(10^1) + 6(10^0)$

5. $20{,}101 = 2(10^4) + 0(10^3) + 1(10^2) + 0(10^1) + 1(10^0)$

7. $1{,}268{,}721 = 1(10^6) + 2(10^5) + 6(10^4) + 8(10^3) + 7(10^2) + 2(10^1) + 1(10^0)$

9. $66{,}006{,}600 = 6(10^7) + 6(10^6) + 0(10^5) + 0(10^4) + 6(10^3) + 6(10^2)$
$\qquad\qquad\quad + 0(10^1) + 0(10^0)$

II.

1. 8	3. 1	5. 1	7. 1728	9. 17
11. 125	13. 2	15. 10,000	17. 33	19. 20,000

III.

1. 3^3	3. 5^7	5. 10^{k+m}
7. 18^{31}	9. a^3	11. 10^9

IV.

1. 29 is 2 sets of *ten* elements each and 9 sets of *one* element each.

3. 92 is 9 sets of *ten* elements each and 2 sets of *one* element each.

5. 289 is 2 sets of *one hundred* elements each, 8 sets of *ten* elements each, and 9 sets of *one* element each.

7. 950 is 9 sets of *one hundred* elements each and 5 sets of *ten* elements each.

9. 4023 is 4 sets of *one thousand* elements each, 2 sets of *ten* elements each, and 3 sets of *one* element each.

Exercise Set 3.5

I.

1. $82 + 13 = [8(10^1) + 2(10^0)] + [1(10^1) + 3(10^0)]$
$\qquad\quad\;\, = [8(10^1) + 1(10^1)] + [2(10^0) + 3(10^0)]$ [Commutative and associative laws for addition]
$\qquad\quad\;\, = [8 + 1](10^1) + [2 + 3](10^0)$ [Distributive law]
$\qquad\quad\;\, = 9(10^1) + 5(10^0)$ [Definition 2]
$\qquad\quad\;\, = 95.$

11. $87 + 23 + 14 + 5 = [8(10^1) + 7(10^0)] + [2(10^1) + 3(10^0)]$
$\qquad\qquad\qquad\qquad\; + [1(10^1) + 4(10^0)] + 5(10^0)$
$\qquad\qquad\qquad\; = [8(10^1) + 2(10^1) + 1(10^1)]$
$\qquad\qquad\qquad\qquad\; + [7(10^0) + 3(10^0) + 4(10^0) + 5(10^0)]$
$\qquad\qquad\qquad\; = [8 + 2 + 1](10^1) + [7 + 3 + 4 + 5](10^0)$
$\qquad\qquad\qquad\; = [8 + 2 + 1](10^1) + 19(10^0)$
$\qquad\qquad\qquad\; = [8 + 2 + 1](10^1) + [10 + 9](10^0)$
$\qquad\qquad\qquad\; = [8 + 2 + 1](10^1) + 10^1 + 9(10^0)$
$\qquad\qquad\qquad\; = [8 + 2 + 1](10^1) + 1(10^1) + 9(10^0)$
$\qquad\qquad\qquad\; = [8 + 2 + 1 + 1](10^1) + 9(10^0)$
$\qquad\qquad\qquad\; = 12(10^1) + 9(10^0)$
$\qquad\qquad\qquad\; = [10 + 2](10^1) + 9(10^0)$
$\qquad\qquad\qquad\; = 10(10^1) + 2(10^1) + 9(10^0)$
$\qquad\qquad\qquad\; = 10^2 + 2(10^1) + 9(10^0)$
$\qquad\qquad\qquad\; = 1(10^2) + 2(10^1) + 9(10^0)$
$\qquad\qquad\qquad\; = 129.$

Exercise Set 3.6

I.

1. $79 \times 10^2 = [7(10^1) + 9(10^0)] \times (10^2)$
$= 7 \times 10^1 \times 10^2 + 9 \times 10^0 \times 10^2$
$= 7(10^3) + 9(10^2)$
$= 7(10^3) + 9(10^2) + 0(10^1) + 0(10^0)$
$= 7900.$

3. $872 \times 10^2 = [8(10^2) + 7(10^1) + 2(10^0)] 10^2$
$= 8 \times 10^2 \times 10^2 + 7 \times 10^1 \times 10^2 + 2 \times 10^0 \times 10^2$
$= 8 \times 10^4 + 7 \times 10^3 + 2 \times 10^2$
$= 8(10^4) + 7(10^3) + 2(10^2) + 0(10^1) + 0(10^0)$
$= 87,200.$

5. $6 \times 10^4 = [6(10^0)]10^4$
$= 6 \times 10^0 \times 10^4$
$= 6 \times 10^4$
$= 6(10^4) + 0(10^3) + 0(10^2) + 0(10^1) + 0(10^0)$
$= 60,000.$

7. $97 \times 10^4 = [9(10^1) + 7(10^0)]10^4$
$= 9 \times 10^1 \times 10^4 + 7 \times 10^0 \times 10^4$
$= 9 \times 10^5 + 7 \times 10^4$
$= 9(10^5) + 7(10^4) + 0(10^3) + 0(10^2) + 0(10^1) + 0(10^0)$
$= 970,000.$

II.

5. $806 \times 53 = 806[5(10^1) + 3(10^0)]$
$= 806 \times [5(10^1)] + 806 \times [3(10^0)]$
$= [806 \times 5]10^1 + [806 \times 3]10^0$
$= 4030(10^1) + 2418(10^0)$
$= 40,300 + 2418$
$= 42,718.$

Exercise Set 3.7

I.

1. $\{20, 30, 40, 100, 110\}$ 3. $\{33, 34, 40, 41, 42, 43, 44, 100, 101, 102\}$

5. $\{441, 2242\}$ 7. $\{1421, 1422, 1423\}$

9. $\{31020\}$

II.

1. $32_5 = 3(\text{five}^1) + 2(\text{five}^0) = 3(10^1) + 2(10^0)$

5. $401_5 = 4(\text{five}^2) + 0(\text{five}^1) + 1(\text{five}^0) = 4(10^2) + 0(10^1) + 1(10^0)$

9. $423025_5 = 4(\text{five}^{\text{five}}) + 2(\text{five}^4) + 3(\text{five}^3) + 0(\text{five}^2) + 2(\text{five}^1) + 5(\text{five}^0)$
$= 4(10^{10}) + 2(10^4) + 3(10^3) + 0(10^2) + 2(10^1) + 5(10^0)$

III.

1. $32_5 = 3(5^1) + 2(5^0)$ 3. $242_5 = 2(5^2) + 4(5^1) + 2(5^0)$

5. $401_5 = 4(5^2) + 0(5^1) + 1(5^0)$ 7. $2134_5 = 2(5^3) + 1(5^2) + 3(5^1) + 4(5^0)$

9. $423020_5 = 4(5^5) + 2(5^4) + 3(5^3) + 0(5^2) + 2(5^1) + 0(5^0)$

IV.

1. $32_5 = 17_{10}$

3. $242_5 = 72_{10}$

5. $401_5 = 101_{10}$

7. $2134_5 = 294_{10}$

9. $423020_5 = 14,135_{10}$

V.

1. $3_5 + 42_5 = 100_5$

3. $12_5 + 13_5 = 30_5$

5. $223_5 + 314_5 = 1042_5$

7. $2012_5 + 3122_5 = 10134_5$

9. $2024_5 + 4444_5 = 12023_5$

VI.

1. $3_5 \times 42_5 = 231_5$

3. $4_5 \times 34_5 = 301_5$

5. $223_5 \times 314_5 = 132132_5$

VII.

1. 4444

3. 44

5. 10000

VIII.

1. $124 + 112 = [1(\text{five}^2) + 2(\text{five}^1) + 4(\text{five}^0)] + [1(\text{five}^2) + 1(\text{five}^1) + 2(\text{five}^0)]$

$= [1 \text{ quarter} + 2 \text{ nickels} + 4 \text{ pennies}]$
$+ [1 \text{ quarter} + 1 \text{ nickel} + 2 \text{ pennies}]$

$= [1 \text{ quarter} + 1 \text{ quarter}] + [2 \text{ nickels} + 1 \text{ nickel}]$
$+ [4 \text{ pennies} + 2 \text{ pennies}]$

$= [2 \text{ quarters}] + [3 \text{ nickels}] + [6 \text{ pennies}]$

$= [2 \text{ quarters}] + [3 \text{ nickels}] + [(5 \text{ pennies} + 1 \text{ penny})]$

$= [2 \text{ quarters}] + [3 \text{ nickels}] + [1 \text{ nickel} + 1 \text{ penny}]$

$= [2 \text{ quarters}] + [3 \text{ nickels} + 1 \text{ nickel}] + [1 \text{ penny}]$

$= [2 \text{ quarters}] + [4 \text{ nickels}] + [1 \text{ penny}]$

$= 241.$

3. $233 + 123 = 411$

IX.

+	0	1
0	0	1
1	1	10

×	0	1
0	0	0
1	0	1

1. 1100

3. 11110

5. 10100

7. 11001

9. 100101

11. 11001

X.

1. $\begin{array}{l} 101_2 \leftrightarrow 5_{10} \\ +111_2 \leftrightarrow +7_{10} \\ \hline 1100_2 \leftrightarrow 12_{10} \end{array}$

3. $\begin{array}{l} 110_2 \leftrightarrow 6_{10} \\ \times 101_2 \leftrightarrow \times 5_{10} \\ \hline 11110_2 \leftrightarrow 30_{10} \end{array}$

5. $\begin{array}{l} 111_2 \leftrightarrow 7_{10} \\ +1101_2 \leftrightarrow +13_{10} \\ \hline 10100_2 \leftrightarrow 20_{10} \end{array}$

7. $\begin{array}{l} 101_2 \leftrightarrow 5_{10} \\ \times 101_2 \leftrightarrow \times 5_{10} \\ \hline 11001_2 \leftrightarrow 25_{10} \end{array}$

9. $\begin{array}{l} 1000_2 \leftrightarrow 8_{10} \\ +11101_2 \leftrightarrow +29_{10} \\ \hline 100101_2 \leftrightarrow 37_{10} \end{array}$

11. $\begin{array}{l} 111_2 \leftrightarrow 7_{10} \\ \times 111_2 \leftrightarrow \times 7_{10} \\ \hline 110001_2 \leftrightarrow 49_{10} \end{array}$

XI.

1. $3e$ 3. 1910 5. $180e$

7. $9e040$ 9. $3ee$ 11. $2019t$

XII.

1.
```
   9  4  3
+  4  4  0
----------
 □  8  3
```

3.
```
   □  □  □
+  □  □  □
----------
 1 □  8  □
```

5.
```
   9  □  □
+  2  □  9
----------
 □  8  5
```

7.
```
   □  0  □
+  □  □  □
----------
18 □  6
```

XIII.

1. $507 = [125 + 125 + 125 + 125 + 5 + 1 + 1]$ (base *ten*)
$ = [4 \times 125 + 1 \times 5 + 2 \times 1]$ (base *ten*)
$ = [4 \times 125 + 0 \times 25 + 1 \times 5 + 2 \times 1]$ (base *ten*)
$ = [4(5^3) + 0(5^2) + 1(5^1) + 2(5^0)]$ (base *ten*)
$ = [4(10^3) + 0(10^2) + 1(10^1) + 2(10^0)]$ (base *five*)
$ = 4012_5.$

3. $609 = [125 + 125 + 125 + 125 + 25 + 25 + 25 + 25 + 5 + 4]$ (base *ten*)
$ = [4 \times 125 + 4 \times 25 + 1 \times 5 + 4 \times 1]$ (base *ten*)
$ = [4(5^3) + 4(5^2) + 1(5^1) + 4(5^0)]$ (base *ten*)
$ = [4(10^3) + 4(10^2) + 1(10^1) + 4(10^0)]$ (base *five*)
$ = 4414_5.$

5. $912 = 12122_5$ 7. $3125 = 100000_5$

9. $16{,}724 = 1013344_5$

XIV.

1. $63 = [32 + 16 + 8 + 4 + 2 + 1]$ (base *ten*)
$ = [1(2^5) + 1(2^4) + 1(2^3) + 1(2^2) + 1(2^1) + 1(2^0)]$ (base *ten*)
$ = [1(10)^{101} + 1(10)^{100} + 1(10^{11}) + 1(10^{10}) + 1(10^1) + 1(10^0)]$ (base *two*)
$ = 111111_2.$

3. $143 = ee_{12}$ 5. $143 = 1033_5$

7. $65{,}535 = \;\square\;\square\;\square\;\square\;_{16}$ 9. $101 = 1100101_2$

XV.

1. 67 3. 71 5. 74 7. 78 9. 82

Exercise Set 4.1

I.

1. No   3. Yes   5. Yes   7. Yes   9. Yes

II.

1. Because there is no unique counting number k such that $0 \cdot k = 0$. That is, $0 \cdot k = 0$ for any counting number k and hence k is not unique, as required by Definition 3.

3. Because there is no counting number k such that $3 \cdot k = 17$, as required by Definition 3.

III.

1. 0, 5, 10, 15, 20, 25, 30, 35, 40, 100
3. 0, 2, 4, 6, 8, 10, 12, 14, 16, 18
5. 0, 8, 24, 32, 40, 48, 56, 64, 72, 80
7. 0, 10, 20, 30, 40, 50, 60, 70, 80, 90
9. 0, 400, 800, 1200, 1600, 2000, 2400, 2800, 3200, 3600

IV.

1. 1, 11, 121

3. 1, 2, 3, 6, 9, 18, 27, 54

5. 1, 5, 11, 55

7. 1, 2621

9. 1, 4987

V.

1. Let a be any counting number. Since $a \cdot 1 = a$ for every counting number a, it follows that $a \mid a$. (QED)

3. Since $a \cdot 0 = 0$, for any counting number a, it follows that $a \cdot 0 = z$ for any counting number a and for $z = 0$. Hence $a \mid z$ and, since the choice of a is arbitrary, every counting number divides z. Since every counting number divides z, certainly every counting number greater than z divides z. (QED)

VI.

1. Because $a - b$ has been defined for $a \geq b$ but not for $a < b$.
3. $b = a - c$

5. $b = x - 2a$

Exercise Set 4.2

I.

3. prime

7. prime

III.

1. 3, 5

3. 2, 5

5. 2, 11

7. 2, 11

9. 101

IV.

1. 1, 3, 5, 15, 25, 75

3. 1, 2, 4, 5, 8, 10, 16, 20, 40, 80

5. 1, 2, 11, 22

7. 1, 2, 4, 11, 22, 44

9. 1, 101

V.

3. 19

5. 23

7. 23

9. 29

VI.

1. Any counting number other than 1 which has no divisors except itself and 1 is called a *prime number*.

Any nonzero counting number which has at least one divisor other than itself and 1 is called a *composite number.*

The counting number one is called a *unit.*

Exercise Set 4.3

I.

1. $30 = 2 \cdot 3 \cdot 5$

3. $105 = 3 \cdot 5 \cdot 7$

5. $143 = 11 \cdot 13$

7. $144 = 2 \cdot 2 \cdot 2 \cdot 2 \cdot 3 \cdot 3$

9. $15,400 = 2 \cdot 2 \cdot 2 \cdot 5 \cdot 5 \cdot 7 \cdot 11$

II. $D_a \cap D_b =$

1. $\{1, 5\}$

3. $\{1, 5\}$

5. $\{1, 7\}$

7. $\{1\}$

9. $\{1\}$

III.

1. 5

3. 5

5. 7

7. 1

9. 1

IV. $M_a \cap M_b =$

1. $\{30, 60, 90, \ldots\}$

3. $\{100, 200, 300, \ldots\}$

5. $\{70, 140, 210, \ldots\}$

7. $\{70, 140, 210, \ldots\}$

9. $\{150, 300, 450, \ldots\}$

V.

1. 30

3. 100

5. 70

7. 70

9. 150

Exercise Set 4.4

I.

1. 3

3. 12

5. 2

7. 2

9. 2

II.

1. 1260

3. 2520

5. 8662

7. 278,460

9. 198,900

III.

1. The product of 45 and 84 is 3780. The LCM of 45 and 84 is 1260, and the GCD of 45 and 84 is 3. The product of 1260 and 3 is 3780.

IV.

1. The largest element in the set of all common divisors of the nonzero counting numbers a, b, and c is the *greatest common divisor of a, b, and c.*

3. The largest element in the set of all common divisors of the nonzero counting numbers a, b, c, and d is the *greatest common divisor of a, b, c, and d.*

Exercise Set 4.5

I. There are 15 twin prime pairs (p, q) such that $q < 200$. The first eight pairs are (3, 5), (5, 7), (11, 13), (17, 19), (29, 31), (41, 43), (59, 61), and (71, 73).

II. [*Note:* These representations are not necessarily unique. For example, $28 = 5 + 23 = 11 + 17$.]

$4 = 2 + 2$	$38 = 19 + 19$	$70 = 11 + 59$
$6 = 3 + 3$	$40 = 11 + 29$	$72 = 13 + 59$
$8 = 3 + 5$	$42 = 11 + 31$	$74 = 7 + 67$
$10 = 3 + 7$	$44 = 13 + 31$	$76 = 5 + 71$
$12 = 5 + 7$	$46 = 5 + 41$	$78 = 5 + 73$
$14 = 7 + 7$	$48 = 5 + 43$	$80 = 7 + 73$
$16 = 5 + 11$	$50 = 7 + 43$	$82 = 11 + 71$
$18 = 5 + 13$	$52 = 11 + 41$	$84 = 11 + 73$
$20 = 7 + 13$	$54 = 11 + 43$	$86 = 13 + 73$
$22 = 11 + 11$	$56 = 13 + 43$	$88 = 5 + 83$
$24 = 11 + 13$	$58 = 5 + 53$	$90 = 7 + 83$
$26 = 13 + 13$	$60 = 7 + 53$	$92 = 13 + 79$
$28 = 11 + 17$	$62 = 19 + 43$	$94 = 11 + 83$
$30 = 13 + 17$	$64 = 23 + 41$	$96 = 13 + 83$
$32 = 3 + 29$	$66 = 23 + 43$	$98 = 19 + 79$
$34 = 3 + 31$	$68 = 7 + 61$	$100 = 11 + 89$
$36 = 13 + 23$		

III. *First perfect number:* $2^2 - 1 = 3$, and 3 is prime. Now, $2^{2-1}(2^2 - 1) = 2(3) = 6$. Thus, by Theorem 7, 6 is a perfect number.

Sixth perfect number: $2^{17} - 1 = 131,071$, and $131,071$ is prime. Now, $2^{17-1}(2^{17} - 1) = 2^{16}(131,071) = 65,536(131,071) = 8,589,869,056$. Thus, by Theorem 7, $8,589,869,056$ is a perfect number.

Exercise Set 5.1

I.

1. 5   3. 5   5. $^-5$ 7. 3/2   9. $^-3$

II.

1. 1, 2, 3, 4, 5, 6, 7, 8, and 10

3. 1, 2, 3, 4, and 10

III.

1. $(^-2)(^-3) = {}^+6$ 3. $^-2 + {}^+1 = {}^-1$

5. $\sqrt{9}$ is the rational number 3   7. $(\frac{1}{2})(4) = 2$

9. $\frac{1}{4} + \frac{3}{4} = 1$

Exercise Set 5.2

I.

1. $R = R_a \cup I_r$ 3. $R = C_0 \cup I^- \cup F_r \cup I_r$

5. $R_a = I \cup F_r$ 7. $R_a = I^+ \cup \{0\} \cup I^- \cup F_r$

9. $I = I^+ \cup \{0\} \cup I^-$

II.

1. $I = R_a \setminus F_r$ 3. $C_0 = I \setminus I^-$ 5. $I^+ = C_0 \setminus \{0\}$

III.

1. Since $(2)(3) = (^-3)(^-2)$ and $^-3$ and 3 are nonzero, then $2/^-3 = ^-2/3$.
7. Since $^-8(5) = ^-10(4)$ and $^-10(5) \neq 0$, then $^-8/^-10 = 4/5$.
9. $^-2 \times 5 \times ^-3 = ^-(2 \times 5) \times ^-3$
$= ^-10 \times ^-3$
$= 10 \times 3$
$= 30.$

IV.

1. 2 is an element of each of the following sets: R, R_a, I, C_0, I^+.
3. R, R_a, I, I^- 5. R, R_a, I, C_0, $\{0\}$
7. R, I_r 9. R, R_a, I, C_0, I^+
11. R, R_a, F_r 13. Same as No. 11
15. Same as No. 11   17. R, I_r
19. Same as No. 9

V.

1. 2   3. 2   5. 8/15   7. 12/35   9. 1

VI.

1. 0.8   3. $0.\overline{285714}$ 5. 1.125   7. $1.0\overline{6}$ 9. $0.\overline{6}$

VII.

1. 41/333   3. 61/495   5. 111/900   7. 179/33   9. 271/50

VIII.

1. $A \neq \emptyset$, $B \neq \emptyset$, $A \cap B = \emptyset$, $A \cup B = R$, and each a in A is less than every element in B; according to the Dedekind law, A contains a greatest element or B contains a least element. The least element in B is 3.
3. A and B do not satisfy the hypothesis $A \cap B = \emptyset$; 5 is the greatest element in A and 5 is the least element in B.
5. A and B do not satisfy the hypothesis $A \cup B = R$.

X.

1. F1, F2, F5, F6, F7, F8, F10, and F11
3. F1, F2, F3, F5, F6, F7, F8, F10, and F11
5. F1 through F11
7. None, since F1 and F6 are not obeyed

Exercise Set 5.3

III.

1.

$\oplus$	0	1	2	3	4	5	6
0	0	1	2	3	4	5	6
1	1	2	3	4	5	6	0
2	2	3	4	5	6	0	1
3	3	4	5	6	0	1	2
4	4	5	6	0	1	2	3
5	5	6	0	1	2	3	4
6	6	0	1	2	3	4	5

3. The sum, $a \oplus b$, of two elements a and b of M_7 is defined as follows: $a \oplus b$ is the remainder in the division of $a + b$ by 7.

IV.

1.

$\oplus$	0	1	2	3	4	5
0	0	1	2	3	4	5
1	1	2	3	4	5	0
2	2	3	4	5	0	1
3	3	4	5	0	1	2
4	4	5	0	1	2	3
5	5	0	1	2	3	4

7.

$\oplus$	0	1
0	0	1
1	1	0

9.

$\oplus$	0	1	2	3
0	0	1	2	3
1	1	2	3	0
2	2	3	0	1
3	3	0	1	2

V.

1. Yes   3. No   5. No

Exercise Set 5.4

I.

1. $(M_{10}, \oplus, \otimes)$ does not obey F9; 2, 4, 5, 6, and 8 do not have multiplicative inverses. They are not relatively prime to the modulus. However, 1, 3, 7, and 9 are relatively prime to the modulus.

3. $(M_{12}, \oplus, \otimes)$ does not obey F9; 2, 3, 4, 6, 8, 9, and 10 do not have multiplicative inverses. They are not relatively prime to the modulus.

5. $(M_{15}, \oplus, \otimes)$ does not obey F9; 3, 5, 6, 9, 10, and 12 do not have multiplicative inverses. They are not relatively prime to the modulus.

7. $(M_{13}, \oplus, \otimes)$ obeys F9. Each element of M_{13} is relatively prime to 13.

9. $(M_{19}, \oplus, \otimes)$ obeys F9. Each element of M_{19} is relatively prime to 19.

II.

1. $x = 2$ 3. $x = 5$ 5. $x = 3$

7. $x = 6$ 9. $x = 7$

III.

1. $2 \otimes 0 = 0$, Since $2 \otimes x \neq 1$ for any x in M_6, it follows that $2 \otimes x = 1$
   $2 \otimes 1 = 2$, has no solution in $(M_6, \oplus, \otimes)$.
   $2 \otimes 2 = 4$,
   $2 \otimes 3 = 0$,
   $2 \otimes 4 = 2$,
   $2 \otimes 5 = 4$.

IV.

1. $2 \otimes 0 = 0$, Since $2 \otimes x \neq 1$, $2 \otimes x \neq 3$, $2 \otimes x \neq 5$, and $2 \otimes x \neq 7$ for
   $2 \otimes 1 = 2$, any x in M_8, it follows that $2 \otimes x = 1$, $2 \otimes x = 3$, $2 \otimes x = 5$,
   $2 \otimes 2 = 4$, and $2 \otimes x = 7$ do not have solutions in $(M_8, \oplus, \otimes)$.
   $2 \otimes 3 = 6$,
   $2 \otimes 4 = 0$,
   $2 \otimes 5 = 2$,
   $2 \otimes 6 = 4$,
   $2 \otimes 7 = 6$.

V.

1. The GCD of x and m is 1.

Exercise Set 6.1

I.

1. $(1 + {}^{-}1) \notin S$. Hence Law G1 of Definition 1 is not obeyed.

3. Since $(S, +)$ is not a group, $(S, +, \times)$ does not obey Law 1 of Definition 3. Therefore $(S, +, \times)$ is not a field.

II.

5. Since $3 \in M_4 \setminus \{1, 2\}$, $3 \oplus 3 = 2$ (mod 4), and $2 \notin M_4 \setminus \{1, 2\}$, it follows that $(M_4 \setminus \{1, 2\}, \oplus)$ does not obey Law G1 of Definition 1. Therefore $(M_4 \setminus \{1, 2\}, \oplus)$ is not a group.

III. Let $x \in S$ and $y \in S$. It follows from the defining table that $x \# y$ is a unique element of S. Hence Law G1 of Definition 1 is obeyed. It follows from the defining table that $(x \# y) \# z = x \# (y \# z)$ for any x, y, and z in S. Hence Law G2 of Definition 1 is obeyed. Let $x \in S$. It follows from the defining table that $x \# i = i \# x$. Hence Law G3 of Definition 1 is obeyed.

Let $x \in S$. By the defining table there is exactly one element $\bar{x} \in S$ such that $x \# \bar{x} = \bar{x} \# x = i$ ($\bar{i} = i$, $\bar{a} = c$, $\bar{b} = b$, and $\bar{c} = a$). Hence Law G4 of Definition 1 is obeyed.

Since Laws G1, G2, G3, and G4 of Definition 1 are obeyed, it follows that $(S, \#)$ is a group.

Law G5 follows from the defining table. Therefore, according to Definition 2, $(S, \#)$ is a commutative group.

V.

1. If $a \# b = a \# c$, then

$\bar{a} \# (a \# b) = \bar{a} \# (a \# c)$,	[by G1]
$(\bar{a} \# a) \# b = (\bar{a} \# a) \# c$,	[by G2]
$i \# b = i \# c$,	[by G4]
$b = c$.	[by G3]

   If $b = c$, then

$a \# b = a \# c$.	[by G1]

VI. If $a_1, a_2, \ldots, a_k$ are any elements of G, then all punctuations of $a_1 \# a_2 \# \cdots \# a_k$ yield the same element of G.

VII. If $a_1, a_2, \ldots, a_k$ are any elements of G, then all arrangements and punctuations of $a_1 \# a_2 \# \cdots \# a_k$ yield the same element of G.

VIII.

1. Since $0 \notin (F \setminus \{0\})$, then (i) Law G1 of Definition 1 does not guarantee that $a \times 0$ and $0 \times a$ are elements of F for each $a \in F$, and (ii) Law G5 of Definition 2 does not guarantee that $a \times 0 = 0 \times a$ for each $a \in F$. Therefore Law 2 is necessary to establish these two facts.

Exercise Set 6.2

I.

1. $(a \# b) \# c = x \# c$
   $= b$
   $= a \# x$
   $= a \# (b \# c)$

5. $(b \# x) \# y = c \# y$
   $= b$
   $= b \# i$
   $= b \# (x \# y)$

3. $(a \# y) \# x = c \# x$
   $= a$
   $= a \# i$
   $= a \# (y \# x)$

II.

1. $a \# x = b$,
   $x \# a = c$,
   $b \neq c$

5. $i \# a = a$,
   $a \# i = a$,
   $a = a$

3. $y \# b = c$,
   $b \# y = a$,
   $c \neq a$

7. $x \# y = i$
   $= y \# x$

III.

1. $(u \# v) \# w = w \# w$
   $\qquad\qquad\quad = v$
   $\qquad\qquad\quad = u \# u$
   $\qquad\qquad\quad = u \# (v \# w)$

3. $(w \# u) \# v = i \# v$
   $\qquad\qquad\quad = v$
   $\qquad\qquad\quad = w \# w$
   $\qquad\qquad\quad = w \# (u \# v)$

5. $(w \# v) \# u = u \# u$
   $\qquad\qquad\quad = v$
   $\qquad\qquad\quad = w \# w$
   $\qquad\qquad\quad = w \# (v \# u)$

IV.

1. $\begin{pmatrix} 1 & 2 & 3 & 4 & 5 \\ 4 & 5 & 1 & 2 & 3 \end{pmatrix}$

3. $\begin{pmatrix} 1 & 2 & 3 & 4 & 5 \\ 4 & 2 & 5 & 3 & 1 \end{pmatrix}$

V.

1. A commutative group

3. Not a group

Exercise Set 6.3

I.

1. The only divisors of 3 are 1 and 3. See Lagrange's theorem.

3. 1, 2, 3, and 6.

II.

1. r_0, r_1, r_2, r_3

3. 0, 1, 2, 3

III.

1. $(\{0\}, \oplus), (\{0, 6\}, \oplus), (\{0, 4, 8\}, \oplus),$
   $(\{0, 3, 6, 9\}, \oplus), (\{0, 2, 4, 6, 8, 10\}, \oplus),$ and $(M_{12}, \oplus)$

3. $(\{0\}, \oplus)$ and $(M_7, \oplus)$

Exercise Set 7.1

I.

1. $\mathscr{D}(f) = A$ by Definition 3.

3. Since f is a function and $x \in \mathscr{D}(f)$ (that is, $x \in A$), it follows from Definition 2 that x is the first coordinate of exactly one element (x, y). Hence $(x, y) = (x, y')$. Therefore $y = y'$.

5. Definition 2 prescribes that each element of A shall have exactly one image in B.

7. Definition 1 prescribes that each element of A must have an image in B.

II.

1. Function

3. Function

5. Not a function

7. Not a function

9. Function

III.

1. Function

3. Not a function

5. Function   7. Not a function

9. Not a function

IV.

1. Function   3. Function

5. Not a function   7. Not a function

9. Function

Exercise Set 7.2

I.

1. $\mathscr{D}(f) = R; \mathscr{R}(f) = R$
3. $\mathscr{D}(f) = R; \mathscr{R}(f) = \{y: y \in R \text{ and } y \le 0\}$
5. $\mathscr{D}(f) = R; \mathscr{R}(f) = \{y: y \in R \text{ and } y \ge 5\}$
7. $\mathscr{D}(f) = \{t: t \in R \text{ and } t \ge 0\}; \mathscr{R}(f) = \{y: y \in R \text{ and } y \le 0\}$
9. $\mathscr{D}(f) = \{s: s \in R \text{ and } s \ne 0\}; \mathscr{R}(f) = \{y: y \in R \text{ and } y > 0\}$

II.

1. 15   3. $^-50$ 5. 30   7. $^-15$ 9. 2/25

III.

1. 12/5   3. $^-32/25$ 5. 141/25   7. $^-6$ 9. 25/8

IV.

1. $\{0, 1, 2, 3, 4, 5, 6\}$
3. $f(x) = x^2 - 1$; x is the independent variable and $f(x)$ is the dependent variable.

V. Let $f(x) = x^2 - 1$ be a rule of correspondence which defines the function $f: R \rightarrow R$.

1. 0   3. 0   5. $\{y: y \in R \text{ and } y \ge ^-1\}$
7. 8   9. $x^2 + 6x + 8$

Exercise Set 7.3

I.

1.

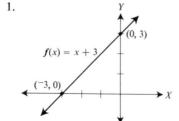

5.

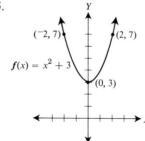

15.

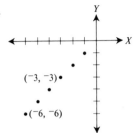

$y = x;\ \mathfrak{D}(f) = \{x: x \in I^-\}$

Other points with coordinates
$(^-7, ^-7), (^-8, ^-8), (^-9, ^-9), \ldots$,
are also part of the graph.

II.

1. The element 2 in the domain corresponds to more than one element in the range.

3. Each element in the domain corresponds to 3 and to $^-3$.

5. $0 \in \mathscr{D}(f)$, and $(0, 2)$ and $(0, ^-2)$ are elements of the set of ordered pairs.

7. $1 \in \mathscr{D}(f)$, and $(1, 2)$ and $(1, ^-2)$ are elements of the set of ordered pairs.

9. $1 \in \mathscr{D}(f)$, and $(1, 2), (1, 3), (1, 4)$ are elements of the set of ordered pairs.

Exercise Set 7.4

I.

1. Slope is $^-3$; x-intercept is $\frac{2}{3}$; y-intercept is 2.

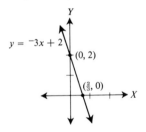

3. Slope is $\frac{2}{3}$; x-intercept is $^-6$; y-intercept is 4.

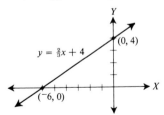

5. Slope is $\frac{6}{11}$; x-intercept is $\frac{11}{3}$; y-intercept is $^-2$.

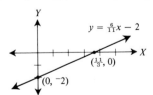

7. Slope is $^-2/3$; x-intercept is 3; y-intercept is 2.

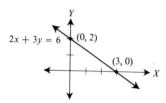

9. Slope is $\frac{3}{5}$; x-intercept is $^-5$; y-intercept is 3.

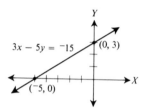

III.

1.

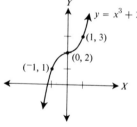

3.

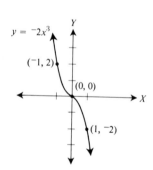

5.

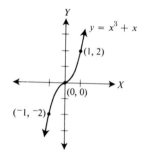

7.

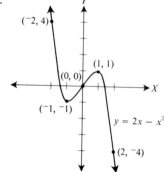

9.

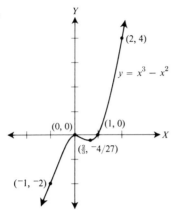

IV.

1. Linear   3. Linear   5. Cubic   7. Cubic   9. Quadratic

V.

3. Since $y = 6$ and $6 = 0x + 6$ for all real x, then $y = 0x + 6$. Hence 0 is the slope of $y = 6$ (by Definition 10).

Since $0x + 1y = y$ and $y = 6$, then $0x + 1y = 6$. It follows from Definition 9 that $6/1$ (i.e., 6) is the y-intercept.

VI. Slope $= a = \dfrac{ax}{x} = \dfrac{ax + b - b}{x - 0} = \dfrac{y - b}{x - 0} = \dfrac{\text{rise}}{\text{run}}$, provided $x \neq 0$.

Exercise Set 7.5

I.

1.

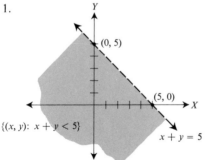

5.

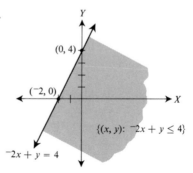

15.

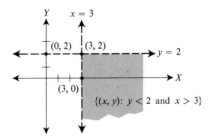

II.

1. $\{(x, y): y = 3\}$ is a function because to each x in the domain (i.e., in R) there corresponds exactly one element 3 in the range (i.e., in $\{3\}$).

   However, $\{(x, y): x = 3\}$ is *not* a function because to 3 in the domain (i.e., in $\{3\}$) there corresponds more than one y in the range (i.e., in R).

   For example, $(3, 0)$, $(3, 1)$, $(3, 2)$ are all elements of $\{(x, y): x = 3\}$, and this is contrary to Definition 1.

3. Exactly one point.

5. No, because some vertical line intersects the circle in 2 points; i.e., some element of the domain is paired with more than one element of the range. In fact, each element of the domain, except two of them, is paired with two elements of the range.

7. Yes, because to each x in the domain there corresponds exactly one element x^2 in the range.

9. Yes, because to each x in the domain there corresponds exactly one element in the range. The domain and range of $\{(x, y): x \in R$ and $y = 0\}$ are R and $\{0\}$, respectively.

Exercise Set 8.1

I.

| 1. 49 | 3. 113 | 5. 113 | 7. 18.6 | 9. 17.016 |

II.

| 1. 0 | 3. 0 | 5. 1 | 7. 4 | 9. 6 |

III.

| 1. 3 | 3. $4x$ | 5. 3 | 7. $^-1/x^2$ |

IV.

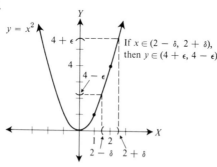

Exercise Set 8.2

I.

1. $\lim_{x \to 5} f(x) = 26 = f(5)$

3. $\lim_{x \to 5} f(x) = 30 = f(5)$

5. $\lim_{x \to 5} f(x) = 32 = f(5)$

7. $\lim_{x \to 5} f(x) = 7/2 = f(5)$

9. $\lim_{x \to 5} f(x) = 1/20 = f(5)$

II.

1. None   3. None   5. None

7. 3   9. 0 and 1

III.

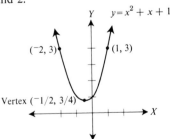

$f(x) = \dfrac{x^3}{x} + 1$

$(-3, 10)$ $(3, 10)$

$(-2, 5)$ $(2, 5)$

$(-1, 2)$ $(1, 2)$ $(0, 1)$ is *not* a point on the graph of f

$0 \notin \mathfrak{D}(f)$

V.

1. $\lim_{x \to 2} f(x)$ fails to exist, and $f(2)$ fails to exist

3. $f(2)$ fails to exist

5. $\lim_{x \to 2} f(x) = 1$ and $f(2) = 2$; that is, $\lim_{x \to 2} f(x) \ne f(2)$

7. $f(2)$ fails to exist

9. $\lim_{x \to 2} f(x)$ and $f(2)$ both fail to exist

Exercise Set 8.3

I.

1. 1   3. 2   5. $^-2$ 7. $^-1$ 9. 4

II.

1 and 2.   5 and 6.

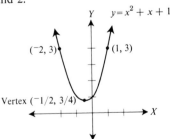

$y = x^2 + x + 1$

$(-2, 3)$ $(1, 3)$

Vertex $(-1/2, 3/4)$

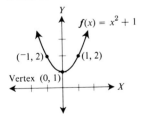

$f(x) = x^2 + 1$

$(-1, 2)$ $(1, 2)$

Vertex $(0, 1)$

III.

1. 3   3. $2x$ 5. $3x^2$ 7. $^-3x^2$ 9. x^2

Exercise Set 8.4

I.

1. $f'(x) = 1; \mathscr{D}(f) = \mathscr{D}(f') = R$
3. $f'(x) = 2 - 2x; \mathscr{D}(f) = \mathscr{D}(f') = R$
5. $f'(x) = 1 + 2x - 3x^2 + 20x^3; \mathscr{D}(f) = \mathscr{D}(f') = R$
7. $f'(x) = {}^-1 + 2x - 3x^2 + 4x^3 - 5x^4; \mathscr{D}(f) = \mathscr{D}(f') = R$
9. $f'(x) = 10x^9 - 8x^7 + 12x^5 - 12x^3 + 2x; \mathscr{D}(f) = \mathscr{D}(f') = R$

II.

1. $f'(x) = 2(x + 3)(5x + 8)(2x - 1)^2; \mathscr{D}(f) = \mathscr{D}(f') = R$
3. $f'(x) = 2(2x + 5)(12x^2 + 15x - 2); \mathscr{D}(f) = \mathscr{D}(f') = R$
5. $f'(x) = x^2(7x^4 - 4x + 3); \mathscr{D}(f) = \mathscr{D}(f') = R$
7. $f'(x) = 2/(x + 1)^2; \mathscr{D}(f) = R \setminus \{{}^-1\} = \mathscr{D}(f')$
9. $f'(x) = 2(3x^2 + 21x - 5)/(2x + 7)^2; \mathscr{D}(f) = \mathscr{D}(f') = R \setminus \{{}^-7/2\}$

III. In each of the following, $c \in R$; that is, c is any real constant.

1. $f(x) = c$ 3. $f(x) = 2x + c$
5. $f(x) = \frac{1}{2}x^2 + c$ 7. $f(x) = x^5 + c$
9. $f(x) = (1/n)x^n + c$

In each of the above, there are as many distinct functions as there are real numbers c.

Exercise Set 8.5

I.

1. $(3/2, {}^-1/4)$ is a relative minimum point.

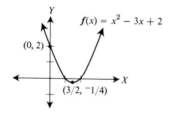

3. $(3/2, 1/4)$ is a relative maximum point.

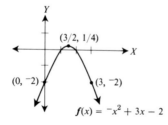

5. $(0, {}^-9)$ is a relative minimum point.

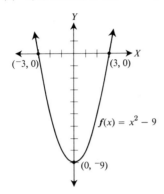

7. $(0, {}^-1)$ is a point of inflection.

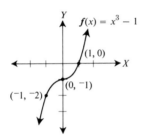

9. $(0, 4)$ is a relative maximum point.

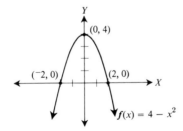

II.
1. Relative minimum: $(0, 0)$ 3. Relative minimum: $(0, 0)$
5. Relative maximum: $(0, 2)$ 7. Relative maximum: $(0, 1)$
9. Relative minimum: $(0, {}^-2)$

III.
1. $(0, 0)$ 3. $(0, 2)$ 5. $(0, 1)$ 7. $(0, 2)$ 9. $(0, 1)$

Exercise Set 8.6

I.

1. To verify that $f(x_1) = 125{,}000$ is really a maximum, we may compute $f'(225)$ and $f'(275)$:

$f'(225) = 1000 - 4(225) = 1000 - 900 = 100,$
$f'(275) = 1000 - 4(275) = 1000 - 1100 = {}^-100.$

Since $f'(225) > 0$, $f'(275) < 0$, $225 < x_1 = 250 < 275$, and $f'(x) > 0$ for each $x \in [225, 250)$ and $f'(x) < 0$ for each $x \in (250,275]$, it follows from Theorem 12 that $\big(250, f(250)\big)$ is a relative maximum point. Hence the maximum area that can be enclosed with 1000 ft of fencing is 125,000 sq ft.

II. 20 ft by 20 ft

III. 2 in.

Exercise Set 8.7

I.

1. $F(x) = x^3 + c$

3. $F(x) = x^4 - x^3 + c$

5. $F(x) = \frac{3}{2}x^2 + 2x + c$

7. $F(x) = x^9 + c$

9. $F(x) = x^{10} - x^9 + c$

II.

1. $y = 5x + {}^-7$

3. $y = 4x + 14$

5. $y = {}^-7x + 26$

7. $y = {}^-4x + 4$

9. $y = 3$

III.

1. $F(x) = x^3 - x^2 + 2x;$
$F({}^-3) = {}^-42$

3. $F(x) = x^4 - x^3 + 2x + 5;$
$F(1) = 7$

Exercise Set 8.8

I. Compute the area of the triangle with vertices $(0, 0)$, $(5, 0)$, and $(5, 5)$; compute the area of the triangle with vertices $(0, 0)$, $(2, 0)$, and $(2, 2)$. Then subtract.

II.

$$\int_{-1}^{2} x^3\, dx = \int_{-1}^{0} x^3\, dx + \int_{0}^{2} x^3\, dx = \frac{{}^-1}{4} + \frac{16}{4} = \frac{15}{4}.$$

The area of (1) the shaded region below the x-axis is $\frac{1}{4}$ (i.e., $|{}^-1/4|$), and (2) the shaded region above the x-axis is $\frac{16}{4}$. Obviously, ${}^-1/4 + \frac{16}{4} \neq \frac{1}{4} + \frac{16}{4}$.

III.

1. 12.5

3. 3

5. 64

7. 20

9. $\frac{38}{3}$

11. $\frac{93}{4}$

13. 24

15. $\frac{1}{6}$

17. $\frac{7}{64}$

19. $\frac{1}{12}$

IV. $\frac{1}{6}$

V. $\frac{1}{2}$

VI. $\frac{1}{12}$

VII. $\frac{4}{15}$

VIII.

1. 112 ft/sec.

Exercise Set 9.1

I.

1. {(1, 1), (1, 2), (1, 3), (1, 4), (1, 5), (1, 6)
   (2, 1), (2, 2), (2, 3), (2, 4), (2, 5), (2, 6)
   (3, 1), (3, 2), (3, 3), (3, 4), (3, 5), (3, 6)
   (4, 1), (4, 2), (4, 3), (4, 4), (4, 5), (4, 6)
   (5, 1), (5, 2), (5, 3), (5, 4), (5, 5), (5, 6)
   (6, 1), (6, 2), (6, 3), (6, 4), (6, 5), (6, 6)}

3. {(1, 2), (2, 1)}

5. {(1, 4), (2, 3), (3, 2), (4, 1)}

7. {(1, 6), (2, 5), (3, 4), (4, 3), (5, 2), (6, 1)}

9. {(3, 6), (4, 5), (5, 4), (6, 3)}

11. {(5, 6), (6, 5)}

13. { }

15. E is the sample space in 1

17. E is the union of the events in 3, 5, 7, 9, and 11

19. {(1, 2), (2, 1), (1, 5), (2, 4), (3, 3), (4, 2), (5, 1), (3, 6), (4, 5), (5, 4), (6, 3), (6, 6)}

II.

1. {(h, h, h), (h, h, t), (h, t, h), (h, t, t), (t, h, h), (t, t, h), (t, h, t), (t, t, t)}

3. $\{A_h, K_h, Q_h, \ldots, 3_h, 2_h, A_d, K_d, Q_d, \ldots, 3_d, 2_d, A_s, K_s, Q_s, \ldots, 3_s,$
   $\qquad\qquad\qquad\qquad\qquad\qquad 2_s, A_c, K_c, Q_c, \ldots, 3_c, 2_c\}$

5. $\{A_h, K_h, Q_h, \ldots, 3_h, 2_h\}$

7. $\{(A_h, A_d), (A_h, A_s), (A_h, A_c), (A_d, A_s), (A_d, A_c), (A_s, A_c),$
   $\qquad\qquad (A_d, A_h), (A_s, A_h), (A_c, A_h), (A_s, A_d), (A_c, A_d), (A_c, A_s)\}$

9. $\{\{A_h, K_h, Q_h, 10_h, \ldots, 3_h, 2_h\}, \{A_d, K_d, \ldots, 3_d, 2_d, A_c, K_c, \ldots,$
   $\qquad\qquad\qquad\qquad\qquad\qquad 3_c, 2_c, A_s, K_s, \ldots, 3_s, 2_s\}\}$

III.

1. {(h, h), (h, t), (t, h), (t, t)}

3. {(h, h)}

5. {(h, t), (t, h)}

7. {(h, t), (t, h), (t, t)}

9. {(t, t), (h, t), (t, h)}

11. {(h, h), (h, t), (t, h), (t, t)}

13. {(t, t)}

IV.

1. $\{(h, h, h), (h, h, t), (h, t, h), (t, h, h), (h, t, t), (t, h, t), (t, t, h), (t, t, t)\}$
3. $\{(h, h, h), (h, h, t), (h, t, h), (t, h, h)\}$
5. $\{(h, t, t), (t, h, t), (t, t, h)\}$
7. $\{(h, h, h)\}$

V.

1. $\{\ \ \}$
5. $\{(h, h, h), (t, h, h), (h, t, h), (h, h, t), (t, t, t)\}$
9. $\{(h, h, h)\}$

VI.

1. $\{r, w, b\}$
3. $\{r, w\}, \{r, b\}, \{w, b\}, \{r, w, b\}$
5. $\{r, w, b\}$
7. $\{r, b\}$
9. $\{w\}$

VII.

1. $\{(r, w), (r, b), (w, b)\}$
3. $\{(r, w), (r, b)\}, \{(r, w), (w, b)\}, \{r, b), (w, b)\}, \{(r, w), (r, b), (w, b)\}$
5. $\{(r, b), (w, b)\}$
7. $\{(r, w), (r, b), (w, b)\}$
9. $\{\ \ \}$

VIII.

1. $\{(t, h), (t, t), (h, 1), (h, 2), (h, 3), (h, 4), (h, 5), (h, 6)\}$
3. $\{(h, 2), (h, 4), (h, 6)\}$
5. $\{\ \ \}$
7. $\{(t, h), (h, 1), (h, 2), (h, 3), (h, 4), (h, 5), (h, 6)\}$
9. $\{(h, 1), (h, 2), (h, 3), (h, 4), (h, 5), (h, 6)\}$

IX.

$\{(1, h), (2, h), \ldots, (52, h), (1, t), (2, t), \ldots, (52, t)\}$

X.

$\{(h, 1), (h, 2), \ldots, (h, 52), (t, 1), (t, 2), \ldots, (t, 52)\}$

The event in IX is $\{1, 2, \ldots, 52\} \times \{h, t\}$; the event in X is $\{h, t\} \times \{1, 2, \ldots, 52\}$. $E = \{(h, 1), (h, 2), \ldots, (h, 52)\}$; $\tilde{E} = \{(t, 1), (t, 2), \ldots, (t, 52)\}$. $\tilde{E}$ is the event that a head does not occur.

Exercise Set 9.2

I.

1. $\frac{1}{36}$ 3. $\frac{1}{9}$ 5. $\frac{5}{36}$ 7. $\frac{1}{36}$ 9. $\frac{7}{36}$

II.

1. $\frac{1}{2}$ 3. $\frac{1}{2}$ 5. $\frac{1}{4}$ 7. $\frac{3}{4}$ 9. $\frac{1}{2}$

III.

1. $\frac{5}{13}$ 3. $\frac{1}{13}$ 5. $\frac{7}{52}$ 7. 1   9. 0

IV.

1. $\frac{1}{3}$ 3. 0   5. $\frac{1}{3}$ 7. 1

V.

1. $\frac{1}{4}$ 3. $\frac{1}{4}$ 5. $\frac{3}{4}$ 7. $\frac{1}{2}$ 9. 0   11. $\frac{1}{2}$

VIII. Since P is the equiprobable function, it follows from Theorem 2 that

$P(A) = n(A)/n(S) = n(A)/k$.   (QED)

Exercise Set 9.3

I. If there are k_1 possible ways of making a first choice, and for each of the k_1 possible ways there are k_2 possible ways of making a second choice, . . ., and for each of the k_{m-1} ways there are k_m possible ways of making an mth choice, then there are $k_1 \times k_2 \times \cdots \times k_m$ possible ways of making the m choices.

1. 18   3. 6
                                6
                                36

II.

1. $20 \times 19 \times 18$ 3. $5 \times (15 \times 14)$

5. $55 \times 54 \times 53$ 7. 4!

III.

1. $\dfrac{13!}{2!\,3!}$ 3. $\dfrac{11!}{16}$ 5. $\dfrac{8!}{6}$ 7. $\dfrac{7!}{2!}$

9. 4!   11. $\dfrac{13!}{8 \times 3!}$ 13. $\dfrac{8!}{4}$

IV.

1. It contains 720 ordered triples of the form (h_w, h_p, h_s).

3. E_2 is the event that horse No. 3 wins, horse No. 1 places, and horse No. 2 shows.

5. E_1 or E_2 is the event that either horse No. 10 wins, horse No. 5 places, horse No. 2 shows; or horse No. 3 wins, horse No. 1 places, horse No. 2 shows.

7. E_2 or E_3 is the event that either horse No. 3 wins, horse No. 1 places, horse No. 2 shows; or horse No. 1 wins, horse No. 6 places, horse No. 4 shows.

9. 101/1000   11. 211/1000   13. 89/100

15. 79/100   17. 889/1000   19. 720

Exercise Set 9.4

I.

1. $C(52 : 13) = \dfrac{52!}{13! \, (52 - 13)!} = \dfrac{52!}{13! \, 39!}$

3. $C(20 : 5) = \dfrac{20!}{5! \, (20 - 5)!} = \dfrac{20!}{5! \, 15!}$

5. 6
   5
   30

7. $\frac{1}{30}$

II.

1. $C(25 : 20) = \dfrac{25!}{20! \, (25 - 20)!} = \dfrac{25!}{20! \, 5!}$

3. $C(20 : 15) = \dfrac{20!}{15! \, (20 - 15)!} = \dfrac{20!}{15! \, 5!}$

III.

1. $\dfrac{C(5 : 3)}{C(8 : 3)} = \dfrac{5}{28}$

3. Let E be the event that 3 black marbles are drawn. Then $1 - P(E)$ is the event that at least one white marble is drawn. Since $P(E) = \frac{5}{28}$ by Exercise 1, then $1 - P(E) = \frac{23}{28}$.

5. The numbers of ways in which 2 white marbles may be chosen is $C(3 : 2) = 3$. The number of ways in which 1 black marble may be chosen is $C(5 : 1) = 5$. Hence there are $3 \cdot 5 = 15$ ways of choosing 2 white marbles and 1 black marble. The number of ways in which 3 marbles can be chosen is $C(8 : 3) = 56$. Hence the probability of getting 2 white marbles and 1 black marble is $3 \cdot 5/56 = 15/56$.

IV.

1. 1   3. 1   5. 2   7. 1   9. 3

V.

1. 2 diagonals   3. 9 diagonals   5. 44 diagonals

VI.

1. $C(4 : 2) - 4 = 6 - 4 = 2$ 3. $C(6 : 2) - 6 = 15 - 6 = 9$

5. $C(11 : 2) - 11 = 55 - 11 = 44$

VII.

1. $C(m : 0) = \dfrac{m!}{0! \, (m - 0)!} = \dfrac{m!}{0! \, m!}$

3. $C(m : 1) = \dfrac{m!}{1! \, (m - 1)!} = \dfrac{m(m - 1)!}{1! \, (m - 1)!} = \dfrac{m}{1!} = m$

5. $C(m : k) = \dfrac{m!}{k! \, (m - k)!} = \dfrac{m!}{(m - k)! \, k!}$

   $= \dfrac{m!}{(m - k)! \, [m - (m - k)]!} = C(m : m - k)$

Exercise Set 9.5

I.

1. $(x + y)^7 = x^7 + 7x^6y + 21x^5y^2 + 35x^4y^3 + 35x^3y^4 + 21x^2y^5 + 7xy^6 + y^7$

3. $(x + y)^{10} = x^{10} + 10x^9y + 45x^8y^2 + 120x^7y^3 + 210x^6y^4 + 252x^5y^5$
$$+ 210x^4y^6 + 120x^3y^7 + 45x^2y^8 + 10xy^9 + y^{10}$$

5. $(x + y)^5 = x^5 + 5x^4y^1 + 10x^3y^2 + 10x^2y^3 + 5xy^4 + y^5$

7. $(2x - y)^5 = 32x^5 - 80x^4y + 80x^3y^2 - 40x^2y^3 + 10xy^4 - y^5$

9. $(x + b)^6 = x^6 + 6x^5b + 15x^4b^2 + 20x^3b^3 + 15x^2b^4 + 6xb^5 + b^6$

II.

1. $x^8 + 8x^7y^1 + 28x^6y^2 + 56x^5y^3 + 70x^4y^4 + 56x^3y^5 + 28x^2y^6 + 8xy^7 + y^8$

3. $x^9 + 9x^8y + 36x^7y^2 + 84x^6y^3 + 126x^5y^4 + 126x^4y^5 + 84x^3y^6$
$$+ 36x^2y^7 + 9xy^8 + y^9$$

5. $x^6 - 6x^5y + 15x^4y^2 - 20x^3y^3 + 15x^2y^4 - 6xy^5 + y^6$

7. $x^5 - 10x^4y + 40x^3y^2 - 80x^2y^3 + 80xy^4 - 32y^5$

9. $(a + 2y)^4 = a^4 + 8a^3y + 24a^2y^2 + 32ay^3 + 16y^4$

III.

1. $C(9:4)x^5h^4 = 126x^5h^4$ 3. $C(5:4)xy^4 = 5xy^4$

5. $C(6:4)x^2y^4 = 15x^2y^4$ 7. $C(7:4)x^3(^-y)^4 = 35x^3y^4$

9. $C(9:4)(2x)^5y^4 = (126)(32x^5)y^4 = 4032x^5y^4$

IV.

1. $C(12:7) = \dfrac{12!}{7!\,5!}$ 3. $C(12:4) = \dfrac{12!}{4!\,8!}$

5. $C(8:7) = 8$ 7. $C(17:7) = \dfrac{17!}{7!\,10!}$

9. $C(7:3)(^-2)^3 = {}^-8\left(\dfrac{7!}{3!\,4!}\right) = {}^-280$

V.

1. 2   3. 8   5. 32   7. 128   9. 512

VI. Same as V.

VII.

1. 2^{20} 3. 2^{50} 5. 2^{60} 7. 2^{100} 9. 2^{500}

IX.

1. $\dfrac{C(10:3)}{2^{10}}$ 3. $\dfrac{C(10:4)}{2^{10}}$ 5. $\dfrac{C(10:5)}{2^{10}}$

7. $\dfrac{C(13:2)}{2^{13}}$ 9. $\dfrac{C(13:13)}{2^{13}} = \dfrac{1}{2^{13}}$ 11. $\dfrac{1}{2^{11}}$

Exercise Set 9.6

I.

1. $P(E_1 \mid E_2) = \dfrac{P(E_1 \cap E_2)}{P(E_2)} = \dfrac{\frac{2}{36}}{\frac{6}{36}} = \dfrac{1}{3}$

3. $P(E_1 \mid E_2) = \dfrac{P(E_1 \cap E_2)}{P(E_2)} = \dfrac{\frac{1}{36}}{\frac{6}{36}} = \dfrac{1}{6}$

II.

1. $\frac{1}{2} \cdot \frac{1}{6} + \frac{1}{2} \cdot \frac{1}{2} = \frac{1}{3}$

3. $\frac{1}{2} \cdot \frac{3}{6} + \frac{1}{2} \cdot \frac{2}{6} = \frac{5}{12}$

5. $\frac{1}{3} + \frac{1}{4} = \frac{7}{12}$

7. $\frac{5}{12} + \frac{1}{4} = \frac{2}{3}$

9. $1 - \frac{1}{3} = \frac{2}{3}$

III. $P(E_1 \mid E_2) = \dfrac{P(E_1 \cap E_2)}{P(E_2)} = \dfrac{.20}{.40} = \dfrac{1}{2}$

IV. $E = E_1 \cap E_2$, in which E_1 is the event that the plane is defective and E_2 is the event that the plane is an A-506 model. $P(E) = P(E_1 \cap E_2) = P(E_1 \mid E_2)P(E_2) = (.20)(.30) = .06 = \frac{6}{100}$.

V. All independent

VI.

1. Independent   3. Dependent   5. Dependent

VII.

1. $\frac{1}{25}$ 3. $\frac{1}{8}$ 5. $\frac{1}{4}$ 7. $\frac{1}{16}$ 9. $\frac{1}{50}$

VIII.

1. $\frac{3}{19}$ 3. $\frac{3}{19}$ 5. $\frac{3}{19}$

Index

ABCDE 79876543210